Correspondence:
Henry E. Sigerist – Charles Singer
1920–1956

(*Medical History*, Supplement No. 30)

Correspondence:
Henry E. Sigerist – Charles Singer
1920–1956

Edited and annotated by

MARCEL H. BICKEL

Department of the History of Medicine,
University of Bern, Switzerland

(*Medical History*, Supplement No. 30)

London
The Wellcome Trust Centre for the History of Medicine at UCL
2010

Table of Contents

Preface

Henry E. Sigerist (1891–1957) is recognized as the foremost historian of medicine of his time. In addition, he was an activist in the fight for a reform of the American health system and, last but not least, he was a scholar with an exceptional breadth of interests and with engaging human qualities.

Charles Singer (1876–1960) was an outstanding British medical historian. As a colleague he first came into contact with Sigerist, who was fifteen years younger, at an early stage of his career as a medical historian in Switzerland. Their correspondence lasted from 1920 through all of Sigerist's career, almost to his death in 1957.

Most of Sigerist's correspondence had been a hidden treasure for a long time until the publication of the incomplete correspondence with George Rosen (Viseltear, 1978) and with George Urdang (Sonnedecker, 1983). In 2008, an edition of Sigerist's correspondence with four Swiss historians of medicine (A. C. Klebs, B. Milt, H. Fischer, E. Hintzsche) was published (Bickel, 2008), and two years later, that between Sigerist and the American colleagues Welch, Cushing, Garrison, and Ackerknecht (Bickel, 2010).

There are several reasons that make an edition of Sigerist's correspondence worthwhile:

1) Most of the correspondence is stored in a well-organized and accessible form in only two archives.
2) Not only do they contain the letters received and collected by Sigerist, but also the carbon copies of his own letters since about 1923.
3) Most of them are almost complete with very few letters missing.

These three facts are rarely combined in editions of correspondence and are therefore an invaluable advantage. To this must be added the interest in both Sigerist and Singer. This correspondence is therefore likely to allow a true insight into the lives and mentalities of the two correspondents, including their private lives and scientific work, as well as relationships with persons, books, and topics. Hence, the correspondence is a source for the correspondents' biographies and for many topics and features of the twentieth century.

I have tried to adopt modern criteria for the edition of correspondence (Steinke 2004). The three reasons given above have allowed an edition of all the surviving letters to and by Sigerist in a chronological sequence, and without selection, which in any case would have been questionable. A complete edition with totally transcribed letters was also feasible because the correspondence is limited in size and contains very few trivialities. Future editors will need to add letters missing in this edition and alter the footnotes.

Problems of transcription are dealt with in the introduction (chapter 1.3.1). The footnotes follow the transcribed letters, and a bibliography of most of the literature mentioned in the letters and footnotes is also given (chapter 3). All persons mentioned in the letters and major topics of the correspondence are listed in the index.

Most of the letters to and by Sigerist are stored in the following archives:

1) Manuscripts and Archives
   Yale University Library

P. O. Box 208240
New Haven, CT 06520–8240
(the Sigerist-Singer correspondence of 1920–1925 [incomplete] and 1947–1956).

2)   The Alan Mason Chesney Medical Archives
     The Johns Hopkins Medical Institutions
     5801 Smith Avenue, Suite 235
     Baltimore, MD 21209
(the correspondence of 1932–1947).

Both archives have lists of the correspondence under the heading "Henry E. Sigerist Papers". Letters of 1925–1932 are in the Universitätsarchiv Leipzig (incomplete). The collection of Sigeristiana at the Department of the History of Medicine of the University of Zurich, although extensive, contains but few letters.

Both Sigerist and Singer played a major role in medicine and academic life in the United States and Britain. Their correspondence is more voluminous than the ones previously edited, except for that of Ackerknecht. It is one between two colleagues, showing their plans and achievements, books read and people met. The reader becomes acquainted with the two personalities and watches as the first half of the twentieth century unfolds in many of its aspects.

For the present edition I am grateful to many who have helped me in many ways. The university archives of Yale, Johns Hopkins, and Leipzig mentioned above, were kind enough to let me publish their materials. Their staff's competence, co-operation, and friendly advice is highly appreciated. I extend my thanks to my colleagues in the departments of the history of medicine in Bern and Zurich for stimulation and help with the transcription and footnotes: Urs Boschung, Pia Burkhalter, Gertraud Gamper, François Ledermann, Luc Lienhard, Iris Ritzmann, and Hubert Steinke. Nora Sigerist-Beeson, Sylvia Bonner, Martina Fierz, and many others offered their help, as did my wife Leni and our daughter Susanne. I wish to express my gratitude in particular to Vivian Nutton and Caroline Overy for their critical dealing with the manuscript, for their improving it by adding new footnotes, and for all other help and cooperation. I also thank The Wellcome Trust Centre for the History of Medicine at UCL for offering to publish this work as a Supplement to *Medical History*.

Bern, 2010

Bickel, Marcel H. (ed.) (2008) *Henry E. Sigerist. Vier ausgewählte Briefwechsel mit Medizinhistorikern der Schweiz* (Bern, Peter Lang Publishing Group).
Bickel, Marcel H. (ed.) (2010) *Henry E. Sigerist. Correspondence with Welch, Cushing, Garrison, and Ackerknecht* (Bern, Peter Lang Publishing Group).
Sonnedecker, Glenn (ed.) (1983) *The American correspondence between George Urdang and Henry E. Sigerist 1941–1948* (Graz).
Steinke, Hubert (2004) 'Why, what and how? Editing early modern scientific letters in the 21st century', *Gesnerus*, **61**: 282–295.
Viseltear, Arthur J. (ed.) (1978) 'The George Rosen—Henry E. Sigerist correspondence', *Journal of the History of Medicine and Allied Sciences*, **33**: 281–313.

Introduction

1. Introduction

1.1. Henry Sigerist (1891–1957)

Sigerist was born in 1891 in Paris, the son of Swiss parents. After schooling in Paris and Zurich he began studies of oriental languages in Zurich and London, then studied medicine in Zurich and Munich. Immediately after obtaining his MD in 1917 he entered the field of the history of medicine as a result of his being encouraged by Karl Sudhoff in Leipzig, the doyen of medical historians. For eight years Sigerist was an independent scholar in Zurich, stimulated by some of his teachers and, above all, by his cooperation with colleagues such as Sudhoff, Charles Singer, and Arnold C. Klebs. He became a lecturer in the history of medicine at the University of Zurich, giving courses and guiding doctoral students. The considerable number of papers and edited books were proof of his productivity and success at this early stage. No wonder, therefore, that in 1925 he was called to fill the leading chair of medical history as the successor of Karl Sudhoff at the University of Leipzig.

In Leipzig, as professor and director of a department, Sigerist's possibilities widened and so did the range of his interests. The Leipzig Institute, which had been Sudhoff's realm, now attracted ever more students and co-workers and opened up to international communication with medical historians and other intellectuals. Sigerist even succeeded in being independent of, and peacefully co-existing with, the authoritarian and vain Sudhoff, who was still present in the Institute. Sigerist also managed things successfully in spite of the difficult political and economic situation in post-World War I Germany. Part of his success was due to his abilities as an organizer. In addition to a variety of publications, Sigerist wrote his three most personal books in Leipzig: *Man and medicine*, *Great doctors*, and *American medicine*. It was also in Leipzig that Sigerist came into personal contact with the foremost American medical historians such as William H. Welch, Fielding H. Garrison, and Harvey Cushing. These contacts led to an invitation for a lecture tour in the United States for the winter of 1931/32 where Sigerist met many American colleagues, gave lectures from coast to coast, and studied American medicine in action. His hosts were so impressed that the Johns Hopkins medical faculty offered him the Chair of the History of Medicine and thus the succession of Welch. Back in Leipzig, Sigerist realized that his chances in the United States were clearly superior to those in Germany with its rapidly deteriorating political situation shortly before the Nazis seized power.

Sigerist's most important time began in 1932 as William H. Welch Professor of the History of Medicine at the Johns Hopkins University in Baltimore. He re-organized teaching, built up a staff of both Americans and exiled European victims of Nazism, and secured the means for the necessary budget. Contacts with the Old World were maintained by spending every summer of the 1930s in Europe, although he never returned to Germany. After his experiences in Germany, and as a liberal democrat, the way of life in America was much to his liking. He continued the research on mediaeval medicine he had begun in Zurich and Leipzig. However, his work soon covered the whole of the history of

Figure 1   Henry E. Sigerist
Courtesy: Archive, Department of the History of Medicine, University of Bern

medicine and the subject's methodology. He also founded the *Bulletin of the History of Medicine*, which soon became, and still is, one of the leading journals on the subject.

Sigerist's writings and the multitude of his lectures all over the U.S. and Canada were a major contribution to the professionalization of the field of the history of medicine in America. Soon, however, his major interests shifted towards the sociology and economics of medicine, the organization of medical services and public health, and he became an ardent advocate of compulsory health insurance. The study of these aspects took him to Soviet Russia and South Africa, and, during World War II, to the Canadian province of Saskatchewan and to India. During the War many of his writings had little to do with medicine, but much with the world situation, education, and building a better world. His final years in the U.S. were overshadowed by overwork and health problems, by merely occasional successes in his medico-political endeavours, and by the threat of McCarthyism. This led him back into his original field and let him begin his multi-volume *A history of medicine*, planned years before and now marked as top priority. Soon after the War, however, he realized that progress of this work was impossible on top of all his duties in research, teaching, and administration. He therefore made the courageous decision to resign his post at Johns Hopkins in early 1947.

In order to write the eight volumes of his *A history of medicine* Sigerist returned to Switzerland after twenty-two years and found a new home in the village of Pura in the canton of Ticino where he spent the final decade of his life (1947 to 1957). Once more he was an independent scholar, now supported by grants from Yale University and the Rockefeller Foundation. He enjoyed his escape from the burdens of his former position as well as a new kind of life in solitude and in the beautiful natural surroundings of the Italian Alps. However, he now missed the facilities and stimulation a university provided. This was but one factor that delayed progress of his *magnum opus*, which eventually amounted to only two volumes. Other factors were an unforeseen number of secondary publications, out-of-town lectures, new editions of his books, etc., as well as a stream of visitors and failing health. Sigerist died on 17 March 1957 in Pura.

An indefatigable writer, Sigerist produced many books and hundreds of papers. His bibliography comprises of some 520 items (Miller, 1966). To this should be added two volumes with selected Sigerist papers on the history of medicine (Marti-Ibañez, 1960) and on the sociology of medicine (Roemer, 1960). Sigerist's works, combined with his rhetorical talent and his charisma, stimulated many authors to write about him. This secondary literature (Berg-Schorn, 1978) (Fee/Brown, 1997) (Becker, 1991) amounts to about 170 titles (excluding the 57 obituaries and many reviews of his books) and shows even an increasing tendency in the half century since Sigerist's death (Bickel, unpublished). It contains much information on his life and times, and work. There are also autobiographical texts that have been edited (Sigerist Beeson, 1966). In addition to his scientific work Sigerist also wrote an enormous number of letters. They were his link to hundreds of correspondents all over the world, among them medical historians as well as representatives of a large spectrum of cultural life. For instance, in the early 1950s, he wrote some one thousand letters per year (Bickel, 1997), a fact on which his friend John F. Fulton commented:

Sigerist was as greatly interested in men as he was in books – men of all lands, persuasions, and occupations - and so conscientious was he in maintaining lines of communication with his ever-widening circle of friends that, toward the end of his life, his correspondence became so vast that it interfered with his more serious writing. (Fulton, 1960).

The works given below may serve as a key to the secondary literature on Sigerist.

Becker, Cornelia (1991) *Schriften über Henry Ernest Sigerist (1891–1957) – Eine Bibliographie*, in S. Hahn and A. Thom (eds) (1991) *Ergebnisse und Perspektiven sozialhistorischer Forschung in der Medizingeschichte. Kolloquium zum 100. Geburtstag Sigerists* (Leipzig), 37–45.

Berg-Schorn, Elisabeth (1978) *Henry E. Sigerist (1891–1957)* (Cologne).

Bickel, Marcel H. (1997) 'Henry E. Sigerist's annual "Plans of Work" (1932–1955)', *Bulletin of the History of Medicine*, **71**: 489–498.

Fee, Elizabeth and Brown, Theodor M. (1997) *Making medical history. The life and times of Henry E. Sigerist* (Baltimore / London).

Fulton, John F. (1960) 'Foreword', in F. Marti-Ibañez (ed.) (1960), *Henry E. Sigerist on the history of medicine* (New York), ix-xi.

Marti-Ibañez, F. (ed.) (1960) *Henry E. Sigerist on the history of medicine* (New York).

Miller, Genevieve (1966) *A bibliography of the writings of Henry E. Sigerist* (Montreal).

Roemer, Milton I. (ed.) (1960) *Henry E. Sigerist on the sociology of medicine* (New York).

Sigerist Beeson, Nora (ed.) (1966) *Henry E. Sigerist: autobiographical writings* (Montreal).

1.2. Charles Joseph Singer (1876–1960)

Charles Singer was born in London on 2 November 1876, the son of a distinguished Hebrew scholar. He studied classical languages at an early age. In 1893 he started studies in pre-clinical subjects and biology at University College London, then continued in Oxford for another three years as a student and instructor in zoology. Back in London he studied medicine at St Mary's Hospital Medical School, where he qualified as an M.D. in 1903. There followed years of medical practice at English hospitals and work at research institutions, even medical expeditions to Abyssinia and Singapore. In 1910 he married the mediaevalist, Dorothea Waley Cohen, who had written on alchemical and other mediaeval manuscripts. She became his life-long collaborator and source of inspiration. This also marked Singer's turn to the history of medicine, which became complete when William Osler invited him to a post in pathology at Oxford where he could devote part of his time to the study and teaching of the history of biology. Unfortunately, World War I interrupted Singer's career, since he served with the Royal Army Medical Corps in England, Malta, and Salonika. Thus, his full-time career as an historian began only in 1918 at over forty years of age. In 1920 he began his correspondence with Henry E. Sigerist in Zurich. Sigerist, fifteen years his junior, was at the beginning of his career as a medical historian, and less than thirty years old.

Also in 1920 Singer returned to University College London, this time as lecturer in the history of medicine. Ten years later he was elected professor with an honorary chair in this subject. This was the first period of Singer's research and literary productivity in the history of medicine and science. Highlights of this period were his presidencies of the International Congress of the History of Medicine in 1922 and of the International Congress of the History of Science in 1931.

Figure 2 Charles Singer
Courtesy: Wellcome Library, London

In 1929 and 1932 Singer spent some time in the United States, giving lectures at Johns Hopkins University in Baltimore and teaching at the University of California in Berkeley. When William H. Welch's Chair of the History of Medicine in Baltimore became vacant in 1931, Singer was asked to succeed. However, he declined because he had been elected professor at University College in London. The one to be given the chair was Sigerist.

From 1934, the Singers spent the winter months in an old house, "Kilmarth", on the south coast of Cornwall. Kilmarth became their permanent home after Singer's retirement in 1942 at the age of sixty-seven. Both Singer and his wife were alarmed when Hitler came to power in 1933, and even more so in view of the fate of many of their academic colleagues in Germany who became victims of Nazi rule. The Singers felt it their duty to actively provide moral and material help for the exiled colleagues to find entry and posts in Britain or, with Sigerist's help, in America. From 1933 to the outbreak of World War II in 1939, this became almost a full-time activity, which took its toll in terms of the Singers' financial resources, time and, hence, scholarly productivity. Singer also supported the war effort, for example, by teaching biology, including laboratory courses in his house in Cornwall, for an evacuated school from Canterbury. Once emigration and war had ended in 1945 Singer had another active phase as an historian that lasted up to his death in 1960.

Singer was the author or editor of many books in addition to some two hundred scientific articles and an equal amount of book reviews. His early works dealt with Hildegard von

Bingen, followed by two volumes of *Studies in the history and method of science*. Among his most important subjects were the history of anatomy, ancient Greek medicine and biology, mediaeval medicine and biology including Anglo-Saxon, and early herbals. Only rarely did he touch periods beyond the Renaissance. He enthusiastically studied early manuscripts in detail, often translating and publishing them, but he was also a master of historical synthesis. This is shown in his *Short histories* of medicine, of biology, and of medicine and scientific ideas. During Singer's fertile post-World War II period, studies on Vesalius and Galen were followed by the monumental five-volume *History of technology*, of which he was the chief planner and editor.

It is notable that Singer's bibliography shows many titles remote from both medicine and history. Examples showing his versatility are: *The teaching of English*; *Woman doctors*; *On growing old*; *The blind; Historical relations of religion and science*; *The legacy of Israel*; *The German universities and national socialism*; *The refugee problem*; *The Christian failure*; *A depressing world*; *The happy scholar*.

The two-volume Festschrift of 1953 in Singer's honour, a monumental work edited by Singer's colleague and son-in-law, E. Ashworth Underwood, contained articles by ninety-five contributors, many of them friends and colleagues. Singer was also the recipient of numerous awards.

Singer travelled the world and lectured in many places. He was in close touch with historians of medicine and science, not only in Britain, but also with early international leaders such as Sudhoff, Sigerist, A. C. Klebs, Sarton and others. He died on 10 June 1960 in his home, Kilmarth, in Cornwall. For literature on his biography see Underwood (1953, 1960), Cope (1960), Hall (1960), Clarke (1961), Jilla (1991). Singer's complete bibliography is in Underwood (1953 and 1960).

For an eminent historian of medicine and science like Singer one would have wished a long-lasting legacy and a secondary literature dealing with his work and influence. This is clearly not the case. The following facts may serve as starting points for explanations. Singer was never given a chair and a full professorship in the history of medicine or science, and after his retirement in 1942, his "department" disappeared. No pupils had been trained who would continue and develop Singer's work. His lack of influence was also due to the fact that soon after his death the historiography of medicine turned against the former positivism and scientism, and that medical men as authors were supplemented by social historians of both sexes for the rest of the century. A twenty-first-century observer comes to the conclusion that Singer does not seem to have left a fertile legacy (Mayer, 2005). As a scholar and as a personality, however, he remains an outstanding figure of the twentieth century.

Cantor, G. (1997) 'Charles Singer and the early years of the British Society for the History of Science', *British Journal for the History of Science*, **30**: 5–23.

Clarke, Edwin (1961) 'Charles Joseph Singer', *Journal of the History of Medicine and Allied Sciences*, **16**: 411–419.

Cope, Zachary (1960) 'Charles Joseph Singer (1876–1960)', *Bulletin of the History of Medicine*, **24**: 471–473.

Fischer, Hans (1960) 'Charles Singer (1876.1960)', *Gesnerus*, **17**: 73–74.

Hall, A. Rupert (1960) 'Charles Joseph Singer (1876–1960)', *Isis*, **51**: 558–560.

Jilla, Cyrus (1991) 'Charles Singer, his life, aims and achievements in the history of medicine' (BSc Dissertation, London).

Mayer, Anna-K. (2002) 'Fatal mutilations: educationism and the British background to the 1931 International Congress for the History of Science and Technology', *History of Science*, **40**: 445–472.

Mayer, Anna-K. (2005) 'When things don't talk: knowledge and belief in the inter-war humanism of Charles Singer (1876–1960)', *British Journal for the History of Science*, **38**: 325–347.

Miller, Genevieve (1985) 'Charles and Dorothea Singer's aid to Nazi victims', *Koroth*, **8**: 11–2, 207–7, 210.

Underwood, E. A. (ed.) (1953) *Science, medicine and history. Essays on the evolution of scientific thought and medical practice, written in honour of Charles Singer*, 2 vols (London).

Underwood, E. A. (1960) 'Charles Singer', *British Medical Journal*, **i**: 1897–1899.

Underwood, E. A. (1960) 'Charles Singer (1876–1960)', *Medical History*, **4**: 353–358.

Weindling, Paul (1998) 'History of science and medicine journals in Great Britain', in M. Beretta, C. Pogliano, and P. Redondi, (eds), *Journals and History of Science* (Biblioteca di Nuncius XXXII, Firenze), 145–152.

Weindling, Paul (1999) 'Medical refugees and the renaissance of medical history in Great Britain, 1930s-60s', in Ralf Bröer (ed.), *Eine Wissenschaft emanzipiert sich. Die medizinhistoriographie von der Aufklärung bis zur Postmoderne* (Pfaffenweiler) 139–147.

1.3. The Correspondence

1.3.1. Technicalities and Explanations

The number of preserved letters is shown in the following table:

	Sigerist	Singer
1920–1925 (Sigerist in Zurich)	2	170
1925–1932 (Sigerist in Leipzig)	25	0
1932–1947 (Sigerist in Baltimore)	61	79
1947–1956 (Sigerist in Pura, Switzerland)	30	34
	118	283

These figures include a few telegrams and some letters of the correspondents' secretaries which fill gaps in the exchange of letters. Clearly missing are almost all of Sigerist's letters from Zurich, and Singer's to Sigerist in Leipzig. Otherwise, there are only occasional letters clearly missing. The missing letters after 1932 are predominantly Sigerist's, in all likeliness long-hand letters of which he did not make carbon copies.

Most of the letters are in English; only Sigerist's letters from Leipzig were dictated in German. These are followed in this edition by an English summary of their contents. Practically all letters are clearly dated, and the majority of the letters are typed. Part of Singer's letters are in long-hand. These occasionally contain indecipherable words which in the transcription are indicated by the sign [....] or are followed by the sign [?]. Sigerist liked to write in long-hand, yet he used typewriters from the mid-1920s in order to have his own carbon copies. Spelling errors have been transcribed as such but are followed by the sign [sic], whereas the frequent errors in punctuation have been left unchanged and unmarked as long as they did not distort the sense of a sentence. The sign [ ] has also been used if Sigerist's signature was missing on the carbon copies used. Literary works are given as, e.g., Ackerknecht (1931), and listed in the bibliography (chapter 3).

Footnotes follow each transcribed letter. They are meant to help understand the contents of the letters rather than to interpret them and are therefore kept to a minimum, referring to persons and subjects only at their first mention; they also serve as links to previous or subsequent letters and notes. Persons sufficiently characterized and explained in the letter may not appear in the footnote. The term "medical historian" for the characterization of persons is used in a wide sense as, e.g., members of the American Association of the History of Medicine. A few persons, most of them mentioned only once, could not be identified and are marked as such in the footnote. However, all persons mentioned in the letters are listed in the index, as are major topics of the correspondence in addition to institutions, journals, locations, and publishers.

1.3.2. Characteristics and topics of the correspondence

The correspondence covers Sigerist's whole career in Zurich, Leipzig, Baltimore, and Pura, Switzerland. In particular, it sheds light on Sigerist's early years in Zurich since it starts as early as 1920. At that time Singer, in London, was an academically established medical historian of forty-four years of age, whereas Sigerist, in Zurich, was at the beginning of his career aged twenty-nine. Their co-operation and mutual help during these early years was very intense, as shown by sixty-three letters from Singer in the one year 1923. Singer's letters of these years are mainly dealing with the correspondents' research. They acknowledge and refer to Sigerist's (missing) letters, so these are likely to be reflected in Singer's (preserved) letters.

The same can be said for the lack of Singer's letters during Sigerist's years in Leipzig (1925–1932). Sigerist's letters suggest an on-going but less intense cooperation, probably due to his new responsibilities and challenges as director of a university department.

This first period of the correspondence (1920–1932) is an exchange on work, e.g., on mediaeval manuscripts, publications, journals, congresses, and institutions such as scholarly societies, departments, libraries, publishers and others. In dozens of letters one follows the progress and setbacks in the creation of the *Festschrift* for Karl Sudhoff, edited by Singer and Sigerist, an excellent example of the problems with the editing of multi-author books. A particular topic in these years was Singer's staunch opposition to the (French) exclusion of colleagues from "enemy countries" (Germany, Austria) from participation at international congresses in the post-World War I years. The two correspondents' attempts at the creation of an international journal of the history of medicine are also remarkable.

From Sigerist's transfer to Baltimore in 1932 and almost through to his death, the correspondence becomes bilateral with only occasional missing letters. From the beginning of this period the correspondence also becomes more intimate, the colleagues becoming friends. Despite the difference in age there is never a trace of condescension on the part of Singer. In fact, Singer often seeks Sigerist's advice or lets him have the freedom of choice between proposals or alternatives.

The list of topics of the correspondence gradually extends far beyond academic subjects. From 1933 politics becomes a topic of increasing importance. Both correspondents are increasingly disgusted with the developments in Germany under the Nazis' ghastly rule and horrified by the fate of their colleagues who have become victims of the regime. Both, as well as Dorothea Singer, are active in helping German and Austrian intellectuals seeking immigration and continued activity, some prominent examples being the medical historians Ludwig and Emma Edelstein, Walter Pagel, Max Neuburger, and Isidor Fischer. Singer became overwhelmed by these activities, to such a degree that his scientific output was clearly diminished. In these pre-war years Sigerist also informs Singer of his study tours to Europe, the Soviet Union, South Africa, Canada, and India.

The war then becomes another topic in the correspondence after its outbreak in 1939. Singer provides impressive insights into life in Britain after the retreat from Dunkirk, during the German bombing of British cities, and at the time of the collapsing Nazi war machine. Sigerist provides information on the war effort on the other side of the Atlantic. With the end of emigration and the defeat of Nazi Germany, Singer's productivity increases again, yet he deplores the sixteen years of his life lost to both World War I and Hitlerism:

It is maddening to think of all the years that I have lost by these detestable wars. The last word should, of course, be in the singular for it is all one war. (Letter 302)

After World War II, with Sigerist in Pura, Switzerland, (1947–1957) and Singer retired in Cornwall, new topics appear in the correspondence. Both correspondents are busy with their multi-volume opera magna: Sigerist with *A history of medicine* and Singer as editor of *A history of technology*. The slow progress of Sigerist's *History*, and finally his idea to finish the work with the help of co-authors, is a major topic at that time. Still discussed are the correspondents' secondary works, the ones projected, in progress, or achieved. Books, reprints, and other materials are still exchanged or discussed, as are the new and often surprising problems of these postwar years. Sigerist happily mentions his travels for lectures and congresses, particularly the ones to England, a country he is increasingly fond of. In the final years, deteriorating health becomes a topic too. Singer informs Sigerist of the not-so-smooth development of the Wellcome Historical Medical Museum and Library. The letters also happily mention the correspondents' continuing encounters in Switzerland, London, and Cornwall.

No fewer than about 200 books and papers and about 450 people are mentioned in the correspondence (see chapters 3 and 4). Some of the people appear time and again, and are characterized in a straightforward way and thus become familiar to the reader. The correspondence is also a document of an impressive friendship, based on common interests, congeniality, confidence, and the will for mutual help in a generous way. There are congratulations without flattering, mutual admiration of capabilities and achievements, and thus mutual stimulation. The correspondents' families are important, and Dorothea Singer is ever present. There is humour, too. In summary, the whole correspondence is a document reflecting many political, cultural and academic aspects of the first half of the twentieth century and the first decade after World War II.

2. The Letters

1

Singer to Sigerist, Oxford, 10 March 1920[1]

My dear Sir,

Many thanks for your letter of March 6 which I was very glad to have. You shall certainly have photographs of the work of Heliodoros[2] and I will arrange for them to be taken at once. I am of course very pleased to help you in any way I can, and much look forward to seeing your edition of this work.[3]

I am examining the two Hunterian MSS. and hope to publish a full account of them. I am therefore especially pleased that you are throwing light on this particular section. As you are working on somewhat similar lines to myself, perhaps you would be good enough to tell me which of the other MSS. you propose to publish. I ask this so that I may avoid working on the same, because I am going through all the early pre-Constantine MSS. in this country. I do not of course wish to begin on any to which you are applying yourself.

I am delighted to be of service to you and to hear of the advancement of our studies in Switzerland and of the news of my friend Klebs.[4]

Yours sincerely,

Charles Singer

Are there good modern Catalogues of the libraries at St. Gallen & Einsiedeln?[5] If so can you give me their authors & publishers & dates?

C.S.

I shall be glad to hear from you again. The Catalogue of MSS is now complete but the question of printing is a serious one.[6] I think we shall bring it out in sections. But it is always open for any one to use. You may care to see my wifes [sic] account of it which I send in another envelope.

As regards Galen. My idea is to have a translation of the more important works into English & an <u>abstract</u> of the less important. I am waiting until the Corpus Medicorum Graecorum has progressed a little.

I am interested to hear that you study [studied?] at University College, London. I have recently been appointed lecturer on the History of Medicine there.[7] I expect you know Prof. Priebsch – the Professor of German there – who recently published an interesting Low German medical text.[8]

---

[1] This may have been the answer to Sigerist's first letter to Singer. The letter-head reads "Westbury Lodge, Norham Road, Oxford". Sigerist's letters of these years are missing, probably because he had not yet made copies of them.

[2] Heliodoros, a surgeon of the first century AD; see Guy Sabbah, Pierre-Paul Corsetti and Klaus-Dietrich Fischer, *Bibliographie des Textes médicaux latins. Antiquité et haut moyen Age*, Centre Jean-Palerne, Mémoires 6, (Saint-Étienne: Université de Saint-Étienne, 1987), no. 310, p.93. The photos Sigerist was looking for were those of Glasgow, Hunterian T.4.13 (96), stated note 3, p.145 of Henry E. Sigerist, 'Die "Lecciones Heliodori"', *Archiv für Geschichte der Medizin*, 1921, **13**: 145–156. Recent research suggests that neither tract is in any way genuine.

[3] Henry E. Sigerist, 'Die "Cirurgia Eliodori"', *Archiv für Geschichte der Medizin*, 1920, **12:** 1–9 and Sigerist (1921). Sigerist and Singer both worked on medical manuscripts of Antiquity and early Middle Ages.

[4] Arnold C. Klebs (1870–1943) son of the pathologist Edwin Klebs, physician and medical historian in the U.S. and Switzerland; after WWI he lived in Nyon on Lake Geneva. See Leona Baumgartner, 'Arnold Carl Klebs, 1870–1943', *Bulletin of the History of Medicine*, 1943, **14:** 201–216.

[5] Swiss monasteries with famous libraries.

[6] This possibly refers to the card catalogue of pre-1600 Western scientific manuscripts created by Singer's wife, Dorothea Waley Singer: *Catalogue of Latin and vernacular alchemical manuscripts in Great Britain and Ireland dating from before the XVI Century*, 3 vols (Brussels: Lamertin, 1928–1931). The card catalogue is now held in the British Library.

[7] Sigerist had studied Oriental Languages at University College in 1911.

[8] Robert Priebsch (1866–1935), German scholar; see *The Times*, May 28, 1935; p.21; *ibid*, May 29, 1935, p.16; *ibid*, May 31, 1935; p.21 and H. Menhardt, 'Robert Priebsch', *Germanisch–romanische Monatsschrift*, 1936, **24:** 144–8. For a portrait see Negley Harte and John North, *The world of University College, London, 1828–1978* (London: University College, 1978), 153.

2

Singer to Sigerist, Oxford, 22 March 1920

Dear Dr. Sigerist,

Many thanks for your letter of March 17th. Could you give me the name of a reliable bookseller in Switzerland as I should like to order catalogues of the old Swiss libraries?

I am glad to have the list of the MSS. on which you are working. London, Harleian 5792, f. 273–276 I have already transcribed and was about to publish. I will, however, carefully keep off the others. I am glad you are dealing with the Hunterian material and I will not discuss the part that you are investigating in my account of them except in a few lines and will mention that you have the matter in hand.[1]

Yours sincerely,

Charles Singer

The Hunterian MS is being photographed for you & you will have them in a few days.

C.S.

[1] The two scholars' work on medieval manuscripts required careful demarcation to avoid any conflict; see the correspondence between Sigerist and Klebs in 1923, in Marcel H. Bickel (ed.), *Henry E. Sigerist: Vier ausgewählte Briefwechsel mit Medizinhistorikern der Schweiz* (Bern, 2008).

3

Singer to Sigerist, Oxford, 1 June 1920

Dear Dr. Sigerist,
Very many thanks for those reprints which I am exceedingly glad to have, especially the one on Heliodorus.[1] I trust that you found the rotographs satisfactory.[2]
With kind <u>regards,</u>
Yours sincerely,
Charles Singer

[1] See letter 1 and Sigerist (1920).
[2] Rotograph, a process of photogravure.

4

Singer to Sigerist, Oxford, 10 September 1920

My dear Dr. Sigerist,
Very many thanks for Overbeck's delightful book.[1] I am really very much obliged to you for it. But you have not or rather the bookseller has not sent me the bill. Do please ask him to do so.
I am for the next two years president of the Historical Section of the Royal Society of Medicine. If you have any thing suitable for them I hope you will send it to me & I will endeavour to get it printed. You know what the difficulties of printing now are but I would do my best, & I should like, if possible, to have something from your pen.
We are preparing a scheme for a meeting, symposium, summer school or whatever you like to call it, next August on the History of Science, probably in Oxford. It would be pleasant if you were able to come.
Klebs paid us a flying visit the other day; I wish it could have been a longer one.
With kind regards,
Yours sincerely,
Charles Singer

[1] Probably Franz Overbeck, *Vorgeschichte und Jugend der mittelalterlichen Scholastik* (Basel, 1917).

5

Singer to Sigerist, Oxford, 8 October 1920

My dear Dr. Sigerist,

Many thanks for your letter of 2.10.20.

I am much looking forward to having an article from you & I will do my very best to get it printed. If you can send me anything that bears definitely on the History of Science (in the restricted sense) I can guarantee publication because I have full control of the "Studies".[1] But with [the History of] Medicine there is some times difficult [sic]. Still I have every hope that all difficulties will be overcome & that we shall not have to reduce our publication[.]

I wish I had been able to see Sudhoff again.[2] I am much looking forward to his & Meyer-Steineg's book.[3] Is it out yet?

I enclose cheque for 7 francs for the Overbeck. Are you sure that is enough[?]

With kind regards,

Yours sincerely,

Charles Singer

[1] Charles Singer (ed.), *Studies in the history and method of science*, 2 vols (Oxford: Clarendon Press, 1917–1921).

[2] Karl Sudhoff (1853–1938) medical historian in Leipzig, Singer and Sigerist's mentor. See Henry E. Sigerist, 'Karl Sudhoff 1853–1938', *Bulletin of the History of Medicine*, 1939, **7 (2):** 801–804; and Henry E. Sigerist (ed), 'A celebration of the eightieth birthday of Professor Karl Sudhoff', *Bulletin of the Institute of the History of Medicine*, 1934, **2:** 1–25.

[3] Theodor Meyer-Steineg and Karl Sudhoff, *Geschichte der Medizin im Ueberblick mit Abbildungen* (Jena, 1921).

6

Singer to Sigerist, Oxford, 25 November 1920

My dear Dr. Sigerist,

I am not quite sure if I have replied to your letter of Nov. 4th suggesting that we should make some common plan for editing a "Collectio prae Salernitana".[1] I greatly like the idea and think that we might at any rate as a preliminary, put together a catalogue of the MSS. without a great deal of labour. This I will do for this country during the first weeks of the coming year and I will send you a copy. You will perhaps let me have a similar copy of the Swiss, German and Austrian material. We must of course avoid overlapping and work always from the best MS. in whatever country it may be.

I think that when we come face to face with the material we shall find that the practical way is for each of us to take up special texts rather than special MSS. But this is a matter we can decide when we have indexed what there is.

I have been very busy with lecturing this Term but expect to have a little more leisure next Term.[2]

With kind regards,

Yours very sincerely

Charles Singer

---

[1] Both Sigerist and Singer published on pre-Salernitan medicine: Henry E. Sigerist, *Studien und Texte zur frühmittelalterlichen Rezeptliteratur* (Leipzig, 1923); Charles Singer and Dorothea Singer, 'The origin of the Medical School of Salerno', in Charles Singer and Henry E. Sigerist (eds), *Essays in the history of medicine presented to Karl Sudhoff on the occasion of his seventieth birthday November 25th 1923* (London/Zurich, 1924), 121–138.

[2] Singer had a new appointment at the University College London.

7

Dorothea Singer to Sigerist, London, 20 December 1920

Dear Dr. Sigerist,

We are delighted to hear that you are coming to Paris the week-end of the 6th. We also are arranging to arrive on Friday Jan. 6th. We have been recommended to the Hotel Lutetia, 43 Boulevard Raspail. I have written to engage rooms there, and it will be delightful if you are there too. We shall hope to find you when we arrive at dinner time. Monsieur Lavastine[1] has asked us to dinner on the 7th and tells us that we shall also have the pleasure of seeing you then.

My husband wonders whether we may take this opportunity of carrying you off to London. It will be a great pleasure if you can come with us.

With our best regards,

Yours sincerely,

Dorothea Waley Singer[2]

---

[1] Maxime Laignel-Lavastine (1875–1953) French medical historian. See I. Simon, 'Maxime Laignel-Lavastine, historien de la médecine (1875–1953)', *Revue d'histoire des sciences et de leurs applications*, 1954, **7**: 81–83, and *British Medical Journal*, 1953, **ii**: 781.

[2] Dorothea W. Singer, née Cohen (1882–1964), medievalist, was Singers's wife and co-worker. See Anita McConnell, 'Singer , Dorothea Waley (1882–1964)', *Oxford dictionary of national biography* (Oxford: Oxford University Press, 2004), vol. 50, 774–775.

8

Singer to Sigerist, Champex, Switzerland, 25 June 1921

My dear Sigerist,

Very many thanks for "Vom Altertum zur Gegenwart".[1] It's a useful compilation &
I am extremely glad to have it. It contains many hints for my paper for Livingstone's
book which is at present haunting me.[2] It really was good of you to have remembered.

We are both looking forward to seeing you in Paris.

We find it delightful here & are making arrangements to come again next year.

With best regards to Mrs. Sigerist[3] & yourself in which my wife joins,

Very sincerely yours

Charles Singer

I have just received Frank's translation of Choulant for Nature & the British Medical
Journal[4] & Wedels [sic] Astrology & Bacon's secretum for Nature.[5]

[1] F. Norden, *Vom Altertum zur Gegenwart*, (Leipzig/Berlin, 1921).
[2] C. Singer, 'Medicine', in R. W. Livingstone (ed.), *The legacy of Greece* (Oxford, 1921), 201–248.
[3] Mrs. Emmy Sigerist-Escher.
[4] Ludwig Choulant, *History and bibliography of anatomic illustration: in its relation to anatomic science and
the graphic arts*, translated and edited with notes and a biography by Mortimer Frank (Chicago: The University of
Chicago Press, [1920]), reviewed by Singer in the British science journal *Nature*, 1921, **108:** 141–142 and in the
British Medical Journal, 1921, **ii:** 12–13. Ludwig Choulant (1791–1861) German medical historian; see
Rodolphine J.Ch.V. ter Laage, 'Reflections on Johann Ludwig Choulant and medico-historical bibliographies',
in P. Smit & R.J. Ch. V. ter Laage (eds), *Essays in biohistory* (Utrecht: International Association for Plant
Taxonomy, 1970), 115–133.
[5] Roger Bacon (1214–1294) English philosopher; his *Opera hactenus inedita Rogeri Baconi, Fasc. V, Secretum
Secretorum cum glossis et notulis*, ed. by R. Steele (Oxford: Clarendon Press, 1920), and Theodore O. Wedel's, *The
Medieval attitude towards astrology* (New Haven: Yale University Press, 1920) were reviewed in Charles Singer,
'Astrology', *Nature*, 1921, **107:** 771–772.

9

Singer to Sigerist, Oxford, 30 July 1921

My dear Sigerist,

Many thanks for your letter of July 24th containing the membership form[1] which
I have sent on to Rolleston and Thompson.[2] Many thanks too for the kind things you
say about my "Studies".[3] I will let you have information in the course of the next fortnight about MS. Add. 17063.

I would very much rather publish the Harleian Antidotarium <u>with you</u>. Do please give
in about it. I think that we could make a nice article for the Classical Quarterly between
the two of us, and if you will send me your material I will see what I can do about it.

Especially I want your remarks about its sources & the classification of early Antidotaries [.] If I find that I cannot add enough to it on my own account I will publish it in your name without adding mine, but I should very much like to publish something conjointly with you.

I will send you off my spare copy of Smith's Early History of Veterinary Literature[4] as soon as the Post Offices open. At present they are closed for two days as it is our bank holiday.

I am reviewing E. G. Browne's Arabian Medicine for "Nature".[5] It is a good book but I must confess to finding myself a little disappointed. I did hope that an author with the very special knowledge that Browne has [,] would give us something that is inaccessible elsewhere. His work is good, thorough and interesting, but it hardly fills a gap.

Congratulations on your appointment in Zürich.[6] I have just finished my article on Medicine for Livingstone's book The Legacy of Greece and it has gone to Press. I was to have collaborated with D'Arcy Thompson in the article on Biology. Now he has failed and I have to write that alone which is very annoying. It is keeping me here for a week grinding hard.[7] My wife has gone to Marvin's Summer School at Birmingham where I join her in a day or two.[8]

Have you ever read the Hippocratic treatise *peri physios paidon De Natura Pueri*? I marvel more attention has not been paid to it. Surely Aristotle must have had predecessors for his De Generatione Animalium!

With best regards from us both,

Yours ever,

Charles Singer

P.S. Horrors! I think I must have given my second copy of Smith away, and I rather think I must have sent it to Garrison,[9] but I will have another hunt. In the meantime I have written to see if there is a copy left.

C.S.

[1] Membership of the Royal Society of Medicine, see letter 10.

[2] Humphry Rolleston (1862–1944), British physician and medical historian; see Mark W. Weatherall, 'Rolleston, Sir Humphry Davy, first baronet (1862–1944)', *Oxford dictionary of national biography* (Oxford: Oxford University Press, 2004), vol. 47, 623–625; D'Arcy W. Thompson (1860–1948), professor of natural history at St. Andrews, Scotland. See W. T. Calman, 'Thompson, Sir D'Arcy Wentworth (1860–1948)', rev. D. S. Falconer, *Oxford dictionary of national biography* (Oxford: Oxford University Press, 2004), vol. 54, 411–412.

[3] Singer (ed.), (1917–1921).

[4] Frederick Smith and Fred Bullock, *Early history of veterinary literature*, (London 1919–1933).

[5] Edward G. Browne, *Arabian medicine* (Cambridge, 1921), reviewed by Singer 'Greek and Arab medicine', *Nature*, 1922, **109**: 438–440.

[6] Sigerist's appointment as a Privatdozent (reader) at the University.

[7] Charles Singer, "Biology", in. R. W. Livingstone (ed.), *The legacy of Greece* (Oxford, 1921), 163–200.

[8] Francis S. Marvin (born 1863), educationist and League of Nations activist, gave a summer school on Evolution of World Peace.

[9] Fielding H. Garrison (1870–1935), medical historian, see H. E Sigerist (ed.) *Bulletin of the Institute of the History of Medicine*, 1937, **5 (4):** (Fielding H. Garrison memorial number); for a biographical introduction and Sigerist's correspondence with Garrison, see Marcel H. Bickel (ed.), *Henry E. Sigerist: Correspondences With Welch, Cushing, Garrison and Ackerknecht* (Bern: Peter Lang, 2010), 95–155.

10

Singer to Sigerist, Oxford, 18 August 1921

My dear Sigerist,

A line to say that I have received your splendid piece of work on the Antidotaria.[1] Is this a duplicate copy or am I to return it to you without delay. I ask this because of course a paper such as I am contemplating will take some time to prepare and in the meantime I should much like to have your work by me.

I am glad to see that the Harleian MS is quite a short one, and I hope to be able to get something about it at any rate into the Classical Quarterly. Of course you shall see what I draw up.

I observe a rather irritating note of old Sudhoff about my Lorica[2] on p. 158 of the new number of the Mitteilungen.[3] Of course I acknowledged Wülker[4] in the most specific and detailed fashion as you will see for yourself on p. 12 of my work if you have it by you. Sudhoff really can be an annoying old man when he tries.

With best regards from us both,

Yours ever,

Charles Singer

P.S. Your election at the Royal Society of Medicine has gone through in due order & you will hear about it[.]

[1] Probably a part of the manuscript to Henry E Sigerist, *Studien und Texte zur frühmittelalterlichen Rezeptliteratur* (Leipzig, 1923).

[2] Charles Singer, 'The Lorica of Gildas the Briton (? 547). A magico-medical text containing an anatomical vocabulary', *Proceedings of the Royal Society of Medicine*, 1918–1919, **12:** 124–144.

[3] *Mitteilungen zur Geschichte der Medizin und der Naturwissenschaften und der Technik*, 1921, **20**.

[4] Richard Paul Wülker (1845–1910), Professor of English Literature and Language at Leipzig University. He had colated and edited the second edition of Thomas Wright, *Anglo-Saxon and Old English vocabularies*, 2 vols (London: Trübner & Co, 1883–1884).

11

Singer to Sigerist, Oxford, 24 August 1921

My dear Sigerist,

Many thanks for your letter of August 21st.

About the Antidotarium. I should very much indeed like to tackle it but cannot do so by the middle of October because I am pledged until the end of September to give all my time to Hippocrates which I am working at in collaboration with Professor A. J. Platt (Professor of Greek at University College, London), and after then I have another piece of work to which I am pledged which will take me about four weeks. Until these are off I?cannot settle down to the Antidotarium.

Would you therefore like me to return it to you and let me have it again later? I very much want to do it and once I am able to settle down to it would give all my time to it. If, however, you feel urgently that it should be published I think I had better stand aside for the moment.

With best regards from both to both,

Yours always,

Charles Singer

12

Singer to Sigerist, Oxford, 28 August 1921

My dear Sigerist,

I see in the Mitteilungen an article Wehrli G. A. Die inneren Körperorgane in den Kinderzeichnungen mit einigen ethnographischen Parallelen. Mitteil. Geogr. Ethnogr. Ges. Zurich 1918/19 XIX S. 35–51 Zurich 1920.[1]

If this is any good would you order a copy for me & have it sent with bill.We are just moving. Our new address will be

5 North Grove

Highgate

N6 London From September 5th

Yours very sincerely

Charles Singer

[1] G. A. Wehrli, 'Die inneren Körperorgane in den Kinderzeichnungen mit einigen ethnographischen Parallelen', *Mitteilungen der Geographisch-Ethnographischen Gesellschaft Zürich*, 1920, 35–51.Gustav Adolf Wehrli (1888–1949) Swiss medical historian and collector at the University of Zurich; see Urs Boschung, 'Gustav Adolf Wehrli (1888–1949), Gründer der Medizinhistorischen Sammlung der Universität Zürich', *Gesnerus*, 1980, **37**: 91–103.

13

Singer to Sigerist, London, 15 September 1921[1]

My dear Sigerist,

Many thanks for your letter of September 5th. Your paper on Antidotes shall go off by registered post to-day. I told the Committee of the new Ducange[2] that you and I would help with early medical terms and they were delighted. We must arrange later on a proper campaign. We are still in great confusion here and you will easily forgive my not writing more.

Many thanks for the copies of Wehrli's papers. They arrived safely and I have written to thank him.

With kind regards from us both,

Yours very sincerely,

Charles Singer

---

[1] New address, see previous letter.

[2] In 1920, the Union Académique Internationale proposed to its member Académies a project to prepare a new edition of Charles du Fresne, seigneur du Cange (or Ducange), Glossary of medieval and late Latin, *Glossarium mediae et infimae Latinitatis* (Paris, 1678).

14

Singer to Sigerist, London, 10 October 1921

My dear Sigerist,

Many thanks for your letter of October 6th with the news that you had come back from the meeting of the German Association.[1] Could you give me any public announcement concerning the introduction of the History of Medicine as a compulsory subject in the medical course of the German Universities? If anything of that sort appears I should very much like to publish it here as it may do our subject quite a lot of good.

I know the Cassel Apuleius. It really is a fine document and extremely interesting. That is splendid news that you are to do the Pseudo Apuleius for the Corpus Medicorum Latinorum.[2] It is a thing which badly wants doing and should prove an exceedingly interesting piece of work. It is sufficiently short not to be tedious and contains innumerable problems. I look forward immensely to being of some little assistance to you in it. I have already begun on the new Ducange.[3] I have a pupil here who is working on the anatomical text in the Hunter MS (Xth century) and there are quite a lot of latinised Greek words in it, and I propose to open my Ducange [sic] box with them. I will send you the transcript of it as I expect you will be able to throw light upon it.

As luck will have it I have just come across my second copy of General Smith's book[4] and I was arranging to send it to you. Now you write that you have got one after all!

Our very best regards to Neuburger.[5] We are just back from a meeting at Paris[6] and I want to say some things to you about it which please regard as confidential, though not secret. I hate all these petty personalities but I think it best to put you <u>au fait</u> with what happened.

In order to make some sort of provisional body, names were asked for from each country. When we came to Switzerland Cumston[7] (who was the only Swiss present) suggested your name in addition to his own. Thereon I proposed Klebs and was seconded by Wickersheimer.[8] Cumston objected saying that two were surely enough from Switzerland! I thought under the circumstances it would be best to bide my time so that I could introduce Klebs under the American list but when it came to that again there was difficulty as it was said that Klebs was not an American, and I really was not sufficiently in possession of the facts to press it on this point. But I had another and better reason for dropping the whole matter. On reflection – and the whole thing, you know, only occupied a few minutes – I came to the conclusion that Cumston, if my diagnostic powers are correct, is obviously going downhill in the physical sense, and I thought to myself that it is quite probable that he will not attend further meetings, that you will then come as the representative of Switzerland and that between the two of us, with Wickersheimer to help, the thing will go through automatically and we shall ask Klebs to become an official delegate. That seemed to me better than an unseemly dispute with Cumston. That is the matter as I see it, and I think it only fair to put you in communication with my views. The French, I think, are coming round in the point of view of meeting enemy countries at the next Congress after this.[9] To my surprise the question was not raised at all and there is nothing in the rules of the Association to prevent Germans and Austrians becoming members. It simply requires that a man should be proposed and seconded. I think it wiser not to propose or second any of them for this Congress but we will raise the question in London and I believe it will settle itself by the following year. The important thing is to do nothing! Could not you manage to come to the Paris meeting in December and then come on here and we could do some Ducangeing?

With best regards from us both,

Yours ever,

Charles Singer

P.S. Perhaps you would like the enclosed list.[10]

[1] German Association of the History of Medicine.

[2] Ernst Howald and Henry E Sigerist, *Pseudo-Apulei herbarius* (Leipzig/Berlin, 1927)

[3] See letter 13.

[4] Possibly referring to Frederick Smith and Fred Bullock, *Early History of Veterinary Literature*, see letter 9.

[5] Max Neuburger (1868–1955), Professor of Medical History in Vienna. See Solomon R. Kagan, 'Professor Max Neuburger: a biography and bibliography . . .in honor of his seventy-fifth birthday', *Bulletin of the History of Medicine*, 1943, **14**: 423–448; Robert Rosenthal, 'Max Neuburger', *Bulletin of the History of Medicine*, 1955, **29**: 295–298.

[6] Probably for the organization of the International Society of the History of Medicine, founded in Paris in mid-1921.

[7] Charles G. Cumston (1868–1928) lecturer of the history of medicine at Geneva. See Ernest Wickersheimer, "Charles Greene Cumston", *Janus*, 1928, **32**: 117–118.

[8] Ernest Wickersheimer (1880–1965) French medical historian. See "Ernest Wickersheimer, 1880–1965", *Journal of the History of Medicine and Allied Sciences*, 1966, **21**: 62–63

[9] For years after World War I the French excluded German and Austrian scientists from scientific conventions.

[10] Probably from Paris meeting.

15

Singer to Sigerist, London, 2 November 1921

My dear Sigerist,

Many thanks for your letter of October 30th. I quite understand, sympathise with and agree with your point of view about the Congress. The question is, what is it best to do?

It is natural that there should be a difficulty in starting these international organisations. Someone must begin, no one knows exactly the conditions in other countries, and it is natural that the most pushing get in first. It seems to me that the right thing for the Swiss to do is to hurry forward the organisation of their own Society, and once that is formed you can express your own opinions clearly. Jeanselme is an understanding and tactful man, and I believe has seen through the whole affair.[1] I am in a very difficult position in the matter as being neither Swiss, American nor French. It happens, however, that Cumston is a Vice-President of our English Society.

My own feeling is, however, that if you will have two or three months' patience concerning the International Congress, and will get on with the formation of your Swiss Society,[2] the whole matter will solve itself.

In forming your Swiss association I should be happy if you would put me down as a member if you are able to include foreigners.

I am much upset that Klebs should not be an official representative from Switzerland, & that my proposal of his name did not go through automatically
Yours always
Charles Singer

I am glad to have news of Neuburger who writes to me frequently. Poor fellow. As I daresay he told you I am having a good deal of printing work done through him at Vienna.
With best regards from us both,
Yours very sincerely,
Charles Singer

---

[1] Antoine E. Jeanselme (1858–1935) French physician and medical historian. See M. Laignel-Lavastine 'Edouard Jeanselme Historien', *Bulletin de la Société Française d'Histoire de la Médecine*', 1939, **33:** 145–192; and *British Medical Journal*, 1935, **i:** 1004–1005.
[2] The Swiss Society of the History of Medicine was founded at the end of 1921.

16

Singer to Sigerist, London?, 6 December 1921 (postcard)

Would you be so good as to tell a Swiss bookseller to send me (with bill)
 E. Lichtenhahn [sic] Sprachliche Bemerkungen zu Marcellus Empiricus
 Thèse de Bàle Bâle (Werner Riehm.) 1917[1]
Charles Singer

---

[1] Eduard Liechtenhan, *Sprachliche Bemerkungen zu Marcellus Empiricus* (Basel, 1917); Marcellus Empiricus (*c.* 410 A.D.) medical author in Bordeaux.

17

Singer to Sigerist, London, 13 December 1921

My dear Sigerist,

You may care to have the enclosed articles by me on "Medicine" and "Biology" contributed to Livingstone's "Legacy of Greece", Oxford, 1921.[1] There is a separate article on Aristotle by D'Arcy Thompson.[2]

With kind regards,

Yours very sincerely

Charles Singer

[1] 'Medicine' (Singer 1921c); 'Biology' (Singer 1921b).
[2] D'Arcy Thompson 'Natural Science', in Livingstone (1921), 137–162.

18

Singer to Sigerist, London, 15 December 1921

My dear Sigerist,

There has just turned up at the Cambridge University Library two fragments of a Beneventum Manuscript[1] which are being investigated by Dr. Minns who is Reader in palaeography at Cambridge University.[2] There are, as you know, only thirteen Beneventan medical manuscripts and this makes the fourteenth. If I remember rightly this one and the Glasgow manuscript are the earliest.

I have been asked to identify the fragment which is obviously an Antidotarium and I have explained that you are the authority on the earliest Antidotaria. I am venturing, therefore, to send a typed copy of it to you. It preserves the original alineation and you will see that the ends of the lines are incomplete. With Dr. Minns' permission I am enclosing this to you and I feel sure he would be glad to have your opinion on it.[3]

We are going to Paris on the 6th and my wife has written to you about hotels. It would be delightful if you could come back to us and we could then do some work together.

I quite agree with your views about the Congress and will do my best to support you.[4]

With very best regards from us both,

Yours always,

Charles Singer

[1] Beneventum, a town in southern Italy.
[2] Ellis H. Minns (1874–1953), archaeologist and palaeographer; see Grahame Clark, 'Minns, Sir Ellis Hovell (1874–1953)', rev. *Oxford dictionary of national biography* (Oxford: Oxford University Press, 2004), vol. 38, 359.
[3] The enclosure is titled "Cambridge University Library. MS. Add. 6324 (Transcript by Dr. E. H. Minns, 10. XII.1921)".
[4] Probably for the organization of the International Society of the History of Medicine.

19

Singer to Sigerist, London, 6 January 1922

My dear Sigerist,

The Channel is so rough – & has been all the week – that we shall not cross.[1] It hardly seems worth while to arrive ill & then to leave – as we should have to do in any case – the next day. It is a great disappointment not to have seen you; we were much looking forward to it.

I have had a line from Sudhoff who, rightly feels very hardly about the exclusion of the Germans.[2] I have written to him repeatedly & I say to you also, that it is not by my will & I am altogether against it. I do not in the least mind saying this publicly & I have repeatedly done so. Still time will heal the matter & the thing for the Germans to do is to take as little notice as possible. I shall do my best.

With very best regards from us both,

Yours ever,

Charles Singer

[1] For the Paris Congress, see previous letter.
[2] See letter 14.

20

Singer to Sigerist, London, 10 January 1922

My dear Sigerist,

I have just been reading with much pleasure your article "Lecciones Heliodori" in the Archiv.[1] I congratulate you upon it. There ought to be a really complete description of Hunterian T.IV.13 published.[2] What extraordinary Latin it is. Can you translate the first paragraph of Heliodorus? If so I wish you would let me have your rendering.

I have just been working at Donnolo and Alchandrius which are of the same date.[3] I think the material might interest you.

It was a great bore not getting over to Paris. What is the best Latin edition of the Herbarium of Apuleius up to date? And can you give me any references to writings on the Synonym lists in the Pamphilus and Dioscorides texts?[4]

I have at last found the extra copy of Smith's Veterinary Medicine"[5] which I will send if you still want it.

With best regards from us both,

Yours very sincerely

Charles Singer

---

[1] Henry E. Sigerist, 'Die "Lecciones Heliodori"', *Archiv für Geschichte der Medizin*, 1921, **13**: 145–156.
[2] Hunterian T.IV.13: A manuscript.
[3] Authors of herbals in Antiquity and early Middle Ages.
[4] Apuleius, Pamphilus and Dioscorides are authors of herbals in Antiquity and early Middle Ages.
[5] Smith and Bullock (1919).

21

Singer to Sigerist, London, 21 February 1922

My dear Sigerist,

(1) Many thanks for your letter of Feb. 6th and for your reprints. All which you write I of course always read, and I am extremely glad to have them in separate form as it enables me to classify them among my pamphlets.

(2) About Paris. I have only the English translation of the notes at the Congress as taken down by C.J.S. Thompson's clerk.[1] Had they been in French I might have understood them but being in English they are quite incomprehensible to me! There is one point, however, on which I must get definite enlightenment, and as I do not want to raise the somewhat acrimonious discussion uselessly I write to you to let me know the facts in confidence.

The original arrangement concerning the Germans was this. We agreed with the French that we should not invite the Germans on this occasion, but it was evident that on the next occasion the meeting would probably be in a neutral country and that they therefore might be invited. It was agreed that a new nation might be admitted to the Society on the vote of two thirds of the members. This was in itself a harsh regulation as the committee meetings are to take place in Paris and naturally the French are liable to outnumber other nations; but it was so agreed and might pass.

I now understand, (though I am not quite sure that I understand rightly,) that in Paris at the last meeting, at which I was not present, they made a new rule that to admit any new country they would require the unanimous vote of all the delegates present!! Is this the case? Do I understand the matter rightly? If it is the case, and if I do understand the matter rightly I intend to protest.

You ought to know, and you will be glad to know, that some of our most eminent historians protest most strongly against a Society calling itself "International" when it is not International. Among their names I am entitled to mention Dr. W.H.R. Rivers, who is the President of the Anthropological Institute,[2] and the eminent Orientalist E. G. Browne.[3] My own feelings are no less strong though my eminence is less.

(3) I shall be delighted to join your Swiss Society if you will elect me. You must think me a very careless fellow for I have unfortunately mislaid the card of application. Please, however, consider this as an application and let me know how much I am to pay.

(4) Have you communicated with the Cambridge people about the manuscript? If you have not, I will forward your letter to them.

(5) Yes, the Hunterian MS. T.IV.13 is indeed written in a terrible language. Much of it is absolutely unintelligible. I have myself been trying to translate the section on Anatomy which has most interesting relations with some of the anatomies that Sudhoff has recently been publishing. The linguistic changes in these Dark Age documents are, however, particularly interesting. They ought to go into the new Ducange.[4] Work does crowd on one so but there is no doubt you and I ought some day to put together these medical terms and they would make the document of first-rate importance. They should appeal, I think, to Niedermann who is at Zürich, is he not?[5]

Did I tell you that I have a new Greek papyrus containing figures of plants of the fifth century? It is the property of the Egypt Exploration Fund and I am hoping to publish it in conjunction with Johnson.[6] It is arranged just like Apuleius but in Greek instead of Latin. I suppose Apuleius must be a translation from the Greek?

It will be delightful to see you here in July. We do so much look forward to it.

With very best regards from us both,

Yours always,

Charles Singer

I have just come on the circular & enclose cheque for 10 frans Swiss.

---

[1] Charles J. S. Thompson (1862–1943), historian, author, and Henry Wellcome's assistant; see John Symons, 'Thompson, Charles John Samuel (1862–1943)', *Oxford dictionary of national biography* (Oxford: Oxford University Press, 2004), vol. 54, 408–409.

[2] William H. R. Rivers (1864–1922), anthropologist and psychiatrist. See Michael Bevan and Jeremy MacClancy, 'Rivers, William Halse (1864–1922)', *Oxford dictionary of national biography* (Oxford: Oxford University Press, 2004), vol. 47, 48–49.

[3] Edward G. Browne (1862–1926), Persian scholar. See E. D. Ross, 'Browne, Edward Granville (1862–1926)', rev. John Gurney, *Oxford dictionary of national biography* (Oxford: Oxford University Press, 2004), vol. 8, 155–157.

[4] See letter 13.

[5] Max Niedermann (1874–1954), classical philologist, University of Basel; see Albert Grenier, 'Éloge funèbre de M. Max Niedermann, correspondant étranger de l'Académie', *Comptes-rendus des séances de l'Académie des inscriptions et belles-lettres*, 1954, **98 (1):** 22–24.

[6] The Johnson Papyrus (Wellcome Library, London, MS.5753); a fragment from an illustrated herbal found in 1914 by the classical scholar John de Monins Johnson (1882–1956), at Antinoe, Egypt, whilst he was working for the Egypt Exploration Fund. See Arthur S. Hunt and John Johnson (eds), 'Two Theocritus papyri' *Gnomon*, 1930, **6:** 561–564.

22

Singer to Sigerist, London, 20 March 1922

My dear Sigerist,

There is really no secret about Klebs though the matter is a little awkward. The situation is as follows. I proposed him in the usual way and got Rolleston to second him.[1] Somewhat incautiously perhaps I then asked a third member of our Section, whom I happened to meet, to support the proposal. I think I had better not give you his name, [.] Immediately he raised the question of Klebs' sympathies during the war. I did not quite know what to do in the matter and so consulted privately D'Arcy Power who is our Senior Vice-President and one of the kindest and most broad-minded of men.[2] Power thought the objection absurd, but he also thought it would be advisable to wait awhile, as clearly we do not want to offend any of our old members. That is how the matter stands. The matter rests with me and has never been placed before any others but those I have mentioned. If Klebs will be so generous as to wait awhile in silence I have no doubt it will be perfectly all right. His name has never been put forward, and in my opinion it is preposterous that such questions should be raised at all. My views on these matters are too well known to need repetition again.

Would you perhaps explain all this to Klebs? I have not the least objection to your sending him a copy of this letter or even the letter itself.

I am threshing out this matter of the French and am very unsettled about it. I am writing to Jeanselme this week to say that if necessary I will come over to discuss the whole matter with him, but in my opinion there is nothing for the French to do but alter their decision about a unanimous vote.

Will you in the meantime bring pressure to bear on your side?

Yours ever,

Charles Singer

[1] This probably refers to his being proposed as a member of the History of Medicine Section of the Royal Society of Medicine.

[2] D'Arcy Power (1855–1941), British surgeon and medical historian; see Harold Ellis, 'Power, Sir D'Arcy (1855–1941)', *Oxford dictionary of national biography* (Oxford: Oxford University Press, 2004), vol. 45, 131–132.

23

Singer to Sigerist, London, 22 March 1922

My dear Sigerist,

I forget if I wrote to you that I rather think I can get photographs taken at the Hunterian Library at Glasgow rather cheaper than most people. If you want any others taken you had therefore better have the work done through me. I am most interested to hear that you are getting on with further texts from T 4.13. I am much looking forward to seeing your work. Keep off the anatomical text as I am at work on that and have a good deal to say about it.

I enclose photos of the new Greek papyrus.[1] Please return them but if you want copies I can let you have others. I read on one side

ΣΥΜΦΥΤΟΝ
ΑΥΤΗ ΒΟΤΑΝΗ ΤΡΙΒΟΜΕΝΗ
ΘΕΡΑΠΕΥΕΙ ΠΑCΑΝ
ΚΑΙ ΤΡΑΥΜΑΤΑ
ΚΟΠΑCΚΟλλ
ΤΑΙ ΘΕΡΑΠΕΥΕΙ

& on the other a few letter such as

ΛΑΘ CΟC
ΗC ΒΟΤΑΝ ΗC ΤΟ
ΥΧΟΝ ΚΑΙ ΜΥ(Ε)λΟCΑ
ΑΝΘΟΥC
ΠΟΙΕΙΤΑΙ
ΘΕΡΑΠΕΥΕΙ

It shows

(a) Rigid conventionalisation in [....] MSS of the 5th century closely parallel to the Leyden Apuleius

(b) The existence of a Greek text on similar lines to Apuleius containing uses of herbs but without their description save by figures.

If you think you can make further suggestions as to readings I will send you a more "diplomatic" transcript of the letters.

As always

Charles Singer

---

[1] Charles Singer, 'The herbal in antiquity and its transmission to later ages', *Journal of Hellenic Studies*, 1927, **47**: 1–52, pp31–33. His published text contains very different readings, after consulting Dr H. I. Bell of the British Museum. See Marie-Hélène Marganne, *Inventaire analytique des papyrus grecs de médecine* (Geneva: Droz, 1981), p.51 no. 30 (Wellcome MS 5753), and David Leith, 'The Antinoopolis Illustrated Herbal (P. Johnson + P. Antin. 3.214 = MP 3.2095)', *Zeitschrift für Papyrologie und Epigraphik*, 2006, **156**: 141–156.

24

Singer to Sigerist, London, 30 March 1922 (postcard)

I entirely agree with your letter to the Paris Committee. You could not have acted otherwise. I have not yet had a reply to my protest.

Charles Singer

25

Singer to Sigerist, London, 4 April 1922

My dear Sigerist,

As regards the resolution of the French. I have been considering the matter carefully and if the French law of procedure is anything like the English law of procedure it is impossible to pass such a resolution as that which was passed in Paris demanding a unanimous vote to admit a new national society, <u>except by giving special notice</u>. The English law of procedure is that no motion which affects the constitution of a society can be put on the agenda unless full notice is given of it. This usually means two meetings and should have meant two meetings in this case. If I am right in this we can very easily reverse the decision at the London meeting.[1] If I find it cannot be done I shall certainly resign my membership of the International Society.[2] But I rather gather from a letter recently received from Lavastine that it can be done.

The object of this letter is to urge you to attend the meeting of the Society in London. The more people like yourself will come the more my views may be strengthened by your support.

It was decided at a recent meeting of our Council in London to send an invitation to Zürich University asking them to send a representative, who will of course be yourself.
Yours always,
Charles Singer

[1] The London meeting was to take place on 17–22 July 1922.
[2] International Society of the History of Medicine.

26

Singer to Sigerist, London, 24 May[?] 1922

My dear Sigerist,

I find that there is a letter from you on my table dated March 4th some elements of which are I think still unanswered.

I notice that you are interested in the MSS. of Solomon Negri[1] in the Hunterian Library at Glasgow. It is impossible to photograph them there. But it is possible to get them to London. If you care for this I could, I think, arrange for them to be here for a few weeks during your visit. One has to insure the MSS for a rather large sum (£ 1,000 I think) which costs about £ 3. But I think it could be done.

Write to me if there are any other MSS you would like specially to see or any arrangements you would like to have made for study & I will try to help in every way in my power.

Klebs comes through London next week.

Yours always,

Charles Singer

[1] Salomon Negri (*c*.1660–1729), philologist in Damascus and London.

27

Singer to Sigerist, London, 25 May 1922

My dear Sigerist,

At our International Congress we have, as you know, a section on "The Revival of Medical Knowledge during the 16th century".

We have not yet a title of a paper from you. Could you not perhaps help us with this section?

I enclose a preliminary prospectus and programme.[1]

Yours always,

Charles Singer

[1] Singer was President of the 2nd International Congress of the History of Medicine in July 1922 in London.

28

Singer to Sigerist, London, 29 May 1922

My dear Sigerist,

I see that your meeting of the Swiss Society begins on August 24th.[1] It is just possible that I shall be able to come to it.

I want to get a copy of Ladame's Michel Servet in the Bulletin de l'Institut national genevois Genève 1914 tome XLI.[2] Could you perhaps get one for me sending me the bill? Was it perhaps unprinted?

As always,

Charles Singer

Klebs is here & I am meeting him today.

C. S.

[1] Swiss Society of the History of Medicine; the first meeting after its foundation in 1921.

[2] Paul-Louis Ladame, 'Michel Servet, sa réhabilitation historique; son caractère – son oeuvre comme savant et sa découverte de la circulation pulmonaire', *Bulletin de l'Institut national genevois*, 1914, **41**: 225–319. Paul-Louis Ladame (1842–1919), Swiss neurologist; Michel (Miguel) Servet, (1511–1553) Spanish theologian and physician.

29

Singer to Sigerist, London, 31 May 1922

My dear Sigerist,

You can get a good idea of the character of Salomon Negri's work by looking at the article on "The Life and Works of Rhazes" by J. S.A. Rankin [sic][1] on p.237 of the Section of the History of Medicine of the 17th International Congress of Medicine, London, 1914. This work is entirely taken from Negri's manuscript.

I will arrange to have a list of manuscripts of Apuleius in London ready for you, so as to waste as little of your time as possible.[2] You are quite right that there is a celebrated Anglo-Saxon translation (Cotton Vitellius C.3) at the British Museum. It is printed in Cockayne[3] and one of the illustrations is there reproduced. I have also reproduced several illustrations from it in Vol. II of my "Studies".[4] I have a very large number of other coloured figures of it and have been at work some time on it with an Anglo-Saxon scholar.[5]

It is good news that you are coming to the Congress. I know quite well that it is often much more comfortable for people to stay in hotels and I will not press the matter, but we have, in fact, ample and comfortable accomodation here and should be more than pleased to put you up. It would be a great pleasure to us both. We have so many things to talk about together that I think we should probably get through much more if you were with us. You have but to say the word and rooms will be reserved for you either in this house or close by. I would add that we are 25 minutes from the British Museum and it is much cooler up here than in town.

I have been invited to lecture in Glasgow in November next. It is a long journey – 12 hours each way – and I don't want particularly to go, but I would be partly determined by the question as to whether I could do any good by examining manuscripts. If, therefore, there are any points that you would like me to look up at Glasgow, let me know and that, together with my own needs in the matter, will partly determine my decision.

That is good news about your paper on the "Conflict between the 16th century Physicians and Antiquity".[6] I have put you down for it. It is just the sort of thing we want.

With best regards from us both,

Yours always,

Charles Singer

I have been asked to write an account of the Menon Papyrus[7] for a learned work here. I don't know anything special new on it. Do you?

[1] George S. A. Ranking (1852–1934), British surgeon; see *British Medical Journal*, 1934, **ii**: 336.
[2] Sigerist was engaged in cataloguing the medical manuscripts of Switzerland and was editing Apuleius. Ernst Howald and Henry E. Sigerist (eds), *Pseudo-Apulei herbarius*, Corpus medicorum latinorum; v. 4 (Leipzig/Berlin, 1927).
[3] Thomas O. Cockayne (1807–1873), philologist of Anglo-Saxon, and author of *Leechdoms, wortcunning and starcraft of Early England* (London: Longman, 1864–1866).
[4] See letter 5.
[5] Presumably J. H. G. Grattan, see letter 244.
[6] Probably for the London Congress of July 1922; not published.
[7] This medical papyrus, now in London, includes a list of the opinions of Greek doctors of the 5th and 4th century B.C. which most scholars believe goes back to Menon, the pupil of Aristotle, around 340 B.C.,see W.H.S. Jones (ed.), *The medical writings of Anonymus Londinensis* (Cambridge: University Press, 1947).

30

Dorothea Singer to Sigerist, London, 23 July 1922

My dear Dr. Sigerist

It is too charming of you to have sent me these lovely roses. Thank you so very much. They are filling our room with lovely perfume & are a tangible reminder of the great pleasure we had in seeing you & Mrs. Sigerist. We are so very glad that you were able to come & we much look forward to seeing you in Switzerland next month.

With our warmest greetings to you and Mrs. Sigerist & with again so many thanks for the lovely roses
Yours very sincerely
D. Waley Singer

31

Singer to Sigerist, Lugano, Switzerland, 24 August 1922

My dear Sigerist,

We were so very glad to hear that you are going on well. Of course you must go very slowly and by no means think of answering this letter.

We start from here tomorrow for Mesocco. From there we are walking to Bonaduz where we shall pick up letters and from there to Andermatt where we shall pick up letters again. Perhaps we may be able to look in on you at Zurich later on in September if you are back by then but you and Mrs. Sigerist must on no account think of putting us up. We know quite well that her hands will be very full & we want to save her & you in every way.

I think you will be interested to see the enclosed list of books. They are for sale by an old medical man who has had a hemiplegic stroke. He is willing to let them go for anything at which they are valued by a competent person. I have marked one or two Sig (Sigerist) & one or two A.C.K. and others C. S. (C. Singer) but any you or Klebs take a fancy to, by all means order as I am not set on any except perhaps the Cocchi.[1]

Let me have the list back, quite at your leisure. I have written to old Baker[2] to say that I cannot order any till I get home but asking him to reserve the marked books – which I am sure he will. I have also written to him to let you or Klebs have any you want.

I received Sudhoff's Pagel[3] for the British Medical Journal just before I left but I think it has not been printed yet. I will let you have a copy when it appears. I also write a leader for the Literary Supplement of the Times in which I ventured to use an idea from your paper at the Congress – the notion of the fertilising union of the mediaeval legacy of Greek science with the Renaissance inheritance of Greek letters. It seems to me a most illuminating idea which ought to be worked out in detail.

I called on Spät of L'Art ancien this morning & found him a very intelligent fellow, but not cheap.[4]

Lugano is very hot & we have been staying on Monte Salvatore where it is pleasant and cool though there are rather to many trippers in the afternoon. Today I had a letter from Sudhoff who is full of the exhibition of graphic art at Leipzig and wants me to send one or two things.

With best regards from both to both,

Yours ever,

Charles Singer

Please tell Mrs. Sigerist that we shall be very grateful if she will let us know how you go on.

---

[1] There are several medical authors named Cocchi: Antonio (1695–1758), Antonio-Celestino (1699–1747), Virgilio (1692–1736).
[2] Probably a bookseller.
[3] Karl Sudhoff, *Kurzes Handbuch der Geschichte der Medizin* (Berlin, 1922), a continuation of Julius Pagel's textbook on the history of medicine. Julius L. Pagel (1851–1912), German physician and medical historian. See Walter Pagel, 'Julius Pagel and the significance of medical history for medicine', *Bulletin of the History of Medicine*, 1951, **25:** 207–225.
[4] Probably a bookseller.

32

Singer to Sigerist, San Bernardino, Switzerland, 29 August 1922

My dear Sigerist,

Isn't it beastly. I've just broken my leg here. Fibula only, simple fracture in 2 places. I had to be carried here about $1\frac{1}{2}$ hours. My leg is now in plaster & I shall stay here in bed about 8 days & then try to get to Zurich where I must have massage[,] Rontgen Rays etc.

Do advise me where to stay & whom to consult there?

How are you going on? This is an additional reason for not staying with you but we shall surely see a good deal of you.

I have written also to Klebs[.]

Best regards from both to both

Yours ever

Charles Singer

33

Singer to Sigerist, London, 29 September 1922

My dear Sigerist,

How are you? I hope you have not been doing too much. Do drop us a line to say you are going on all right. We are so grateful to you and your family for your kindness to us.

On arriving home I found on my table H. Kühn, <u>Die Malerei der Eiszeit</u>, published by Delphin Verlag of München.[1] It was bought for me by a friend who was visiting Germany and cost me about 7/6. It has 12 folio plates and a number of other drawings, and is a very beautiful reproduction. I thought you might like to know of this.

Yours ever,

Charles Singer

I also find the long expected solution by[?] Newbold of the Roger Bacon cypher.[2] Absolutely mad!

---

[1] Herbert Kühn, *Die Malerei der Eiszeit* (München, 1922).
[2] Newbold and Roger Bacon cypher not identified.

34

Singer to Sigerist, London, 1 October 1922 (postcard)

I notice that S. Bocca,[1] Via Fontanella di Borghese, 27, Roma 9 has the following 489. Du Cange[2] 1884 edition (the best), bound, 1500 lire 846. Mangetus. Bibliotheca anatomica. Geneva 1685.[3] Round 75 lire 1355[.] Thierfelder Additamenta ad Haeseri Bibliothecum

[sic] 1843[4] 12 lire with 20% addition. These might interest you. Hope you are going on well.

Yours ever

Charles Singer

---

[1] A bookseller.

[2] See letter 13.

[3] Jean-Jacques Manget (1652–1742); Jean-Jacques Manget, *Bibliotheca anatomica* (Geneva, 1685).

[4] Johann G. Thierfelder, *Additamenta ad Henrici Haeseri bibliothecam epidemiographicam* (Meissen, 1943), on a work of the medical historian Heinrich Haeser (1811–1884).

35

Singer to Sigerist, London, 3 October 1922 (postcard)

I saw Elliot Smith[1] for a few minutes yesterday. He will write for the Sudhoff Volume "On the beginnings of Science".[2] I thought you would like to hear this at once.

C. S.

---

[1] Grafton Elliot Smith (1871–1937) British anatomist and anthropologist. See Graham Richards, 'Smith, Sir Grafton Elliot (1871–1937)', *Oxford dictionary of national biography* (Oxford: Oxford University Press, 2004), vol 51, 156–157.

[2] Charles Singer and Henry E. Sigerist (eds), *Essays in the history of medicine presented to Karl Sudhoff on the occasion of his seventieth birthday November 25th 1923* (London/Zurich, 1924); see Letter 64, note 2.

36

Singer to Sigerist, London, 11 October 1922

My dear Sigerist,

We were very glad to get your card and hope things will go on all right now. You will be glad to see the enclosed from Lewis who is delighted to have that Welsh book.[1] Don't return it.

My leg goes on as well as possible and I am getting about in fair comfort. I am told I shall be quite all right in about a month.

I hope you won't attempt to lecture this term and will have a good time at Lugano with no thought of work!

With best wishes from us both to you all,

Yours ever,

Charles Singer

---

[1] Timothy Lewis (1877–1958), scholar in Celtic palaeography. The Welsh book not identified.

37

Singer to Sigerist, London, 5 December 1922

My dear Sigerist,

Thanks for your letter of December 2nd. Please forgive me for not having answered sooner I have been very upset by the very grave illness of my mother.

Comrie,[1] Elliot Smith, Withington,[2] and Streeter[3] have all accepted. To that list you must of course add my name.[4] I have written to Garrison but have not yet had an answer. Now that I have your list I will begin to attack the doubtfuls.

By all means let me have the lantern slides together with an account. The College[5] will pay all right. How many were there?

That is good news that you are properly at work again. I think it is quite all right about Ketham[6] although I have been so buried under with work that I have not had time to think about it. I do not think there is any doubt that Klebs and I are to work for the Italian firm.[7] I do not know about overlapping Sudhoff but I will make a point of sounding him on the subject.

With best regards from house to house,

Yours always,

Charles Singer

[1] John D. Comrie (1875–1939), Scottish historian of medicine. See 'John Dixon Comrie, M.A., B.Sc., M.D.', *British Medical Journal*, 1939, **ii:** 789.

[2] Edward T. Withington (1860–1947), British historian of medicine; see 'E. T. Withington, M.B.', *British Medical Journal*, 1947, **i:** 698.

[3] Edward C. Streeter (1874–1947), medical historian at Yale University, pupil of Sudhoff. See Henry R. Viets, 'Edward Clark Streeter (1874–1947)', *Bulletin of the History of Medicine*, 1947, **21:** 843–845.

[4] Contributors to the Sudhoff Festschrift.

[5] University College London.

[6] Iohannes de Ketham (15th century), poorly identified editor of medical texts and drawings. In 1923 work on Ketham led to certain irritation between Klebs, Sigerist, Singer, and Sudhoff; see the Sigerist-Klebs correspondence in Marcel H. Bickel (ed.), *Henry E. Sigerist: Vier ausgewählte Briefwechsel mit Medizin-historikern der Schweiz* (Bern, 2008).

[7] Lier & Co., publishers, Milan.

38

Singer to Sigerist, London, 5 January 1923

My dear Sigerist,

Many thanks for your letter of Jan 1st. That is good news about the publisher. Now about the plan of the book.[1] I enclose an article I have written for it for your approval.[2] You will note that it [is] in the nature of a review of work done & does not profess to be original. I think it is better so. I also think that a short list of the more important work reviewed – as distinct from bibliography – is better than complete documentation for our purpose.

If you approve of this idea I will at once start getting in my people[3] from this point of view.

I have written to Garrison but have not yet had a reply. I have also written to Maar[4] & Fonahn[5] but as I have not heard from them I'll write again. Wickersheimer I have intentionally left till last.

All my other people have accepted, Comrie, Withington, Streeter, Elliot Smith. If you pass my plan I'll get them to write on similar lines.

I've had a great upset here. My mother died (aged 83) a month ago & I have had much to do looking after her affairs. Now I have lost the use of my secretary for a time & she will not be back till next week.

But the article is done – that's the great thing. Best wishes to you all from us both for the New Year,

Yours ever,

Charles Singer

---

[1] Sudhoff Festschrift, Singer and Sigerist (1924a).

[2] Charles Singer and Dorothea Singer, 'The origin of the Medical School of Salerno', in Singer and Sigerist (1924), 121–138.

[3] Comrie, Withington, Streeter, Smith.

[4] Vilhelm Maar (1871–1940), Danish medical historian; see Edvard Gotfredsen, 'Vilhelm Maar (8. Juni 1871-18. Mai 1940)', *Mitteilungen zur Geschichte der Medizin und der Naturwissenschaften und der Technik*, 1940, **39**: 212–213.

[5] Adolf M. Fonahn (1873–1940), Norwegian orientalist and medical historian.

39

Singer to Sigerist, London, 24 January 1923

My dear Sigerist,

You must really forgive me for being such a very bad correspondent. I feel very guilty about it. But you would not believe how pressed I have been during the last few weeks. I have had to write two articles for a volume edited by Marvin;[1] I have had to get finished my article on "Science" for the "Legacy of Rome";[2] I have had to write an introduction to a school-book on "The History of Science";[3] I have had any amount of reviewing;[4] I have had to prepare my lectures for the term, and I have been getting Hippocrates into its final state.[5] However, I feel a little less rushed now and am able to turn round.

Firstly, I must thank you most sincerely for your two admirable volumes on "Dark Age Texts" and on "Ambroise Paré".[6] They are both most valuable and treasured contributions. Curiously enough, we have sent off to the printer this very week our own little volume on Paré which is to appear in my wife's name.[7]

I have this morning sent letters to Fonahn, Leersum, Maar and Sarton,[8] copies of which I enclose. The four letters differ only as regards one sentence. I have also written to Streeter and Garrison copies of whose letters I also enclose. I have written also to Professor E. G. Browne at your suggestion.

As regards Lier & Co. and their taking up the editing of that series of Kleins.[9] They are quite right that I have been very negligent, but the reason for my negligence is the same as for my negligence of you. It is really pressure of work which is now, I am glad to say, less. I have had their letter on my table for weeks, meaning to answer it.

I should be delighted to join you or Klebs or both of you in editing such a series as you suggest, but having neglected it so long I feel very guilty in the matter. I think the best thing to do would be for you to edit the series and for me to undertake the Ketham either alone or in conjunction with Sudhoff.

I have an idea that I could make it more readable than Sudhoff could, and a volume written in English would probably have a greater sale. If he would like it why not send his plates to me with the material, allow me to write it up, and let it appear in both our names, his of course to come first? This is what I should really like best, and you may assure him that I should be proud to place my name under his in an English work.[10]

As regards the general editing of the series, I really feel that as things have gone so long it would be best for you to take on the whole series as editor and I will back you up as much as I can, and specifically by undertaking this Ketham right away. If, however, you think it would help to add my name you are most welcome to do so, and I should think that Klebs would take the same view. I think I could make some suggestions, particularly in the department of MSS. We have one or two manuscripts in the British Museum which certainly ought to be facsimiled, notably the French Roger of Parma which I could easily do also.[11]

You may absolutely rely on me not to run in any way a rival show of facsimiles. Anything that you settle with Lier I am sure to be content with.

Yours ever,
Charles Singer

---

[1] Charles Singer, 'Ancient medicine', in F. S. Marvin (ed.), *Science and civilization* (London,1923), 43–71; Charles Singer, 'The Dark Ages and the dawn', *ibid.*, 112–160.

[2] Charles Singer, 'Science', in C. Baily (ed.), *The legacy of Rome* (Oxford, 1923), 265–324.

[3] Not published under this title.

[4] In 1922 Singer published 10 book reviews.

[5] 'Hippocrates' not published under this title.

[6] Probably Henry E. Sigerist, *Studien und Texte zur frühmittelalterlichen Rezeptliteratur* (Leipzig, 1923) and Henry E. Sigerist (ed.), *Ambroise Paré, Die Behandlung der Schusswunden* (Leipzig, 1923).

[7] Dorothea W. Singer, *Selections from the works of Ambroise Paré* (London 1924).

[8] E. C. van Leersum: Dutch medical historian; see M. A. van Andel, 'In memoriam Prof. Dr. E. C. van Leersum', *Janus*, 1939, **43:** 81–83. George Sarton (1884–1956) Belgian-American historian of science. See *Isis* George Sarton Memorial Issue, Sept 1957, 48 (3).

[9] J. T. Klein (1685–1759) published on zoology. 'Series of Kleins' not edited by Singer.

[10] Charles Singer (ed.), *The Fasciculus Medicinae of Johannes de Ketham, Alemanus*. With an Introduction by Karl Sudhoff, translated by C. Singer (Milan: Lier, 1924). Singer had corresponded with Sudhoff about Ketham.

[11] Roger Frugard of Parma, 12th century surgeon in southern Italy; not edited by Singer.

40

Singer to Sigerist, London, 29 January 1923

My dear Sigerist,

If you like you may transmit the enclosed letter to Sudhoff, either with or without a covering letter from yourself.

I am sorry to say that Leersum won't hear of contributing to the volume.[1] E. G. Browne would like to but is doubtful if he can find time. I shall try to persuade him, and shall be in Cambridge next month for the purpose.

Yours always,

Charles Singer

---

[1] The Sudhoff volume, Singer and Sigerist (1924).

41

Singer to Sigerist, London, 1 February 1923

My dear Sigerist,

I have written right off to Streeter to suggest that he should do "Renaissance Anatomy" rather than Renaissance Medicine as a whole.

I am so glad you are taking on Lier's job . I'll help all that I can most gladly. My idea was also to reproduce pages from different editions of Ketham and to have a general survey of the book as a whole. We'll see how Sudhoff takes it. I shan't be at all hurt if he does it on his own, but I think it very likely that he will like to collaborate with me.

Of course if we reproduce manuscripts in England it would not be in the least necessary to make the clichées in England. It would only be necessary to make the photographs here, unless perchance we decided to have coloured figures.

Of course I would do the 1478 Mondino.[1] Another suggestion that I would make is Malpighi's De pulmonibus of 1661 (Bologna).[2] There is no copy of this in England and it is excessively rare. Doubtless it is to be found in Italy. You remember that it is the first work containing a description of the capillaries. It is quite short.

Maar and Leersum have just refused with a considerable degree of ferocity! Under the circumstances I decided to invite Fishbein also and have written to him.[3] I think you will approve of this.

I have just had a letter from E. G. Browne to say that he thinks he will be able to do something after all.

Have you seen the article by Breasted[4] in the last number of the Bulletin of the Society of Medical History of Chicago? on the "Edwin Smith Papyrus"? It is earlier than the Ebers and very much more scientific.[5] If Breasted is right he has produced a new document of fundamental value which must entirely alter our views as to the origin of science. Much of what I have written about the beginnings of Greek science will have to be re-written.

With best regards to you all from us both,

Yours ever,

Charles Singer

[1] Mondino de Liucci (*c.*1275–1326), Italian anatomist. See Vern L. Bullough, 'Mondino dei Liucci', *Complete dictionary of scientific biography*, Vol. 9 (Detroit: Charles Scribner's Sons, 2008), 467–469.

[2] Marcello Malpighi (1628–1694), Italian anatomist; Marcello Malpighi, *De pulmonibus observationes anatomicae*, Bologna, 1661. See Luigi Belloni, 'Malpighi, Marcello', *Complete dictionary of scientific biography*, Vol. 9 (Detroit: Charles Scribner's Sons, 2008), 62–66.

[3] Morris Fishbein, (1889–1976), editor of the *Journal of the American Medical Association* and historian of medicine and science; see *Morris Fishbein, M.D.: an autobiography* (Garden City, N.Y.: Doubleday, 1969); and 'Former editor Dr Morris Fishbein dies', *Journal of the American Medical Association*, 1976, **236:** 1820–1822'.

[4] J. H. Breasted, 'The Edwin Smith Papyrus: an Egyptian medical treatise of the seventeenth century before Christ', *Bulletin of the Society of Medical History of Chicago*, 1923, **3:** 58–78. James Henry Breasted (1865–1935), archaeologist and historian, see W. R. Dawson, 'James Henry Breasted', *The Journal of the Royal Asiatic Society of Great Britain and Ireland*, 1936, **1:** 179–184.

[5] Edwin Smith and Ebers, Egyptian papyri.

42

Singer to Sigerist, London, 2 February 1923

My dear Sigerist,

Many thanks for your letter of Jan. 31st. Your suggestion that I should do the 1493 Italian Ketham and Sudhoff the 1491 seems to me quite satisfactory, and I will gladly fall in with your plans.

It seems a pity that the two should not appear at the same time, but I should like to have Sudhoff's material before me while I prepare mine. I think in that way I could make a better job of it. Perhaps I might have proof sheets of the facsimiles sent me?

W. G. Spencer will be coming here one day next week.[1] He has given me that excellent paper that he read on the figures in the Epitome of Vesalius[2] to publish in the next volume of my "Studies". It looks, however, as though Vol. III of my "Studies" will be some time in appearing. I therefore think that it would be a good idea for me to ask him to put the article into our volume for Sudhoff.[3] He has some beautiful clichées for it, and I know he has a great admiration for Sudhoff.

I had a letter from Klebs this morning which rather suggests that he is a little offended about this business with Lier! If he is, it is entirely my fault for not answering letters promptly and you may put it all on to me!

As regards asking the French to contribute to the Sudhoff volume, I have been awaiting a favourable opportunity and clearly that has not yet arrived. I fear there is nothing for it but to leave them as late as possible. When we have a volume with plenty of English and

American names – and it is now certain that we shall have these – we can tell them how the matter stands.

Have you had anything from Italy yet?

Yours ever,

Charles Singer

[1] Walter G. Spencer (1858–1940) English surgeon and medical historian. See *British Medical Journal*, 1940, **ii:** 649–650.

[2] Andreas Vesalius (1514–1564) anatomist; Epitome to his *De humani corporis fabrica* (Vesalius 1552).

[3] Walter G. Spencer, 'The "Epitome" of Vesalius on vellum in the British Museum Library', in Singer and Sigerist (eds), (1924), 237–244.

43

Singer to Sigerist, London, 5 February 1923

My dear Sigerist,

(1) Enclosed from Browne is very difficult to read. The relevant passage runs as follows: -

["]I should like to contribute to Sudhoff's Festschrift[1] but shrink from Bibliography. I would like to write a short account, of my rare Arabic MS Magala [....][2] ("Discourse on the Generation of Man") by Abu'l Hasan Said ibn Hibalu'Nah court physician to the Caliph al-Mugtadi who died in A.D. 1101. My copy was made in A.D. 1096 while the author was still living. There is another MS at Oxford which I have not seen. The book is mostly about Embryology & Psychology, but as yet I have only examined it superficially. We can discuss it when we meet."

I go to Cambridge & stay with him for a day or two next Monday. Of course I shall accept though his suggestion is off our line. It is important & too good to lose. Also he is too eminent to miss. I feel sure you will agree.

(2) I enclose also Fonahn's letter. I am less certain about including him. The article[,] however[,] on the "Grabadin" might be extended a bit to be made of more general interest & something dragged in about the "Mesue" collection.[3]

In favour of including Fonahn is that he is the only Scandinavian that has accepted & it is evident that we shall be short of non-English & non-German contributors.

(3) Poelter[?][4] let me have my article back. I can brush[?] it up a bit & add one or two new facts that I have found. But you can have it the very moment you want to go to Press.

Yours ever,

Charles Singer

[1] Browne did not contribute to the Festschrift, Singer and Sigerist (1924).

[2] Arabic transcriptions are left out.

[3] Grabadin, a medieval compendium of drugs by J. Mesue (Mesue collection).

[4] Poelter or Poetter not identified.

44

Singer to Sigerist, London, 27 February 1923

My dear Sigerist,

You haven't let me have back my MS. of Salerno.[1] There are a few things I should like to alter and amplify in it.

D'Arcy Power has consented to write an article for the Sudhoff volume. It will be on the "History of Antiseptic Surgery since its inception".[2] He can of course write it from personal memory. I have to-day also written to Walter Spencer. I think he will give us the article that he gave at the Congress, and he has some clichées in illustration of it which I think he might lend us.

To-day there comes from Lynn Thorndike his two-volume "History of Magic and Experimental Science during the first thirteen centuries of our era". It looks to me a work of enormous erudition.[3]

Very many thanks for the excellent lantern slides. They are really beautiful, but most unfortunately they do not fit the English lantern. I only discovered this a few days before yours arrived, when I had similarly a number sent to me by Sudhoff. You must, however, let me know the cost so that I may send you a cheque.

The English lanterns are made to hold a slide of 8.1 cms x 8.1 cms. Some of your slides I can cut down, but about two thirds of them I cannot. I think, however, even in these cases I can have other slides made from them.

You will be interested to see the enclosed project for a summer school at Vienna. Our present scheme is to come to Switzerland about the middle of July with a couple of our nieces, to spend a fortnight on walking tour, and then to go on to Vienna. I wonder if you and Mrs. Sigerist would care to come there. I expect you are already booked up.

I have not yet had the plates of Ketham. With best regards from us both to you all,

Yours ever,

Charles Singer

P.S. I enclose a letter from Streeter which explains itself. As he is going to Salerno I have written to him to know if he can secure a photograph of that MS. that Capparoni has been working on.[4] I should think that Capparoni and Wellcome between them are sure to do something that will be quite useless, so that we shall have to get it done anyhow!

[1] Charles Singer and Dorothea Singer, 'The origin of the Medical School of Salerno', in Singer and Sigerist (1924), 121–138.

[2] D'Arcy Power's article did not appear in the Sudhoff Festschrift.

[3] Lynn Thorndike (1882–1965), historian/medievalist at Columbia University; see *Isis*, 1966, **57**: 88–89. Lynn Thorndike, *History of magic and experimental science during the first thirteen centuries of our era* (New York, 1923–1958).

[4] Pietro Capparoni (1868–1947), Italian medical historian; see Andrea Corsini, 'Pietro Capparoni 1868–1947', *Rivista di Storia delle Scienze Mediche e Naturali*, 1947, **27**: i–ii. Pietro Capparoni, *Magistri salernitani nondum cogniti.* (London, 1923) was published in the series of Wellcome Historical Medical Museum Research Studies in Medical History.

45

Singer to Sigerist, London, 7 March 1923

My dear Sigerist,

Many thanks for your letter. No matter about the diapositives. Although they do not fit our ordinary lanterns, I find that, as a matter of fact, there are a good many lanterns that they <u>can</u> be used for with a little manipulation, and as you kindly sent the photographs I can have slides made from them by our college photographer.

Thanks, too, for the bill. I am passing it through the college account and you will be paid in a few weeks. If, however, you would like to be paid earlier, let me know, and I daresay it could be managed.

Walter Spencer, I think I wrote to you, will let us have that excellent article on Vesalius,[1] which should especially appeal to Sudhoff for it contains figures of the Epitome (of which he will lend the clichées) which have never before been used.

Sarton is entirely in sympathy with the idea of giving a volume to Sudhoff, but feels he cannot do anything as he is so very rushed. Fishbein, however, has consented.[2]

We shall be taking a walking tour in Switzerland during the last fortnight in July with one of my nieces. When we know your movements we shall be able to arrange to meet, I have no doubt.

I have been reading a good deal of Lynn Thorndike's book. It is undoubtedly a very fine piece of work, and will enormously facilitate future researches. It might, I think have been a good deal condensed without diminishing its usefulness, but one must be grateful to him for what he has done, and must not cavil at minor defects. Among his other achievements he has codified and rendered accessible all the work of Steinschneider.[3] I shall review it in the most friendly possible fashion.[4]

Yours ever,

Charles Singer

Thanks for the Salerno article safely received.[5] You shall have it back again in due course.

I am telling contributors to the Sudhoff volume that their articles must be in in May.

I hope that you are keeping well & getting all the open air you can.

[1] Spencer (1924).

[2] Fishbein has no article in the published Sudhoff Festschrift.

[3] Moritz Steinschneider (1816–1907) published on Arabic and Hebrew Literature.

[4] Charles Singer, 'Review of L. Thorndike: A history of magic and experimental science', *Observer*, 13 May 1923, p.5.

[5] Singer and Singer (1924).

46

Singer to Sigerist, London, 23 March 1923

My dear Sigerist,

I find on looking through some of the letters on my table, that there is a point in your last which I had not answered. I should be quite satisfied with £15 for doing Ketham for Lier.

There is one matter in which I might be able to help him. I have the negative, full size, of the very fine dissection scene in the 1493 Italian edition of Ketham. This I would gladly place at his disposal. I have made several attempts to get it coloured in accordance with the original, but all of these have so far failed. The difficulty is that the colours have of course different tone-values in the photograph. Therefore, to get a satisfactory picture, the artist must first get a tracing of the photograph itself and then fill in the colours. It occurs to me as a possible solution that we might send to Italy a print of the photograph and get someone there to trace it, and then have it re-coloured at the British Museum. It is in the tracing that the British artist always seems to break down.

Yours ever,

Charles Singer

I've asked Thorndike to write for the volume.[1]

[1] Lynn Thorndike, 'Disputed dates, civilization and climate, and traces of magic in the Scientific Treatises ascribed to Theophrastus', in Singer and Sigerist (1924), 73–86.

47

Singer to Sigerist, London, 5 April 1923

My dear Sigerist,

Just a line to say that today I have sent off signed my contract to Lier. I go away today to Belgium returning on April 21st.[1]

On my return I will at once set about getting in the papers for the Sudhoff Festschrift. These should be in by the end of May.

On June 6th my lectures end. I will then start on Ketham at once. Fishbein has accepted to write to Sudhoff. I have not yet heard from Thorndike.

Yours always,

Charles Singer

P.S. Poor old Klebs was fuzzing about London last week.

I wonder if Sudhoff would really have a chance for the Nobel Prize? You can hardly call him a 'literary' man & as a scholar I fear he would come after Wilamowitz[2] or

Heiberg.[3] But, of course, if they do award the prize for medical history there could be no two opinions that Sudhoff is the man.

We like Silberschmidt very much.[4] I've been able to put him in touch with the people he wants who all like him.

[1] To the Congress of Historians.
[2] Ulrich von Wilamowitz (1848–1931) German classical philologist.
[3] Johan Ludvig Heiberg (1854–1928), Danish philologist.
[4] William Silberschmidt (1869–1947) Swiss hygienist, was Singer's guest.

48

Singer to Sigerist, Brussels, 13 April 1923

My dear Sigerist,

(1) While at the Congress of Historians here I have visited the Royal Library at Bruxelles to see the well known IXth-Xth cent. MS. of Muscio.[1] It is suitable for reproduction in your series. If you like the idea I would edit it. No colours are needed though on several pages they are desirable. All the pages also have <u>some</u> red words in them[?] but these need not be rendered red. The pages to be reproduced are MS 3701-15 folio 15 recto to 31 verso included.

The pages that it would be desirable to colour are 16v, 26v, 27, 27v, 28, 28v & 29. Arthur Langsberg, Avenue Victor Jacobs 60, Bruxelles will take photographs of the MS 18x24 cms (practically full size) at Belgian 9 francs per negative & 1.80 for each print. The present exchange is 25 Swiss francs = 81 Belgian francs.

(2) Mme Wickersheimer[2] spoke to me of the possibility of your being invited to succeed Sudhoff. I do hope you will be & I hope also you would accept but that they will provide a proper position[?] for you at Zurich. If I were in your place I think I would rather have a small post in Zurich than a large one at Leipzig!

But can I do anything to help? Can I, for instance write to any one at Leipzig? You know we have [....] a "Board of Studies" at London University for the "Principles History & Method of Science" at which I have now been officially appointed Secretary. I could write in that capacity. The chairman of the Board is Prof A. N. Whitehead who is very well known as a philosopher & mathematician.[3] I daresay he would sign such a letter. But let me know frankly because I don't want to do anything that would injure you. Perhaps I could write to some one at Zurich?
Best regards from both to both,
Yours ever,
Charles Singer

This Congress is very tiring

[1] Muscio or Mustio (*c.*500 A.D), supposed author of a treatise of gynaecology.
[2] Wife of Ernest Wickersheimer, see letter 14.
[3] Alfred N. Whitehead (1861–1947), mathematician and philosopher. See E. T. Whittaker, 'Whitehead, Alfred North (1861–1947)', rev. I. Grattan-Guinness, *Oxford dictionary of national biography* (Oxford: Oxford University Press, 2004), vol. 58, 652–654.

49

Singer to Sigerist, London, 22 April 1923a

My dear Sigerist,

Many thanks for your card & letter which reached me, after some wandering, at Ghent. It is good of you to have offered to do anything for me at Rome but I had no need at the moment.

On my return from Belgium I find this article from Garrison awaiting me.[1] I send it on to you at once because, as Garrison lives such a very long way away, in the Phillipine [sic] Islands, I think it would be a good thing if this particular article for the Sudhoff volume were set up in type at once so as to give Garrison time to care of the proofs. You might perhaps ask the publishers if this could not be done.

Best regards,

Yours ever,

Charles Singer

[1] Fielding H Garrison, 'The newer epidemiology', in Singer and Sigerist (1924), 255–268.

50

Singer to Sigerist, London, 22 April 1923b

My dear Sigerist,

Thanks for your letter of 15. 4. 23.There are several figures of the 1493 Ketham which are among the finest woodcuts ever made. These must be included.

I agree[,] however[,] that the Latin text of 1495 is more valuable than the Italian of 1493.

The situation is therefore that I should publish in one volume

(a) The figures of the Italian Ketham of 1493

(b) The Latin text of 1495 including that of Mondino[1]

(c) The figures of the 1495 edition where they differ from those of 1493 sufficiently to be of importance

(d) Such figures from other editions as illustrate the subsequent history of the work.
Yours ever,
Charles Singer

---

[1] Mondino (Mundinus), probably da Luzzi, 13th century; there are several medieval medical authors of that name. See letter 41.

51

Singer to Sigerist, London, 23 April 1923

My dear Sigerist,
    I have spent the day at the British Museum in the editions of Ketham of which there are 10 copies there.
    I came to the conclusion that the following would make the best publication if it can be done: – (1). A complete facsimile of the 1493 edition. This is the largest page, the best print & much the most beautiful. It contains Mundinus (though in Italian) (2) A reprint (not facsimile) in small print of the text of the 1495 edition. On so large a page as is needed for (1) this would go with a very few pages. (3) A translation into English of passages from (2), notably of the text of Mundinus. (4) Reproductions, which can be on a reduced scale, of certain of the illustrations in the 1495 & later editions. (5) Introductory explanatory & bibliographical matter by myself.
    If this is too ambitious I suggest leaving out some of the facsimile pages that are merely in type of (1).
    Do you know where I can find a copy of the edition of 1509 printed in Milan by Giovanni di Castellione? It is said to have very beautiful figures.
    I am greatly interested in this piece of work & much looking forward to it. I expect I shall have to go over to Paris in the course of doing it.
Yours ever
Charles Singer

52

Sigerist to Singer, Zurich?, 26 April 1923

My dear Singer,
    Many thanks for your last letters. Excuse my not answering them earlier. When I came home from Rome there was so much work waiting for me that I hadn't time for anything.
    I had a letter yesterday from Lier telling me that he hadn't yet got any news from you. Your letter of April 5th must have got lost on the way. Would you write just a few lines to Lier saying that you have sent the contract already and that you agree to his conditions.

About Ketham I like your scheme very much and I will ask Lier to do it as you suggest: 1. A complete facsimile of 1493. 2. A reprint of 1495. 3. An English translation of some passages from 2 (Mundinus) 4. Reproductions of several illustrations 5. Your text.

In the German and Italian edition we could omit 3 easily. If Lier agrees with that scheme, I'll have the facsimile done as soon as we find a good copy in Germany which wont [sic] be difficult. We could also have 2 printed at once. All depends now on Lier and I hope to have his answer soon.

If I'm not mistaken Lier told me that Olschki[1] in Florence has a copy of the 1509 edition on sale just now. Do inquire about it and try to get the British Museum to buy it.

I'm glad that you like that piece of work. It is really fascinating. I hope to be able to send you Sudhoffs [sic] text next week. The facsimile of 1491 is beautiful and 12 plates, 7 of them originally coloured are also ready.

I like your idea of publishing the Muscio MS of Brussels very much too.[2] I'll speak to Lier about it and I hope that we can have it done soon after Ketham. It would be much better to begin our MS-facsimiles with that short and very important MS than with Roger[3] or the Dioscurides Neapolitanus.

It is very kind of [you] to think of helping me in the Leipzig business.[4] I dont know exactly what the prospects are. Diepgen being a German will probably be invited first but I dont know if he'll accept.[5] In that case perhaps they would ask me. Of cause [sic] I dont care spending my life in Germany especially now and I would prefer an ever so modest position in Switzerland or in any other country, but the only possibility for me of getting a professorship in Zurich now is to be calles [sic] abroad. However[,] I think the best to do is just to let things go and not to interfer [sic]. If a letter of you were ever useful to me I would frankly ask you for it.

Now about our Festschrift. I shall meet our publisher[6] in a few days and I will try to have Garrisons [sic] article get into type at once.[7] The first proofs will be sent to the various authors, the second to you and myself. You might then correct the English and I the German and Italian articles. No doubt you have seen Garrisons bibliography of Sudhoffs writings in the Bulletin of Chicago. It is no use reprinting it but I think a subject index of Sudhoffs writings under various headings (antiquity, Dark Ages, Salerno, Paracelsus, Syphilis etc.) would be very useful. What do you think of it? I could easily have it done.[8]

---

[1] A publisher in Florence.
[2] See letter 48.
[3] Possibly Frugard, see letter 39.
[4] Rumors about Sigerist as Sudhoff's successor.
[5] Paul Diepgen (1878–1966) German medical historian. See *Sudhoffs Archiv*, 1966, **50:** 1; and 'Paul Diepgen, 1879–1966', *Journal of the History of Medicine and Allied Sciences*, 1966, **21:** 189–190.
[6] Seldwyla, Zurich.
[7] Garrison (1924).
[8] The following page seems to be missing.

53

Singer to Sigerist, London, 30 April 1923

My dear Sigerist,

Many thanks for your letter of April 26th. I think the English title for the volume should be

"Essays on the History of Medicine
Presented to
KARL SUDHOFF
On the occasion of his 70th
Birthday, Nov. 26th 1923
Edited by
Henry Sigerist
and
Charles Singer"

I think perhaps there could be no harm in having the introduction in German and English and French. As we can't get French contributors would it not be possible for the Swiss contributors to write in French? If you write the introductory words in German I could of course translate them into English.

We have no English word for Festschrift. Yesterday E. G. [sic] Streeter was here. He is well on with with his essay, but looking through some of my material he discovered five anatomical drawings in the Hunterian Library at Glasgow in which he was extremely interested. I begged him to publish them said they would do very well for his contribution to the Sudhoff volume, but he simply won't do this unless my name is also attached. Under these circumstances I suggest that he and I write this article together in our joint names, and that my other article appears in the joint name of my wife and myself.[1] This article of Streeter will only occupy two pages, but will need illustrations for which he will pay.

I said it seemed a pity that he should not also publish the article which he had originally designed, because he has taken a great deal of trouble over it. I explained to him, of course, that I must obtain your consent for such a course.

I had a card this morning from Capparoni at Rome which says you have visited him. He very much wants me to become a member of his Institute, and says you were delighted with it. What do you think of it really?

The Wellcome Museum has a rotograph of a manuscript of Ketham which they <u>say</u> comes from the Leyden University Library and is dated 1435. I am almost certain that the date is wrong, and, from my knowledge of the Wellcome Museum, I should think it quite likely that the Library is also wrong. To me it looks like a manuscript copy of the 1491 Ketham – I mean a manuscript taken from the printed book. I am in correspondence

with Sudhoff about it, and I gather from a card received from him this morning that he had not heard of it. This would be easily explained if date and place are wrong!
With best regards,
Yours ever,
Charles Singer

P.S. A matter for you to turn over in your mind. It is pretty evident that Archiv must come to an end. I have been wondering whether we could have an international journal under the editorship of yourself, Wickersheimer, Streeter and myself. Streeter would, I think, endow it with a 1,000 dollars a year, and it might perhaps be made to pay except for the cost of illustrations.[2] We might conceivably get over the German difficulty with Wickersheimer by making French the official language on condition that articles were accepted in English, French, Italian or German. Of course Wickersheimer could leave the correspondence with the German contributors to you or me.
C. S.

[1] Edward C. Streeter and Charles Singer, 'Fifteenth century miniatures of extramural dissections', in Singer and Sigerist (eds), (1924), 207–210; and Singer and Singer (1924).
[2] *Archiv für Geschichte der Medizin*, later *Sudhoffs Archiv*, still existing; the planned international journal of the history of medicine did not materialize.

54

Singer to Sigerist, London, 2 May 1923

My dear Sigerist,
  I wonder if you would be good enough to ask Olchki [sic] to let me have information concerning his 1509 Ketham? I was at the British Museum yesterday and they said they would consider it if I had any information about it. I don't know Olchki's address, and from my experience of the Italian Post Office I don't suppose the letter would arrive if I didn't address it fully.
  If they could let me have a photograph or two of some of the pictures, all the better.
Yours ever,
Charles Singer

55

Sigerist to Singer, Zurich?, 5 May 1923

My dear Singer,

Many thanks for your letters of April 30th and May 2nd. Of cause [sic] I fully agree with any arrangement you would like to make with Streeter.[1] I would like to have his article in any case, especially as mine has been quite altered. It was nearly written, but then I change the whole scheme. I call it now "Die Geburt der abendländischen Medizin".[2] It will be rather revolutionary and I wonder how you will like it.

I saw our publisher two days ago.[3] He will start printing the book at once. I have already received most of the German and Swiss MSS. Do let me have the English as soon as possible, especially those with illustrations. I have got a very good portrait of Sudhoff which has recently been taken in Leipzig. I'll put it at the beginning of the volume. The publisher will give each author 50 reprints of their respective articles, and we shall each get five copies of the book free. I think it quite decent of him. I am sorry that I cannot ask the Swiss contributors to write their articles in French. Klebs will write his in English. The others are all German Swiss and as for me, I would hurt Sudhoff's feelings by writing this special article in French.

My "delight" with the Roman Institute was mostly out of politeness towards Capparoni.[4] It is only an embryo of an Institute, Carbonelli's not very important collection,[5] and nothing else. Still it will develop one day. As soon as the patients are removed from the Ospedale S. Spirito, they will get several rooms there, and the beautiful Biblioteca Lancisiana will be kept exclusively as a historical library. I would suggest you to become a member as I did. For 500 Lire you are a life member. It helps them and you get their Bulletino regularly which is of the same standard as the Rivista.[6]

About Ketham 1509 I have written to Lier. He told me of Olchki's [sic] copy when I met him in Milan. I asked him for further information. I had a letter from him this morning telling me that he quite agrees with your scheme and that he will gladly have it executed.

The MS of the Wellcome Museum must be wrong.[7] A little while ago I discovered a German translation of a part of Ketham's gynecology. I publish it in the Archiv, but as it will take some time to come out, and as you might care to see it, I am sending you my MS by the same mail.[8]

I would be delighted to collaborate in an international journal. The idea has occupied my mind for a long time. The Archiv is too unsatisfactory in its present state and it obviously wont [sic] get any better.[9] I wrote a long letter to Sudhoff last autumn, suggesting him to make an international Quarterly of his Archiv, with an international editorial board. He didnt [sic] like the idea, so I dropped the thing. Now your scheme would be the very best solution. I am glad that you are coming to Switzerland this summer, so that we can discuss the question. I think we ought to start the paper next January.[10]

I am very sorry that I didn't see Streeter. I hoped he would come through Switzerland on his way back from Italy.

With best regards

Yours sincerely

[Henry E. Sigerist]

[1] Streeter and Singer (1924).

[2] Henry E. Sigerist, 'Die Geburt der abendländischen Medizin', in Singer and Sigerist (eds), (1924), 185–205.

[3] Seldwyla, Zurich..

[4] See letter 53.

[5] Giovanni Carbonelli's collection of medical books. Giovanni Carbonelli (1859–1933), Italian medical historian and book collector, see 'Giovanni Carbonelli', *Rivista di Storia delle Scienze Mediche e Naturali*, 1933, **24:** 121–122.

[6] *Rivista di storia della medicina.*

[7] See letter 53.

[8] Henry E. Sigerist, 'Eine deutsche Uebersetzung der Kethamschen Gynäkologie', *Archiv für Geschichte der Medizin*, 1923, **14:** 169–178.

[9] See letter 53.

[10] Singer means start the journal.

56

Singer to Sigerist, London, 8 May 1923

My dear Sigerist,

Many thanks for your letter of May 5th. I think your publisher is <u>most</u> generous, but at the same time I don't want him to be <u>too</u> generous.[1] Do you mean that each contributor of an article will get five copies of the book free? If you do I think it's rather overdoing it as it would interfere with the sales. I think it ought to be enough if each author gets fifty reprints of his own article without any copy of the book at all. In the case of people who pay for their plates I think we might give a copy of the book, and in the case of German contributors who cannot buy a copy we should stretch a point and let each of them have <u>one</u>. But the others ought to buy their own as they will not have any expense in connection with the volume. My feeling is that we do not want to do our publisher badly because he may subsequently accept similar publications, and it is a good thing, from our point of view, that publishers should find Medical History a not unprofitable concern. As regards you and I, I think we might reasonably take two or three copies each and be allowed to distribute a few more for review purposes, but these latter would be sent by the Publisher on our suggestion.

I see the difficulty about French and suppose it cannot be helped, but as it is I doubt if we shall get a single article in that language.

For our international journal[2] I am exceedingly anxious that we should get one among the editors who is a Frenchman, and I have written to Wickersheimer to know his feeling. Of course neither you nor I would be willing to compromise on the question of accepting German articles – neither of course would consent to edit a journal which refused them. If

pressed, however, and if unable to get Wickersheimer on any other terms, I would personally be willing to accept French as the primary language of the journal, and the language
of its editorial material. I don't want to raise this point until I am forced to, however, as it
is the trump card. Also I feel that French is not the best language for the purpose as far
better material is appearing in English and in German. German appears to me to be out
of it for editorial purposes because it would raise anew the old prejudice, so that it really
lies between French and English. I would accept either but I do not know the American
view.

I think after we have presented Sudhoff with his volume, he could not be hurt at not
being included in the editorial list. If he were[,] the French would not join. I am therefore
anxious not to raise the question publicly until the volume has been presented to him. This
would prevent our starting next January, but I don't see why we should not start a month
or two later. I would like to have your considered opinion on all this – at your leisure.

You can rely on our being in Switzerland in the second half of July. We have, of
course, to pass through Zurich and might stop for a day or two there, but I wonder if
you would not rather that we met in some little country place. Don't hurry to answer,
but I should like to have your considered thoughts on this and on the suggestions about
the journal.

The Wellcome manuscript[3] is of course wrongly dated in the well-known Wellcome
manner! It is called about 1435! I have examined the rotograph and collated it with the
printed editions. There is no doubt that it is a copy of the 1495 edition. It has, however,
a small interest in that the gynaecological section is abbreviated and in Dutch, but the
gynaecological figure is omitted.

Many thanks for your Ketham article which I shall read with great interest.[4] I am getting a rotograph on my own account of the Wellcome (Leiden) manuscript, and am sending it to Sudhoff. If you want a copy of the Dutch section you can either borrow it from
him or I can get another for you. I am afraid the reading of it is beyond my power. I shall
be interested to hear further of the Olchki [sic] copy.

I am bringing out an expanded version of my articles on herbals.[5] It will be of a semi-
popular character and well illustrated. If you know of any figures of plants that you would
particularly like to see reproduced perhaps you would let me know or lend me photographs of them, for which I would of course gladly pay and acknowledge the source.
I have written to the same effect to Sudhoff.

Do you know Herman Koebert De Pseudo-Apulei Herbarum Medicaminibus, Beyr-
euth, 1888?[6]

I'll send Capparoni 500 lire for his institute. You shall have the English communica-
tions as soon as possible, and I hope in any event by the end of May. I have told most
of the contributors that that is the terminal date, and most of them will doubtless choose
the terminal date.[7] The article by Streeter and myself I will send off to-day after I have
been through it, together with some of the photographs for it which will be five in all.[8]
Two or possibly three of the photographs are so bad that they must be taken again.
With best regards to you all,
Yours ever,
Charles Singer

I find on enquiry yesterday that your photographer has not yet been paid for his slides. This is only the usual "official delay". Tell him its [sic] quite all right & I am seeing to it.

[1] See previous letter.
[2] The international journal did not materialize.
[3] See letter 53.
[4] Sigerist (1923c).
[5] Charles Singer, 'Herbals', *Edinburgh Review*, 1923, **237**: 95–112.
[6] Hermann Koebert, *De Pseudo-Apulei herbarum medicaminibus* (Bayreuth, 1888).
[7] Articles for the Sudhoff Festschrift.
[8] Streeter and Singer (1924).

57

Singer to Sigerist, London, 10 May 1923a

My dear Sigerist,

Herewith the article by my wife and myself.[1] I have appended a bibliography which you had better just glance at to see if you think that it is the form Sudhoff would like.

The article by Streeter and myself must wait a day or two until I get the photographs from Glasgow.[2]

Yours ever,

Charles Singer

[1] Singer and Singer (1924).
[2] Streeter and Singer (1924).

58

Singer to Sigerist, London, 10 May 1923b

My dear Sigerist,

Herewith Withington's article for the Sudhoff volume on Roger Bacon.[1] It is very clear writing and I think therefore hardly needs typing.

I found that the Streeter article needed the insertion of a short paragraph which can only be done after I have had one of the figures re-photographed.[2] I have ordered the photographs and the document, together with my other article, shall follow in a day or two, and the others as rapidly as I can gather them in, and all I hope by the end of this month.

Yours ever,

Charles Singer

---

[1] Edward T. Withington, 'Roger Bacon, on the errors of physicians', in Singer and Sigerist (eds), (1924), 139–157.

[2] Streeter and Singer (1924).

59

Singer to Sigerist, London, 11 May 1923

My dear Sigerist,

Herewith Spencer's short article on the Vesalius Epitome.[1] There are some illustrations to it, but he possesses some, at any rate, of the blocks which will save the expense of publication. He has promised to lend them and I have written to him for them. They shall be forwarded to you in due course.

Yours ever,

Charles Singer

---

[1] Spencer (1924).

60

Singer to Sigerist, London, 14 May 1923

My dear Sigerist,

I have just had a line from Glasgow to say that the photographic apparatus there is out of order, and that it will be a week before we shall be able to get those photographs of which I wrote in my last. I had better hold the manuscript up until then.

I don't think I shall succeed in getting anything out of E. G. Browne who pleads advancing age and over work, but on the other hand I think that Clifford Allbutt[1] will let us have something, though rather late. I am having difficulties, too, with D'Arcy Power, but I expect he'll be all right.

I think it quite possible that Elliot Smith will come with us to Switzerland.

Yours ever,

Charles Singer

---

[1] Thomas Clifford Allbutt (1836–1925), British physician and medical historian; see H. D. Rolleston, 'Allbutt, Sir (Thomas) Clifford (1836–1925)', rev. Alexander G. Bearn, *Oxford dictionary of national biography* (Oxford: Oxford University Press, 2004), vol. 1, 764–765.

61

Singer to Sigerist, London, 17 May 1923 (postcard)

Can you by chance let me have a reference of anything that has been written on the list of plant synonyms in the Julia Anicia[1] & in the Apuleius Herbarium? Has any one compared the two?

C. S.

---

[1] The Dioscorides MS, Vienna, med. Gr. 1, was dedicated to the Byzantine princess Anicia Juliana.

62

Singer to Sigerist, London, 18 May 1923

My dear Sigerist,

I enclose in a parcel which comes with this post the following elements for the illustration of Spencer's article.[1]

(1) Two clichées representing the nudes from the Epitome of Vesalius.

(2) Photographs of the five muscle men from the Epitome. I suggest that in the reproduction of these only the figures should appear, and that the letter press around them should be deleted. If the clichée maker would prefer to have the actual negatives I can send them also.

There still remain to be sent two clichées illustrating the arteries and nerves. These Mr. Spencer omitted by error, but I have asked him to let me have them, and I will send them to you as soon as they reach me.

I enclose you also his last letter which is important for you only as containing a sentence which I have underlined in red, which says "You will let me know the cost of the extra blocks". I have answered him, thanking him for his generosity, and I have only sent it to you so that it may go into your dossier.

I am still waiting for Streeter's photographs from Glasgow, but I expect it will come to-day or to-morrow.

I fear Browne and D'Arcy Power are both defaulting. They both write me to say that they are being so fearfully rushed, so I am getting an article from Robert Steele on Roger Bacon,[2] which will go well with Withington's. I hope, too, to get something from Clifford Allbutt. He says he would like to write. But of course he cannot be rushed. We must print him if necessary at the end.[3]

Yours ever,

Charles Singer

[1] Spencer (1924).

[2] An article of Robert Steele (1860–1944) on Roger Bacon had appeared earlier: Robert Steele, 'Roger Bacon', in Charles Singer (ed.), *Studies in the history and method of science*, vol. 2 (Oxford Clarendon Press, 1921), 121–150.

[3] The published Sudhoff Festschrift does not contain articles by Browne, Power, Steele, or Allbutt, although Allbutt writes the dedication; see letter 76.

63

Singer to Sigerist, London, 22 May 1923

My dear Sigerist,

Can you answer these professional points? I am engaged in expanding my article on Herbals into a small volume, and I want them to illustrate it.[1]

1. What are the earliest manuscripts of Apuleius? I should love to have a list of them if you could let me have one.

2. Is there any real evidence of the date of Sextus Placitus Papyriensis?[2] Isn't he mostly extracted from Pliny?[3] Is he found associated with Apuleius in the Leiden Voss MS?

3. Have you ever looked at Constantine's Africanus[4] De Animalibus, printed at the end of the Basle (Henricus Petrus) edition of Constantine, dated 1541. Isn't it Sextus Placitus? It's a puzzling thing, and I wonder whether it has anything to do with Constantine at all. I see no evidence of Arabic influence, and I think it's just a false ascription.

I expect you can answer all these things right off.

I am going to try to run up to Cambridge this week and see Allbutt and secure that article from him. The photographs haven't come from Glasgow yet but I expect they will arrive to-day.

Yours ever,

Charles Singer

I am hoping for an article from Thorndike for the Sudhoff vol.[5] I wrote him again to-day.

Elliot Smith is away but returns tomorrow. I wonder if you & Sudhoff would consent to lend me the bound Rotograph copies of the Apuleius MSS? I would only keep them for a few days. I want them for the purpose of selecting figures. I have a copy of the Leyden Voss. Is it asking too much? Please say so if you feel this.

I had enclosed card from Wickersheimer in answer to my suggestion of an 'Archiv'. Looks hopeful.

[1] Singer (1923e); the planned volume is probably Charles Singer, 'The herbal in antiquity', *Journal of Hellenic Studies*, 1927, **47**: 1–52.
[2] Sextus Placitus Papyriensis (late Antiquity), wrote on medicine.
[3] Caius Plinius (23/24–79 A.D.), Roman naturalist.
[4] Constantinus Africanus (c.1010-c.1087), translator of Arabic medical texts in southern Italy.
[5] Thorndike (1924).

64

Singer to Sigerist, London, 29 May 1923

My dear Sigerist,

(1) Herewith the article of Streeter and myself, all complete and in good order.[1] The figures should appear in the order of the numbers written in <u>green</u> on their backs. I suggest that one of them is left with a few lines of script just to show the palaeographical character of the manuscript. I leave you to choose which. Streeter will pay towards the cost of the illustrations, and will probably pay for the lot. The size of reproduction I leave also to your judgment. I should like the article to appear in Streeter's name but he insists that I should add mine to his as figures were of my finding.

(2) We shall be able to get Elliot Smith's article all right, but it will be a few days before he will have time to write it.[2] Comrie doesn't think that his will be ready until the middle of June, and I expect that Allbutt's will not be ready until about the same date, but I am trying to get down to Cambridge next week to discuss it with him. I am going to try to get an article from Sir Humphrey [sic] Rolleston also, and am going to see him about it to-day.[3] Fonahn writes that it is really impossible for him to let us have anything. This is a blow.

(3) Thinking over the question of the title page, I believe it would be a good thing if we put the names of <u>all</u> the contributors on it, ending up with our own in the same size type but on a different line. I think they should go in alphabetical order, beginning with Allbutt who would naturally come first both in the alphabet and by reason of his seniority.[4]

(4) I have received Lier's proofs of Sudhoff's Ketham. It is simply magnificent both in style and substance, and I most heartily congratulate you on it.[5] It so happens that we have no copy of the 1491 edition in London; I have already started to collate the facsimile with the later editions, and I have got a good way in the translation of Mundinus. I wrote to Lier saying that I would devote the whole of September to their work, and I expect they will be able to deliver me my facsimiles before then.

(5) I have just been called off to the telephone to speak to Humphrey Rolleston. He says he will let us have something if he possibly can, and I propose to give him some

material of my own which he will work up a little, but naturally it must be some days before we can get it over to you.

Yours ever,

Charles Singer

[1] Streeter and Singer (1924),

[2] There was no article by Elliot Smith

[3] Humphry Rolleston, 'The reception of Harvey's doctrine of the circulation of blood in England', in Singer and Sigerist (eds) (1924), 247–254.

[4] The title page appeared exactly as proposed by Singer.

[5] Karl Sudhoff (ed.), *Der Fasciculus medicinae des Johannes de Ketham, Alemanus* (Milan, 1923). This edition appeared in Sigerist's Monumenta medica series.

65

Singer to Sigerist, London, 4 June 1923

My dear Sigerist,

(1) A line to say that I have been talking with Sir Humphrey [sic] Rolleston. He absolutely promises to deliver to me an article by June 14th, and I am sure he will keep his word.

I have had a letter from Fishbein to say that a short article from him of about 1500 words will arrive in a few days' time.

I may not be able to get Comrie's article in until the end of June, and the same applies to Allbutt's.

Elliot Smith I am worrying daily. I think we shall get something out of him all right, but it takes time. (2) During the next day or two I shall be finishing my little volume on the History of the Herbal which is an enlargement of my Edinburgh Review article.[1]

I am having three copies typed. I wonder if you would be sufficiently good natured, to read the part of it which concerns your particular specialty for me and correct the errors?

(3)[2] Many thanks for your list of Apuleius MSS, some of which are quite new to me. May I make a few corrections on it?

The Breslau III F.19 S.IX, is surely not illustrated. It has a certain amount of ornamentation, but no figures of plants.

The Vatican Barberini MS is illustrated, as is also Florence Laurent. 73.41.The Harleian MS 4986 is certainly the XIIth century and not the XIth, and I think the second half of the 12th. There is almost a sister MS to Harleian 4986 at Eton College, of which I have taken photographs. The Eton College MS is early thirteenth. Both Eton College and Harley 4986 are German work.

I have made out a genealogical tree of the MS which I will tidy up and send you. You probably will want to make many alterations in it.

(4) Have you seen photographs of Halberstadt MS and of its figures? I should awfully like to get them. I think Diepgen must have had copies for that article that he wrote in

Janus.[3] Could you let me have Diepgen's address? I should also very much like to have photographs of the Berlin and Hildersheim [sic] fragments.

Can you suggest any one to write to for the purpose?

Yours ever,

Charles Singer

---

[1] Singer (1927) which is an enlargement of Singer (1923e).

[2] (3) and (4) are medieval manuscripts with their official abbreviations..

[3] *Janus*, a journal of medical history. Paul Diepgen, 'Zur Tradition des Pseudoapuleius', *Janus*, 1922, **26**: 104–107.

66

Singer to Sigerist, London, 9 June 1923

My dear Sigerist,

Enclosed letter from Cushing will interest you.[1] Perhaps you would be good enough to send it on to Lier.

I find that we have in London the MS from which I believe the 1483 Rome edition of Apuleius Barbarus was printed. I think a facsimile of that book together with some facsimile pages from the MS might be considered for your series.[2] I believe I shall be able to bring evidence with me to Interlaken[3] to prove my point about the source of the Apuleius Barbarus to you. The Anglo-Saxon illuminated herbal was copied from a closely similar MS, so that most interestingly the Anglo-Saxon herbal and the printed edition are not much further from each other than first cousins.

I have drawn up my genealogical tree, but have still to copy it out and you shall have it in the course of the next few days.

Yours ever,

Charles Singer

Would you like me to look through the <u>English</u> of the translation of Sudhoff's Ketham?[4]

---

[1] Harvey Cushing (1869–1939), neurosurgeon and historian of medicine; see John F. Fulton, Harvey Cushing, a biography (Springfield, Ill.: C.C. Thomas, 1946), and Michael Bliss, *Harvey Cushing: a life in surgery* (New York: Oxford University Press, 2005). For a biographical introduction and Sigererist's correspondence with Cushing, see Marcel H. Bickel (ed.), *Henry E. Sigerist: Correspondences With Welch, Cushing, Garrison and Ackerknecht* (Bern: Peter Lang, 2010), 41–92.

[2] Monumenta Medica.

[3] Interlaken, a town in Switzerland.

[4] Sudhoff (1923).

67

Singer to Sigerist, London, 13 June 1923

My dear Sigerist,

Herewith Sir Humphry Rolleston's article.[1] I have edited it a bit, so I think he'd better have proofs.

I had a card from Allbutt last night which makes it pretty clear that it is quite certain that we shall get something from him.[2] As the doyen of all those who are writing in this volume it is evident that his article should go first, and I hope your printer will be able to arrange for that. Of course his article will be rather late as he has only just started to write it.

It is a great thing to secure both Allbutt and Rolleston, who are, I think, the two most distinguished medical men in this country.

Yours always

Charles Singer

P.S. I enclose Allbutt's card. I don't suppose you can read it, but it runs as follows: "Has anybody put together from a clinical point of view the heart lore before Laennec? – say R. Lower; Albertini; Valsalver [sic]; Senec [sic] and especially Haller, etc. etc.[3] If not I could try to do this for Sudhoff in a few weeks, but perhaps it is done already. C. A."

C. S.

---

[1] Rolleston (1924).
[2] Only a preface appeared by Allbutt in the Sudhoff Festschrift.
[3] Ippolito Albertini (1662–1738), Italian pathological anatomist; Albrecht Haller (1708–1777), Swiss physiologist, botanist, poet, and statesman; René Théophile Hyacynthe Laennec (1781–1826), French professor of medicine; Richard Lower, (1631–1691), British physiologist; Jean-Baptiste de Sénac (1693–1770), French anatomist and cardiologist; Antonio Valsalva (1666–1723), Italian anatomist.

68

Singer to Sigerist, London, 15 June 1923

My dear Sigerist,

(1) I send you in confidence – as to a discreet medical man – the enclosed absurd letter from Klebs.[1] His trouble is, of course, that he hasn't enough work to do. He has a series of photographs of Canano,[2] and owns the negatives. I simply want prints of them in order that I may read the work and make a few lantern slides for use in my lectures on the 'History of Anatomy'. Of course this has nothing whatever to do with the Monumenta

Medica. Of course if Canano is edited in the Monumenta Medica it should be done by a professed anatomist, and I am quite unsuited for the task.[3] Poor old Klebs is trying to fasten on me a perfectly imaginary quarrel in a matter in which I am quite innocent.

(2) I enclose a copy of the Apuleius tree, based on the illustrations.[4] It will be most interesting to see how it fits in with your conclusions based on text. You shall have the MS of my work in a few days, but of course the argument closely follows the figures which are hardly ready yet.

(3) I have had enclosed from Fishbein and from Clifford Allbutt. Fishbein does not matter, but we must not do without Allbutt if we can help it, and I have therefore written to him to say that we shall keep a space for him until the end of July.

(4) I am rather sorry you don't put the names all on the title page.[5] I saw a Festschrift the other day which was treated in this way, and it looked awfully well. Why not ask the publisher to print a trial page in that way and one in the other so that we can compare them. The experiment could hardly cost more than 10 francs.

(5) I quite agree with you that it would be desirable to open with Elliot Smith's article, and that would mean of course that the book would be arranged in the chronological order of the subjects which it treats. I'll try to get hold of Elliot Smith during the next few days, but he is always difficult to find. His trouble is that he has a large family and is very poor! The result is that he has to make money in all kinds of odd ways, which include journalism. But he is an awfully good fellow, extremely generous, and of course very distinguished, and I am in great hopes of getting his contribution.

Yours ever,

Charles Singer

P.S. I went out yesterday to visit an old fellow student who is in practice in the country. He produced an old anatomical book & asked me if I would like to have it. It was the Italian (the best) edition of Valverde[6] which must be very rare. Of course I seized on it. It's a most interesting work & a great stroke of luck to get it in this way.

---

[1] Earlier in 1923 Sigerist had also received 'absurd letters' from Klebs in connection with Canano, see the Sigerist -Klebs correspondence in Marcel H. Bickel (ed.), *Henry E. Sigerist: Vier ausgewählte Briefwechsel mit Medizinhistorikern der Schweiz.* (Bern, 2008).

[2] Giovanni Battista Canano (1515–1579), Italian anatomist. See Giulio Muratori, 'Canano, Giovan Battista', *Complete dictionary of scientific biography*, Vol. 3, (Detroit: Charles Scribner's Sons, 2008), 40–41.

[3] Canano appeared as volume VI in Sigerist's Monumenta Medica series: *Ioannes Baptista Canano, 1515–1578, Girolamo da Carpi, 1501–1556: musculorum humani corporis picturata dissectio (Ferrara 1541?).* Facsimile edition annotated by Harvey Cushing & Edward C. Streeter (Florence: Lier & Co, 1925). This included an article by Klebs.

[4] Genealogical 'tree' of Apuleius manuscripts, see letter 65.

[5] See letter 64.

[6] Juan Valverde de Amusco (c.1520 – c.1588), Spanish anatomist; see Francisco Guerra, 'Juan De Valverde', *Complete dictionary of scientific biography*, vol. 13 (Detroit: Charles Scribner's Sons, 2008), 568–569.

69

Singer to Sigerist, London, 18 June 1923

My dear Sigerist,

Very many thanks for the photographs of the Berlin, Halberstadt and Hildersheim [sic] fragments concerning which I have a few remarks to make.[1]

I quite agree with you and differ from Diepgen that the Halberstadt cannot possibly be the ancestor of the Leyden MS. I should be disposed to place its origin from the main stem before that South Italian recension was formed from which the Leyden is derived.

There are some extremely interesting points, however, in the figures. First I would point out to you that instead of a snake and scorpion fighting on one of the pages – a very usual grouping – we have a snake and cray-fish or lobster. There can be no doubt if you examine the head of the beast that this is the case. Now the cray-fish or lobster is not infrequently represented in the signs of the Zodiac instead of the scorpion. But when this is the case the document is invariably of northern origin. The reason is obvious; it is that the scorpion is unknown in the North, and known only in the South. From this we may infer that the Halberstadt fragment represents a document which, already in the seventh century, had departed considerably from tradition.

The herb persterion [sic][2] on another page of the Halberstadt differs considerably from any herb with a similar name in the Leyden or Cassel MSS. On the same page as this figure, however, is a winged horse-like creature with claws which may give a clue to the origin of the MS.

I have looked all through E. H. Zimmermann's Vorkarolingische Miniaturen and there are quite a number of figures which resemble this very closely.[3] The closest resemblance is given on Tafel 245 of that work. There is here represented figures from the Gospel book of St. Chad now in the Cathedral Library at Lichfield.[4] This MS was written and illuminated in the British Isles, and probably in Wales, in the second half of the eighth century. It is extensively glossed in Anglo-Saxon, and represents late Celtic work under English influence.

If you glance at the lion of St. Mark on this plate you will see a creature with spotted body, open-mouthed with tongue, claws, wings and tail similar to the Halberstadt beast. The head is differently shaped and the spots are of a different type, but in symbols of the other evangelists on the same page you will see similar spots to the Halberstadt. In the same group of MSS on other plates you will see other points of resemblance.

I think the single figure of the Berlin fragment may possibly be related to the Leyden MS.

So far as I am able to make out in general the descent of the figures has curiously little relationship to the descent of the text.

If you own the negatives I wonder if you would be so very kind as to tell your photographer to send me positive prints. They would be easier to distinguish that [sic] the rotographs, for which, however, I am extremely obliged.

By the way, has your man been paid for all those magic lantern slides? The Secretary of the Department told me the other day that she was about to send a cheque, but soon after that was taken ill with pneumonia, and I don't quite know what happened, but I should be very much obliged if you would let me know. There is no need for you to bear the expense.

Yours always,

Charles Singer

---

[1] Berlin, Halberstadt, Hildesheim manuscripts.
[2] Peristerion
[3] Ernst H. Zimmermann, *Vorkarolingische Miniaturen* (Berlin, 1916).
[4] Lichfield, a town in England.

70

Singer to Sigerist, London, 9 July 1923

My dear Sigerist,

(1) Many thanks for the proof of Garrison.[1] I have corrected one copy and return it to you. I think that, as it is another man's work, I had better have another slip proof before it goes into pages.

The other copy I have sent on to Garrison himself.

(2) About the English translation of Sudhoff's Ketham. I have received the English translation from Sudhoff himself together with the original German text.[2]

I am sorry to say that the English translation is badly done, and in some parts really incomprehensible. This is not altogether the translator's fault. It is partly the result of Sudhoff's very involved style and careless writing. But the important point is that it would be quite impossible to publish it in English as it stands.

I have therefore sat down to translate, or rather to re-translate the whole on the basis of the MS that Sudhoff has submitted to me. I have got a fair way with this and will do my best to complete the text before I leave London. But this may be impossible and in that case I must leave the remainder until I get back on August 18th when I can finish the whole thing off in two days. I'll bring the documents with me to Interlaken.

(3) I have had a letter from Dannemann[3] saying that he has heard from you that I am coming to Switzerland and asking me to visit him at Munich. I find Dannemann a perfectly impossible person to deal with. He seems to have no common sense at all. I persuaded an English publishing house to undertake an abridged translation of his big book.[4] They offered him what seemed to me very generous terms. I was to undertake the final editing. But Dannemann has so infuriated them with his interminable letters, un-business-like habits, scrawling writing, refusal to answer the questions he is asked and irritating bargaining with people who are trying to treat him well, that they declare that they will not answer any more of his letters. I'll tell you all about it on the 15th.

(4) I am sorry to say we must drop the idea of Elliot Smith's article. My wife and I called on the Elliot Smiths yesterday and we found the poor old fellow almost in a state of collapse. He's frightfully overworked and generally run down, and of course, as always

happens with men in that nervous condition, he said it was quite impossible for him to take a holiday. After arguing with him for about an hour and a half – the gist being that if he didn't take a holiday he'd have a breakdown – he consented to come with us next Saturday. I was just off to take his ticket this morning when the poor old fellow telephones up to say that he can't come after all.

I shouldn't be surprised if he did come, but he really isn't in a state to be asked to write anything.

We are booking our rooms at an Interlaken hotel to-day, and I'll write you to-morrow which one.

Yours ever

Charles Singer

---

[1] Garrison (1924).

[2] Sudhoff (1923); an English edition, translated by Singer, appeared in 1924.

[3] Friedrich Dannemann (1859–1936) German historian of science; Friedrich Dannemann, 'Über den Parallelismus in der Entwicklung der Naturwissenschaften und der Heilkunde', in Singer and Sigerist (eds), (1924), 349–368.

[4] Friedrich Dannemann, *Grundriss einer Geschichte der Naturwissenschaften*, 2 volumes (Leipzig 1898).

71

Singer to Sigerist, London, 11 July 1923

My dear Sigerist,

I have been working at the English translation of Sudhoff's text for the <u>Monumenta medica</u>,[1] and, as I wrote to you, I am somewhat perturbed by the results. I send you the enclosed documents so that you may think the matter over before we meet to discuss it on the 15th.

It is quite out of the question to print the translation as it stands. A large part of it – perhaps the most part of it – is quite incomprehensible. It is evident that the translator's knowledge of English is not quite perfect, and his knowledge of the actual subject of the work practically negligible.

I first thought to correct the English to make it intelligible, but I found that this meant making practically a new translation.

Moreover there were passages in Sudhoff's original German which were quite incomprehensible except to one, like myself, who knew the antecedent work. Furthermore, there are large passages, e.g. the discussion of the manuscript sources of the "urine disc", which can only appeal to a very small class in any country. That class may safely be relied upon to be able to interpret German for itself.

I enclose 13 typed pages of my retranslation, together with the manuscript of the original, for you to get some kind of idea of its state. Even as it is I have had to excise parts of Sudhoff's material and add a sentence of my own here and there in order to get it into literary English.

Thinking the matter over I make this suggestion as to how it should be treated. Give up the idea of an English translation altogether, but let me write from this translation an abstract in English of Sudhoff's original, occupying, let us say, some 20 small printed pages. This can be slipped into the copies which are sold in England and America and would help the sales. I could get in to 20 pages or so everything except what the highly specialised reader would want to have, and my name added to that of Sudhoff would do something to help the sales.

If you like this idea I will undertake it directly I get back to England in August,[2] and indeed the task is already half done in the typewritten pages which are in your hands. If you don't like the idea, – or if it infuriates Sudhoff too much to be told that he can't write German! – I am quite willing to complete the task in the way in which I have begun it, and do my best to make something of a translation.

If you choose this last course I think I would prefer my name not to be associated with the translation itself because I have a suspicion that it would contain a comic element! And humour you know is a deadly weapon!

Seriously, Sudhoff is sui generis. You can't translate him, you can only abstract him. We who know him and are used to working in manuscripts can afford to smile at the enormous emphasis laid on rotten little manuscripts on urinoscopy, but the average English reader who buys him will not smile but will laugh outright! He will say that Sudhoff is playing a very old tune! Therefore I am all in favour of an abstract and not of a translation.

I send under registered cover the following elements: (a.) a typewritten copy of my new translation as far as it is complete. (b.) Sudhoff's own translation into English divided into two parts, the first part corrected as far as I have gone, and the second part still to be worked upon. (c.) Slip proofs of this original text.

I retain here (a.) page proofs of Sudhoff's German text.(b.) A complete facsimile of the Ketham itself. (c.) A number of pages of illustration which are to go into the appendix.

I suppose I may keep these until I return in the middle of August, particularly as they are very awkward to pack, but if not I can always get my secretary to forward them to you, to Lier & C. or to the printers Messrs. Kurt Wolf.

We much look forward to seeing you at Interlaken on the 15th. We have booked rooms for the whole party at Hotel du Lac. We arrive about 10 o'clock in the morning, and you and I can spend the whole day together. I shall let the others go off by themselves and shall have nothing to do but talk matters over with you.

Yours ever,

Charles Singer

I see no objection to English title pages for the English edition. It would help to sell the book.

[1] English translation of Sudhoff (1923).
[2] After Singer's vacation in Switzerland.

72

Singer to Sigerist, Oberalpsee, Switzerland, 22 July 1923

My dear Sigerist,

Herewith the correction proofs of the second part of Garrison's article.[1] There are a large number of corrections but I must admit that they are most of them the fault of Garrison's MS. I did not realize how bad it was. I had certainly better have another set of slip-proofs before it goes into page form. I found a letter from Garrison waiting for me at this place in which he says I may 'edit' his article as I like.

You had better write to me to Vienna at

Pension Miko

Nedergasse 23/24

Wien XIX where I shall be from August 3–13. If anything urgent turns up a communication addressed Poste Restante, Vättis, Schweiz will find me there until July 30.

I have written enclosed to Sudhoff I hope you approve. I don't make you responsible as you will see.[2]

We have had a fine time here[.] We walked from Brienz over the Brunig through the Aare Gorge to Meiringen & on to Innertkirchen. Spent a day there on a long excursion to the Alp of the Bourg [sic]. From there we walked to the Grimsel Hospiz & spent a day on excursions from there. Next day we walked over the Nageligratli [sic] & Rhone glacier to the Furka where we stayed a day, coming to the Tiefen Gletscher on an excursion. Today we walked here from Furka.[3] All are well & all enjoying it enormously.

Best wishes to Mrs. S & the children[4] from us both,

Yours always,

Charles Singer

I find that Miss Jessie Symmers (Elliot Smith's niece) who comes with us to Wien has not had her passport visaed for Austria. I am writing (in German) to the Austrian consulat [sic] at Zurich saying that she is known to you, asking for a visa.

[1] Garrison (1924).
[2] In his letter to Sudhoff, Singer tries to sell his ideas he had explained in the previous letter.
[3] The itinerary of the Singers in the Swiss mountains was a considerable hiking tour of one week.
[4] Sigerist's two daughters, Erica (1918–2002) and Nora (born 1922).

73

Singer to Sigerist, Vättis, Switzerland, 30 July 1923[1]

My dear Sigerist,

I've had a letter from Sudhoff accepting my suggestions. He says he does not mind my abstracting him provided it occupies a <u>good large space</u>! So that is all right. I'll settle to it as soon as I get back on August 18.

My wife finds she has not paid for the maps. Would Mrs Sigerist let her have a post card to Vienna to say how much they cost?

The walk has been a very great success. We have enjoyed it enormously. The weather has been good & we have crossed several glaciers.

Address till August 13
Pension Miko
Nedergasse 23/4
XIX Wien
As ever
Charles Singer

---

[1] Vättis, a village in eastern Switzerland.

74

Singer to Sigerist, Vienna, 2 August 1923

My dear Sigerist,

We got here yesterday morning. Today I am spending with the Juliana Anicia.[1] (1) I return corrected proofs of the Salerno article.[2] I note that the printer has no letter y. This will doubtless be corrected. (2) I'm sorry about Allbutt. Under the circumstances if he would write a tribute to Sudhoff which we could put directly after your dedication I think it would help the appearance & sale of the book & be of some international[?] value also. I will see that D'Arcy Power and E. G. Browne write personal letters to Sudhoff. Before I left I wrote to Comrie to send you his article. Have you heard from him yet? I'll stir him up if you have not.[3]

Will you write to Allbutt to say that we agree to print his dedication? I return his letter. (3) As regards Garrison's proofs there are four notes that have been incorporated in the text.

Page 3 last paragraph
Page 5 first paragraph
Page 5 third paragraph
Page 5 last line I have put loops[?] round there. Could they be put back to their right place? I don't know how to [....] this to a German printer. Garrison's proofs are greatly improved. (4) As regards the title of Garrison's paper. Did he give us one? I don't think he did. If not I suggest:

SOME MODERN MOVEMENTS IN EPIDEMIOLOGICAL THOUGHT.
By F. H. GARRISON[4]

Manila, Phillippin [sic] Islands
I have been through his proofs again. They can now go into page form if the notes are put in their place.

(5) I have sent their proofs to Spencer & Rolleston. Their addresses are

W. G. Spencer
  2 Portland Place
  W1, London
  Sir Humphry Rolleston KCB
  55 Upper Brook Street
  W2 London
(6) The question arises about titles degrees offices etc. I prefer the German way of only giving names and towns. The difficulty is with titles such as <u>Sir</u> which are really part of the name. In Rolleston's case, too, as President of the College of Physicians his office has a real historic interest & is not inapplicable to the present volume. As regards the English and Americans I am inclined to describe them as follows:
Sir T. C. Allbutt P. C. (i.e. Privy Councilllor = Geheimrat)
Regius Professor of Medicine, Cambridge
Sir Humphry Rolleston K.C.B.
President of Royal College of Physicians
  London
  W. G. Spencer London
  Charles and Dorothea Singer London
  E. T. Withington Oxford
  J. D. Comrie Edinburgh
  E. C. Streeter Harvard
  F. H. Garrison Manila
But I will consult Rolleston himself on the point as soon as I get back to London. (7) What about Spencer's & my own pictures? (8) I have had another letter from Sudhoff who is now quite delighted with my suggestion of abstracting him. (9) This morning comes Miss Bowie[?] (one of our party) from München. She says a revolution in Germany is certain. Prices there she says, have gone up 3 times since yesterday. Most of the shops are closed.

If things should go badly try and get old Sudhoff out of Germany. We could put him up for a while & if it came to the worst & I expect the English would try to make small posts[?] for such people as we have some for the Russian professors. But I daresay this is alarmist nonsense. But it does look bad.
Yours ever,
Charles Singer

Vienna gives an impression of being now fairly prosperous. They say trade is good. We had a professor here last night who told us that he pays 5 shillings a quarter = one pound a year for his flat!

---

[1] Anicia Juliana (462–527/528), a Byzantine princess to whom the Vienna Dioscorides MS was dedicated.

[2] Singer and Singer (1924).

[3] Allbutt, Garrison, Spencer, Rolleston, Withington, and Streeter are authors in the Festschrift; Power, Browne, and Comrie are not.

[4] Garrison (1924), the title in the Sudhoff Festschrift reads 'The newer epidemiology'.

75

Singer to Sigerist, Vienna, 11 August 1923

My dear Sigerist,

(1)[1] Herewith the remaining proofs of Garrison's article.[2] The whole can now go into page proof & had better be returned to me as a whole.

Page 7 paragraph 3 reference should go into a note.

Page 8 paragraph 2 reference should go into a note.

Page 10 paragraph 1. Is it not La Tène not la Tene?[3] It is the type of palaeolithic culture to which Garrison is referring.

(2) I will write the dedication of the volume in English as you suggest. It shall be the first thing I do on my return home. For that purpose would you let me have a complete list of the contributors to the volume addressed to me in London?

(3) Very well let Garrison's title be "The Newer Epidemiology".

(4) Clifford Allbutt's letter is charming and will do admirably. I will get similar but shorter letters from D'Arcy Power, E. G. Browne & Elliot Smith. I anticipate no difficulty. Elliot Smith's article must evidently fail. He is much run down & has been unwell here[?] with some digestive trouble. He is better now but not up to writing. He will however gladly write a letter.

(5) With a view of getting letters from Power, Browne & Elliot Smith I am keeping Allbutt's for the moment but will send it back to you soon after my return.

(6) I called on Neuburger both at his house & in the Josephinum.[4] I had the honour, also, of an interview with Frau N. Poor fellow, it's a queer ménage! But learned men are a queer lot! He's very grateful for what has been done for him.

(7) We get beastly accounts from Germany. I wish I could do something for Sudhoff. I'm sure he'll want it & I'll try my best. One of our party wants to go to Germany but there is great difficulty about visas.

(8) We leave here by the Orient Express[5] early in the morning on Tuesday August 14th & we get to London on the evening of Wednesday August 15th, so all letters are best send [sic] to London.

Best wishes to Mrs S. & the children.

Yours always

Charles Singer

---

[1] (1) to (5) are dealing again with the Sudhoff Festschrift.
[2] Garrison (1924).
[3] La Tène culture: The European Iron Age, 450 to 1st century B.C.
[4] The Vienna Medical-Surgical Academy, later Department and Museum of Medical History
[5] Long-distance train running between Paris and Istanbul.

76

Singer to Sigerist, London, 17 August 1923

My dear Sigerist,

Thanks for your letter of August 14th which reached me yesterday evening.

(1)[1] I have written to Comrie by this post, and also to E. G. Browne and D'Arcy Power. The latter two will, I have no doubt, write letters. Elliot Smith arrives in London on Monday 20th August, and he has promised also to write. I shall go down to his house and stand over him till he does!

(2) I have been thinking over the question of the dedication. With the alteration of a few words in the first sentence – which I have no doubt he would permit – Clifford Allbutt's letter would serve perfectly for the purpose. He is an ideal man to write this dedication. He is probably the oldest practising physician living, besides being a man of great eminence as an historian. I suggest therefore that it won't be necessary for me to write an introduction at all, but that we can simply place this letter, with the alterations that I have made, at the head of the volume. Nothing would, I believe, give Sudhoff greater pleasure. To save time I have written to Allbutt direct asking if he would permit this. I return Allbutt's letter with copy (with alterations) herewith. I have made a few trivial alterations in the text and have sent him a copy.

(3) Many thanks for proofs of Sudhoff's Ketham[2] and the English proofs of your Brunschwig.[3] The latter I will go through to-day and return to you. The English of it looks to me excellent. To Ketham I will immediately apply myself.

(4) I enclose what seems to me to be a satisfactory account in English of Lier's proposed advertisement. I don't think it necessary to mention that there will be simultaneous editions in Italian and German, because to do so appears to me to rather diminish the value of the book, but I have no objection at all to its going in.

(5) I return your letter from the firm Seldwyla.[4] I am sure that the best agents in London for the sale of the Sudhoff volume would be H. K. Lewis, 136 Gower Street, W.C.1. I don't know who Lier's agents are in London, but I think Lewis would be less suitable for the Ketham.

(6) I enclose rotographs of

Harley 4986

„ 5294

Royal Appendix III.

Additional 8928

„ 21115

Harley 1585

Sloane 1975

Additional 17063, wrongly marked 21115 and corrected accordingly. Note that Additional 21115 and 17063 are very similar, and are in fact sister manuscripts by the same hand. Miss Anderson[5] tells me that she has sent you rotographs of

Sloane 1313

„ 3531

Harley 4346

(7) I feel it's about time that I paid you all that I owe. If I remember rightly the slides came to about £5.10.0[6] and the maps that Mrs. Sigerist sent us to about 10s. making £6.0.0 in all. These rotographs cost £1.18.0, and I therefore enclose cheque for £4.2.0. I hope this will be about right.

The rotographs of the 1508 Ketham, together with the photographs of the pictures in it, cost £2.9.3. I suppose I can hardly ask Lier to pay this, can I?

This is a very complicated letter, and I had better leave the rest till next time.

Yours ever,

Charles Singer

---

[1] (1) and (2) are dealing with the Sudhoff Festschrift.
[2] Sudhoff (1923).
[3] Henry E. Sigerist (ed.), *The book of 'Cirurgia' by Hieronimus Brunschwig* (Milan,1923); Hieronymus Brunschwig (c.1450–1512/13) German surgeon.
[4] The Zurich publisher of the Festschrift.
[5] Annie Anderson, Singer's secretary.
[6] £5.10.0 in English currency before 1971 meant 5 pounds, 10 shillings, 0 pence.

77

Singer to Sigerist, London, 18 August 1923

My dear Sigerist,

Herewith the proofs of your Brunschwig.[1] The English is distinctly good. I have made a number of corrections and suggestions. It is very interesting and readable[.] I have done the proofs very carefully.

As regards the reference to the translation into English of Brunschwig on p. 9, I had the book through my hands years ago, and there are copies of both editions entertainingly illustrated in the British Museum. If you want exact information concerning them I will send it to you if you will let me have a postcard to that effect.

I enclose proofs of Streeter's article and of my own Salerno article.[2] Both can now go into page form. I have not yet seen the Streeter figures. Of course you will let me have them together with the page proofs.

I am now hard at work on the translation of Sudhoff.[3] I shall finish it to-day or to-morrow, but it will take at least another day to type.

I have just heard that Miss Anderson is in Oxford, so I will ask her to go through the Oxford manuscripts of Apuleius and order photographs for you.

I go to Oxford on the 30th of this month to examine a candidate for the Ph.D. I shall have a few hours in the Bodleian,[4] so that if there is anything you want let me know in time.

Yours ever,

Charles Singer

I find I have only slip proofs of Sudhoff's Ketham & I am making my translation from that. I returned the final German page proofs to the printer before I went to Switzerland. Could you let me have the page proofs again for my final revision?

---

[1] Sigerist (1923d).
[2] Streeter and Singer (1924); Singer and Singer (1924).
[3] Translation of Sudhoff (1923)
[4] The main research library of the University of Oxford.

78

Singer to Sigerist, London, 22 August 1923

My dear Sigerist,

I have had an awful job with the Sudhoff Ketham,[1] but I have finished it at last and enclose the manuscript. I have re-written the whole thing, rearranging it and at times inserting paragraphs and taking out others. The original translation was quite useless. In one or two places Sudhoff has written so obscurely that I may have missed some of his meaning. In several places the old fool has rushed off into discussing the influence of Ketham on later printed works which was of course to have been my job in Vol. II. I have simply cut these out. I have marked a few doubtful references etc. in red for you or Sudhoff to deal with.

Is it all right for me to put in the reference to Soranus on p. 37 of my MS?[2] Cut it out if it is not.

As the old man may be a little hurt with the alterations I have sent a copy direct to him. As this does not pass through you he cannot be offended with you. I have kept a third copy in my own hands.

I have now translated most of Mondino.[3] I'll work at the 1493 Ketham as soon as I get the proofs of it from Lier.

Corrections[:][4] Thanks for your list of contributors to the volume. As Sir Clifford Allbutt is going to contribute the preliminary letter his name had better remain in. W. G. Spencer of London is Mr. not Dr.; surgeons in England are rather sensitive in England [sic] on the point of being called Mr.! Withington is of Oxford, not London. You may if you like insert Mrs. Dorothea Waley Singer who is writing the article with me. I haven't heard from Comrie yet.

This morning I have the enclosed letter from E. G. Browne. His handwriting is so difficult that I type it together with the letter that he sends to Sudhoff. I have altered Browne's letter in the typed copy in a few details. If you think it advisable this letter of Browne can go into the volume with Allbutt's. As regards Elliot Smith I shall reserve action till I hear from you, but I can easily get a letter from him to the same effect. D'Arcy Power has already written to Sudhoff privately, so there is no need for him to take further action. I am sure it's right to print Allbutt's letter, but I leave you to decide about Browne and Elliot Smith.

I enclose photographs – which I have just found – of the English translation of Brunschwig's Surgery. It was printed in London in 1525 by Peter Treveris. Please return the photographs at your leisure, but I can get copies of them for you if you are sufficiently interested. There is also an English translation of Brunschwig's Distillation book[5] printed in London by Laurens Andrewe, 1527.

Yours ever,

Charles Singer

No need to return Browne's letters

P.S. As regards my translation of Sudhoff's Ketham. It would, of course, not be necessary to reprint the <u>text</u> figures in my work. It would be enough to refer the reader to the German original. As these figures in the German original will always have legends attached to them stating their sources it is not necessary to constantly repeat the press-marks of manuscripts in my text.

PP.S. I enclose another copy of Allbutt's letter with Allbutt's own corrections which are very slight. One, however, is important. We wrote seventeenth for seventieth! See for heaven's sake that the error is kept out of print.

[1] Sudhoff (1923).
[2] Soranos of Ephesos (2nd century A.D.), Greek physician and author on gynaecology.
[3] See letter 41.
[4] This and the following paragraph are dealing with the Festschrift in which the letters of Browne and Smith are not contained.
[5] Hieronymus Brunschwig, *Liber de arte distillandi de compositis* (Strassburg, 1512).

79

Singer to Sigerist, London, 27 August 1923

My dear Sigerist,

I have to-day sent a letter of which the enclosed is a copy to Cushing. Somehow or other these perfectly silly ideas grow, so I thought I'd better get rid of it at once.[1]

Yours ever,

Charles Singer

I don't think it commits you too much. It puts it on Klebs!

[1] In his letter to Cushing, Singer writes: "there has been some misunderstanding about Canano, and that somehow or other an idea has got about that I am going to write on him or to produce an edition on him. .... It is obvious that there is nothing whatever in all this that will in the remotest degree interfere with anything that you or Klebs might write on the subject."

80

Singer to Sigerist, London, 29 August 1923

My dear Sigerist,

Thanks for your note. If you are sure we have enough material for the Sudhoff volume I think we will <u>not</u> print Browne's letter. It is much easier for us both if we don't as Allbutt's then stands[?] as a dedication.

I can easily explain to Browne – indeed I have already done so – he is a very reasonable man. Elliot Smith can then write direct to Sudhoff.

I am glad you like my work on Ketham.[1] I don't think the old man[2] can object. I go to Oxford tomorrow & will look up your MSS.

I don't think I wrote that we should be delighted to see your pupil[3] if she lets us have a line when she is in London.

Yours ever

Charles Singer

[1] Charles Singer (ed.), *The fasciculus medicinae of Johannes de Ketham, Alemanus*. With an Introduction by Karl Sudhoff, translated by C. Singer (Milan: Lier, 1924).

[2] Sudhoff.

[3] Miss Bauer, see letter 86.

81

Singer to Sigerist, London, 1 September 1923a

My dear Sigerist,

I have received this morning enclosed letter from Sudhoff. It is satisfactory that the old man is satisfied. I have written to him telling him that I have incorporated all, or nearly all of his suggestions. Concerning them I have a few observations to make.

I enclose his copy in which these corrections have been made by him and endorsed by me. It is the copy that should go to Lier. Perhaps you will check off these remarks of mine against his letter, which, by the way, you had better keep.

P.1. I think the word "adapted" had better remain on the title page. If it does not[,] people will say I have not 'translated' him. "Tradottori sono traditori".[1]

p.3. Correction made.

p.9. The old man is anxious for this figure to go in. It would cost very little to reproduce and it is really of great interest. It's a picture I found and sent to him from what is I believe a unique copy in the British Museum. It is, I believe, the earliest illustration in a medical printed book.

p.17. Correction made.

p.20. I am not sure that I understand what the old man means. I think it had better been printed as it is now corrected, and wait to see what happens, but you might look through it.

p.23. I think this is all right. I think the old man has misunderstood my English.

p.26 I think the old man is wrong here and I am right, but I have written to him on the matter.

p.34 I gather I may leave in the Arundel reference.[2]

Yours ever,

Charles Singer

[1] Italian proverb, meaning "translators are traitors".

[2] Thomas Howard, 2nd Earl of Arundel (1585–1646); The Arundel Manuscripts: *Catalogue of manuscripts in the British Museum* (London, 1841).

82

Singer to Sigerist, London, 1 September 1923b (postcard)[1]

With reference to the use of cata in the Antidotaries, cp. P. 154, 9 lines from bottom, and p. 159, 18 lines from bottom I notice that the philologist Henry Bradley (editor of the great English Dictionary)[2] writes: "The preposition cata seems to have been generally used by traders from the Levant pretty much as per is used in English business language. Cata unum means 'apiece' hence the Italian caduno." I note also that cata is used in the 'Hisperic' language[3] in which the "Lorica of Gildas"[4] was written.

Charles Singer

[1] This card was addressed to the Swiss resort village of Beatenberg.

[2] Henry Bradley (1845–1923), philologist and lexicographer; see W. A. Craigie, 'Bradley, Henry (1845–1923)', rev. Jenny McMorris, *Oxford dictionary of national biography* (Oxford: Oxford University Press, 2004), vol. 7, 211–212.

[3] Hisperic: A style of Latin originating in the 6th century in Britain.

[4] Lorica of Gildas the Briton (6th century AD).

83

Singer to Sigerist, London, 7 September 1923

My dear Sigerist,

Please note that sheet 6 of Garrison's article is wanting. I am particularly anxious to get his article exactly right because he can have no opportunity of seeing it himself.[1] You will of course let me have page proofs of it.

I also enclose our Salerno article which can now go into page proofs.[2] Two or three of the words are wrongly divided into syllables. I have indicated this in the margin.

According to your directions I am holding the article by Streeter and myself[3] until the clichées arrive. Rolleston's I have sent on to him.[4]

I hope you will have a good time in Germany, and things will be quiet there. My very kind regards to Sudhoff.

Yours ever,

Charles Singer

[1] Garrison (1924); Garrison was on military duty in Manila.
[2] Singer and Singer (1924)
[3] Streeter and Singer (1924)
[4] Rolleston (1924).

84

Singer to Sigerist, Cadgwith, West Cornwall, 26 September 1923[1]

My dear Sigerist,

(1) I have not yet had the proofs of the figures of the article by Streeter & myself.[2] It is getting rather late. Could you hurry up Seldwyla.

(2) Are Withington's proofs going through all right?[3] I have not seen them. His address is 4 Polstead Road, Oxford.

(3) I have had a very nice letter from Cushing, concerning this absurd Canano business.[4] Since then I have found a copy in the British Museum! It is entered under a wrongly spelt name – that is why I did not know it was there. Sudhoff has also lent me his photographic copy so that I am equipped for any Fitzpatrick Lectures.[5]

I wrote to Klebs some time back sending him a book & telling him that to avoid misunderstanding I had no plans for publishing Canano. He writes back that he is going forward with it & is coming to London next week & will look at the B.M. copy.[6]

(4) I am down here for a few days. I return Oct 3rd. It is in the middle of the wildest-coast scenery.

(5) I hear that the facsimile of the 1493 Italian Ketham has arrived. I will set to work on it as soon as I get back.

(6) Is there not some work in Spanish on the 1493 Spanish Ketham? I think you have it [.] If so will you lend it me? Where is there a copy to be found? Is there one in Paris? If so I will have it photographed. Herzberger of Amsterdam[7] has a copy of the Spanish 1517 which he is lending me.

(7) Lier doesn't seem to mind how much he spends on the book is[?] how big the figures are. Nevertheless I think they can be too big & I think Sudhoff's are too large for

convenient reference. I am suggesting therefore that most of mine – other than the facsimile itself – should be reduced.

Yours ever

Charles Singer

[1] Cadgwith, a village and fishing port in Cornwall, England.

[2] Streeter and Singer (1924).

[3] Withington (1924).

[4] See letters 68 and 79.

[5] The Fitzpatrick Lectures delivered at the Royal College of Physicians of London; Singer's were on the history of anatomy and were published as Charles Singer, *The evolution of anatomy: a short history of anatomical and physiological discovery to Harvey: being the substance of the Fitzpatrick lectures delivered at the Royal College of Physicians of London in the years 1923 and 1924* (London; 1925).

[6] British Museum.

[7] Herzberger, probably a bookseller.

85

Singer to Sigerist, London, 3 October 1923

My dear Sigerist,

I arrived home last night and found a letter from you awaiting me, and another one this morning.

To avoid delay I send off at once herewith the legends for Streeter's and my article together with proofs of it. These proofs can go into page form.

Below each figure I have written legends. The figures will naturally be arranged together on a page, and the page as a whole should have the following legend :

Figures Illustrating Extramural Dissection in the XVth century.

From MS 9 (Young-Aitken Catalogue) in the Hunterian Library at Glasgow.

The other matters that you refer to I will attend to later in the day, or to-morrow.

Yours ever,

Charles Singer

86

Singer to Sigerist, London, 4 October 1923

My dear Sigerist,

I enclose my suggestions for the English form of Seldwyla's notice.[1] I send you three copies for your convenience.

I have slightly modified your notice on page 2, but I enclose your original for reference.

As regards page 3 I have altered a little the order of the Table of Contents, making "General Subjects" last, and arranging the material under each head in chronological order.

As regards the question of the sale of the book. I think Seldwyla would be well advised to employ an English firm or agent. Either the Oxford University Press or Messrs. H. K. Lewis of 136 Gower Streeter [sic] would I feel sure be glad to undertake the work. On hearing from you or Seldwyla on the matter I would gladly approach them, or they could write direct.

As regards American sales it is even more necessary to get a local publisher than in England, and although I do not like him I should think that Paul Hoeber, the publisher of the Annals of Medical History[2] would be as good as any one. If, however, Seldwyla employ the Oxford University Press the book could be advertised through their American house. On the whole I would advise the Oxford University Press.

Although I like to see all the contributors on the advertisement I think I agree with you on the whole that the title page is best without them, but I look forward to seeing the proofs.[3]

Many thanks for the Spanish Ketham which arrived yesterday. By the way you say that both Spanish editions of Ketham were known to Daremberg.[4] Can you give me the reference?

Miss Bauer called here yesterday.[5] She seems a nice earnest student, and I was able to help her give her new references. I gave her introductions to the Secretary and to the Superintendent of the British Museum and to the Librarian of the Royal College of Surgeons. We will gladly do what we can for her.

I have just got into my new department which is really delightful.[6] University College house me [sic] extremely well though not on the scale of Sudhoff.

I happened to be calling at Lewis's yesterday on an entirely different matter, and I shewed them the reproduction by Lier of Jenner's book. They are eager to become its agent, and I told them to write direct to Lier with permission to use my name. I shall write a review on the Jenner book in the Times Literary Supplement.[7] I did not discuss with them our Sudhoff volume, and I am inclined to think that that is better placed with the Oxford University Press.

Yours ever,

Charles Singer

[1] Publisher of Sudhoff Festschrift, used Oxford University Press as its English publisher.

[2] *Annals of Medical History* was the first American journal of the subject.

[3] All authors of the Sudhoff Festschrift appeared on the title-page.

[4] Charles Daremberg (1816/17–1872) French medical historian. See A. Hahn, 'Charles-Victor Daremberg 1817–1872: A Great Medical Historian', *British Medical Bulletin*, 1947, **5**: 59–61; and Danielle Gourevitch, 'Charles Daremberg, his friend Émil Littré, and positivist medical history', in Frank Huisman and John Harley Warner (eds), *Locating medical history. The stories and their meanings*, (Baltimore: Johns Hopkins University Press, 2004), 53–73.

[5] Sigerist's student at the University of Zurich, mentioned in letter 80.

[6] Probably new rooms.

[7] Edward Jenner (1749–1823) English surgeon and apothecary; introduced smallpox vaccination; see Derrick Baxby, 'Jenner, Edward (1749–1823)', *Oxford dictionary of national biography* (Oxford: Oxford University Press, 2004), vol 30, 4–8. Charles Singer, 'Jenner and vaccination', article on Jenner's *Enquiry* (facsimile), *Times Literary Supplement*, 20 November 1924.

87

Singer to Sigerist, London, 7 October 1923

My dear Sigerist,

I blush to find among my neglected correspondence the notice from the Swiss Society of the History of Medicine. I enclose cheque for 10 Francs made out to yourself. Let me know if I owe more.

Yours ever,

Charles Singer

A letter from Kurt Wolff [sic][1] of Munich tells me that the proofs of my translation of Sudhoff's Ketham are on their way to me.[2]

Klebs is in London and I am seeing him today.

[1] A printer in Munich.
[2] Singer (1924a).

88

Singer to Sigerist, London, 19 October 1923

My dear Sigerist,

What an awful nuisance. It is most unfortunate too that the same thing happened to me with the only other Festschrift with which I have been connected, that to Sir William Osler.[1] In his case he died before it was ready, and the whole thing made a very bad impression. Be warned in time and don't run any risk of it happening in this case. Sacrifice everything to speed.[2]

Since most of the book is actually in proof and the proofs have been corrected already, it ought not to take long to set them up again from the old proofs. This should be done in such a way that all the corrections can be embodied at once and need not again be referred to the contributors.

I don't think I had better approach the Clarendon Press[3] until I have had a set of proofs. I am very glad to do so then, but after this disappointment I think I must be sure of my ground. Furthermore I don't see how the Press could do anything until they have some sort of idea what the book is like.

Write to me at the first possible moment to let me know whether any estimate can be given as to the actual date that the work will appear. It so happened that Clifford Allbutt wrote also the introduction to the Osler volume!

We were very glad to do anything for Miss Bauer.

I am glad you liked the review. [4]

Yours ever,

Charles Singer

[1] William Osler (1849–1919) Professor of Medicine at McGill University, Johns Hopkins, and Oxford, England; see W. F. Bynum, 'Osler, Sir William, baronet (1849–1919)', *Oxford dictionary of national biography* (Oxford: Oxford University Press, 2004), vol. 42, 53–56. Charles Singer and Dorothea Singer, 'On a miniature, ascribed to Mantegna, of an operation by Cosmas and Damian', in *Contributions to medical and biological research, dedicated to Sir William Osler*, Vol. I, (New York, 1919), 166–176.

[2] This letter reflects panic that the Sudhoff Festschrift would not appear in time for his birthday on 25 November 1923.

[3] The scholarly branch of Oxford University Press.

[4] Singer (1924b).

89

Singer to Sigerist, London, 24 October 1923

My dear Sigerist,

I have this morning received enclosed article for the Sudhoff volume by Lynn Thorndike.[1] If we are to be late in printing we may as well include it as we are a bit short of Americans. The manuscript is a very clear one and should not give a German printer any trouble-

Yours ever,

Charles Singer

[1] Thorndike (1924).

90

Singer to Sigerist, London, 1 November 1923

My dear Sigerist,

You will be interested to hear that Sir Humphry Rolleston has just been appointed personal Physician in-Ordinary to the King.[1]

Under these circumstances I think it would be advisable to do everything you possibly can to press on the publication of the Sudhoff volume. The fact that he contributes to this volume to a German Professor will have a small share in ameliorating international relationships.[2] It is a matter in which he behaved particularly well all through the War. During the War he was President of the Royal Society of Medicine and with great tact he succeeded in preventing the names of German and Austrian Fellows and Members from being removed. Under the circumstances it would be a great pity if the volume were much delayed.

Do try and see what can be done.

Yours ever,

Charles Singer

[1] King George V
[2] Rolleston (1924).

91

Singer to Sigerist, London, 9 November 1923

My dear Sigerist,

Herewith the proofs received yesterday. I have carefully corrected both Rolleston's and Garrison's as far as the latter goes.[1] I did not think it necessary to let Rolleston see his, as I happen myself to possess the transcript of the Power MS.[2] It would, however, be courteous to send him what English printers call "clean sheets". That is to say the final form, before it goes to press.

A few general points on typography in English.

(1) In English quotations are usually given between <u>inverted commas</u> which are written in the way illustrated in this paragraph: -[3]

It is vexing to have the German method constantly adopted by the printer [....] It looks queer to English eyes.

(2) Notes are referred to, if not too numerous as in the case of our volume, by asterisks *, the first note by one asterisk, the next by two **[.] It is not necessary to accompany the asterisk with a bracket. Still less if numbers are used for referring to notes is a bracket necessary. I have never been able to understand why the German printers will insist upon putting these brackets in. They mean nothing. Anyhow they give an unEnglish appearance to the page and are best omitted.

What is the exact day of Sudhoff's birthday?[4] Is it November 23rd? I want to know so as to send the old man a greeting from my wife and myself on that occasion. You might drop me a card on the point.

I have had a note from Lier asking me to call on the Oxford University Press with reference to the sale of the <u>Monumenta medica</u>, and I will do so early next week.

I notice that you advertise Berengar of Carpi's <u>Isagoge Breves</u>.[5] That would be a splendid book to have out. It ought to be accompanied by an English translation. An English translation was made of it in the 17th century (1664). It is, however, excessively rare. There is a copy in the British Museum. I suggest that I have this British Museum copy copied out, and that I modernise the spelling a little and correct any errors in the translation, and that this be published along with the facsimile.[6] It will be an interesting companion to my translation of Mundinus.[7]

In translating Mundinus I have found it easier to adopt a somewhat archaic style, using the English of the earlier eighteenth century. I am sending it off to Lier within the next week.

Yours ever,

Charles Singer

P.S. I notice Rolleston has specially marked Please let me have page proofs [.] Therefore he had better have them but I don't think he will have anything to correct after I have been through them thus.

[1] Rolleston (1924) and Garrison (1924).
[2] There is no D'Arcy Power MS in the Sudhoff Festschrift.
[3] Pasted into the letter.
[4] Sudhoff's birthday is 25 November.
[5] Jacopo Berengario da Carpi, *Isagoge breves prelucide ac uberime in anatomiam humani corporis* (Bologna, 1522).
[6] Singer's translation of Berengario did not materialize.
[7] Charles Singer (ed.), *The Fasciculo di Medicina Venice 1493*, with translation of Anathomia by Mondino da Luzzi, (Florence, 1925).

92

Singer to Sigerist, London, 16 November 1923

My dear Sigerist,

Herewith the proofs of the remainder of Garrison's article and that by Streeter and myself.[1] They were received only this morning, and I return them to you within two hours of their reaching me.

As regards Garrison's article and all the other English articles, keep your eye on the „inverted commas" about which I wrote to you in my last letter.

Concerning the article by Streeter and myself, as each figure is to go on a separate page I have suggested legends for them. There is plenty of room and they will make the page look better. I think I had better have proofs of these with the legends on. With the article itself I am quite content save for the "inverted commas". There are very few corrections.

As regards Sudhoff's Ketham.[2] I have corrected it and was about to return it when the disorders in Munich broke out.[3] I therefore held it up, but am sending it to-day.

I am getting on well, I think, with my Ketham.[4] I have finished with the translation of Mundinus, and am now writing up the introduction.[5] Wolff is behaving very well over proofs, and they are everything that can be desired. I ought to get this work finished by the end of the year, and also Sudhoff's tracts on Syphilis translated into English.[6]

Yours ever,

Charles Singer

POSTSCRIPT:

I have sent off to-day Sudhoff's proofs to Wolff. They are extremely well done and there are not many corrections. I don't quite understand how my translation is to be arranged in connection with Sudhoff's German original. Are the editions to be either English or German? Or is my "adaptation" to be issued along with the German original? If the latter is selected there is no need for the figures to be reproduced twice, and this arrangement would, I think, be the most satisfactory.

I am giving a Seminar this term on "History of Anatomy" for which I have thirteen people entered. I give notes on the subject to my students. Perhaps you would care to see a copy as far as we have got. I enclose it.

C. S.

[1] Garrison (1924). Streeter and Singer (1924).
[2] Sudhoff (1923).
[3] Hitler's failed Putsch attempt.
[4] Singer (1924a).
[5] Singer (1925a).
[6] Karl Sudhoff, *Zehn Syphilis-Drucke aus den Jahren 1495–1498* (Milan, 1924).

93

Singer to Sigerist, London, 19 November 1923

My dear Sigerist,

In answer to your card. Don't you think that 50 reprints is rather a lot to give away? If you haven't already told people of this, I think 25 would be quite enough. If you have told them we will let it stand.

50 will be enough for me of the Salerno article, and I am sure enough for Garrison of his. If 50 are distributed to each, I think you had better strike off 75 of the article by Streeter and myself.[1]

I return the corrected proof of the handbill for the Monumenta medica. As soon as you have one in final form I will take it to the Oxford University Press. I think I had better wait until I get the last proofs of this handbill, and also of the Sudhoff Ketham, together with advanced proofs of my Ketham, before I act with the Oxford University Press. If, however, you or Lier are anxious for me to discuss the matter with them earlier I will gladly do so. I think it best, however, to have something to show them.

Did you get Thorndike's article, and will it be possible to include it? I have received his authority to correct the proofs without reference to him, to save time.[2]

Yours ever,

Charles Singer

[1] Articles for the Sudhoff Festschrift and Ketham.
[2] Thorndike (1924).

94

Singer to Sigerist, London, 21 November 1923

My dear Sigerist,

I think this card[1] is for you to attend to rather than for me, so far as it concerns the Ketham. I don't think really that the corrections that Sudhoff suggests matter in the least, and no harm will be done if they are not inserted, but I have written to the old man to say I will do my best.

Have you seen Capparoni's book on Salerno?[2] If so, I think it will make you smile. I thought I knew English, and I rather prided myself on having studied Salerno, but I really haven't the least idea what Capparoni is talking about!! I got the book for review, but I find myself quite unable to review either favourably or unfavourably a book in which I have hitherto discovered no meaning at all!!

Thanks for your telegram which I replied to at once, though a letter on the subject was already on its way. As regards the Salerno article I should like 50 copies, and as regards the article by Streeter and myself 75. If 75 for both have been printed no harm has been done.

As I wrote, however, in my letter I think it would be wiser to give far fewer reprints all round. The point, however, is not a matter of great importance.
Yours ever,
Charles Singer

P.S. Are Seldwyla in communication with H. K. Lewis or with the Oxford University Press? If not, that ought to be attended to at once, and they had better send me a complete set of proofs for the purpose.

Will Sudhoff receive an advanced copy of the book? I have written to congratulate him to-day as has also my wife.

[1] From Sudhoff to Singer.
[2] Capparoni (1923).

95

Singer to Sigerist, 23 November 1923

My dear Sigerist,

Many thanks for the Withington paper, which shall be typed as you suggest. You shall have it as soon as possible.[1]

You still don't say anything about having received Thorndike's paper.[2]

Both my wife and I have written to congratulate Sudhoff on his seventieth birthday.
Yours ever,
Charles Singer

[1] Withington (1924).
[2] Thorndike (1924).

96

Singer to Sigerist, London, 3 December 1923

My dear Sigerist,
Very many thanks for the Haller and Gesner correspondence. It's a very fine volume and shows wonderful activity on your part.[1]
I am longing to hear how you found old Sudhoff and what is happening in Germany. Did he get my letter and did he like it?
Yours ever,
Charles Singer

[1] Henry E. Sigerist, *Albrecht von Hallers Briefe an Johannes Gesner 1728–1777* (Berlin, 1923). Johannes Gesner (1709–1790), Swiss physician and naturalist; see P. E. Pilet, 'Gessner (Gesner), Johannes', *Complete dictionary of scientific biography*, vol. 5 (Detroit: Charles Scribner's Sons, 2008), 379–380.

97

Singer to Sigerist, London, 6 December 1923a

My dear Sigerist,
Herewith Klebs' proofs.[1] I have done my best with them.
He is such a queer fellow that it would be best to keep these proofs & return them to me. Then if he wants to quarrel afterwards I have them in evidence.
Spencer's have gone to him & will follow to you tonight.[2]
You enclose also Streeter's and my article but this need no further correction & I don't return it.[3]

The Ketham is the finest volume I have ever seen.[4] Of this more later.

Yours ever,

Charles Singer

[1] Arnold C. Klebs, 'The Practica of Gianmatteo Ferrari da Gradi editio princeps', in Singer and Sigerist (eds), (1924), 211–236.

[2] Spencer (1924).

[3] Streeter and Singer (1924).

[4] Sudhoff (1923).

98

Singer to Sigerist, London, 6 December 1923b

My dear Sigerist,

First of all I must most heartily congratulate you on the beautiful Ketham volume. I don't know how to praise it enough. It is certainly the most beautiful production that has yet been turned out in the history of medicine[1].

My translation of the Ketham[2] must still be delayed for a few days because I have never until now had a complete copy of the German version. I must get the proofs for a last time to correct two or three references. I have written to this effect to Wolff, but will return them immediately after receiving them.

Now for some points concerning the Sudhoff volume.[3] I sent off proofs to you this morning which you have doubtless received by now. I find that in the article by Streeter and Singer 3 small corrections are desirable, and I enclose the proof.[4] None are really important but it would be convenient if they could be made.

As regards the advertisement. I return a corrected proof, but want to make some remarks about it.

(a) It is very desirable that Seldwyla should also give the price in English shillings, and should say that he will accept ordinary English cheques. Without this he will not get many English orders.

(b) I think the volume is too dear, if the price is given in Swiss francs. 40 Swiss francs equals about 32/-. I think a proper price for the book would be 15/- or 16/- unbound and 20/- or 21/- bound.

In other respects it looks a very attractive volume[.]

I am so glad to get good news of Sudhoff.

When Seldwyla have a complete set of clean proofs, and when they are [in?] communication with the Oxford University Press, they had better also send them to me, and I can

easily put in a word with the Oxford University Press. I am taking my copy of Sudhoff's Ketham down to the Oxford University Press to-morrow to discuss matters with them.
Yours ever,
Charles Singer

[1] Singer congratulates Sigerist as editor of the Monumenta medica series.
[2] Singer (1924a).
[3] Sudhoff Festschrift, Singer and Sigerist (1924)
[4] Streeter and Singer (1924).

99

Singer to Sigerist, London, 12 December 1923

My dear Sigerist,
I have to-day sent the enclosed to Lier & Co. It explains itself, and I merely send you a copy.
Most unfortunately I have mislaid the proofs of Sudhoff's work on Syphilis, and I have to-day written to Wolff for another copy.[1] I have also sent them the English translation of Mundinus which is now complete.[2] I have put into it a great deal of work, and am now getting on to the other aspects of the Ketham volume.
I can't send you the figures for the second Ketham yet, but you shall have them in a few weeks.
A nice letter from old Sudhoff this morning.
Yours ever,
Charles Singer

P.S. I enclose Lier's letter also
I have sent off the Mundinus translation by this post.

[1] Sudhoff (1924).
[2] Singer (1925a).

100

Singer to Sigerist, London, 13 December 1923

My dear Sigerist,
These proofs need in each case the correction of the letter 9 to the number 9 at their head. Will you see to this? Otherwise they are correct.
Yours ever
Charles Singer

101

Singer to Sigerist, London, 20 December 1923

My dear Sigerist,

It is perfectly mad of me, but I find I have Sudhoff's Syphilis work perfectly safe after all.[1] I had an idea that it was in proof form and I have been hunting everywhere for proofs. But I see that this is not the case. I have the typed document perfectly safe and will embark on it at once.

Will you please explain to Wolff and Lier what has happened? The whole mistake arose from my thinking it was in proof form.

I have nearly finished the 1493 Ketham, and you shall have the material in the first week in January.

With best wishes from us both to you all for a happy Christmas.

Yours ever,

Charles Singer

[1] Sudhoff (1924).

102

Singer to Sigerist, London, 22 December 1923

My dear Sigerist,

(1) I have to-day sent off to Wolff at Munich the major part of my introduction to the 1493 Ketham. He has already received the translation of Mundinus so that he has now got nearly the whole thing.[1] I expect you would rather not see it until it is in proof but if you want to I have two more copies.

(2) About illustrations for it. I have to-day sent to Lier & Co. a number of illustrations to be turned into blocks. A number of other blocks I can myself supply from the Clarendon Press. Could you let them have the clichées [sic] of these two plates from the Sudhoff volume?

(3) I hope you got my letter saying that I had found the MS of Sudhoff's Syphilis & would work at it at once.[2]

(4) How goes the Sudhoff volume? I have not yet had proofs of Thorndike's article.[3]

Best wishes from both to both for Christmas.

Yours ever,

Charles Singer

[1] Singer (1925a).
[2] Sudhoff (1924).
[3] Thorndike (1924).

103

Singer to Sigerist, London, 31 December 1923

My dear Sigerist,

Many thanks for your letter. I am glad you are to have a quiet holiday.

You shall certainly have the photographs in question in due course.

There is some work that I want done at Munich of which I'll write to you in a few days.

This letter is to tell you of a rather interesting visit that I had the other day. Menno Hertzberger of Amsterdam telephoned me up to say that he wanted to see me.[1] He came here and we spent an hour talking things over.

He had heard – from whom I do not know – that you and I had formed the idea of editing an international journal for the History of Medicine. He told me that Janus was about to die (it's about time) and of course he anticipated the death of the Archiv.[2] His idea is to publish a journal under our editorship guaranteed for two years. I said I thought we'd like Streeter included and that probably the general format of the Archiv was about as good as we could have. I said I didn't mind economising on print but we must have scope for the reproduction of figures.

I said that in a general sense I thought it was probable that you and Streeter would agree to what I suggested and I asked him to go and think it over and write suggestions to me which would be a basis of discussion for us all.

I just thought you'd like to hear of this as soon as possible.

Don't overdo it and take things easy and tell your wife I said so.

With best wishes from us all for the New Year,

Yours ever,

Charles Singer

[1] Menno Hertzberger (died 1982) Dutch antiquarian bookseller.

[2] The planned international journal did not materialize. *Janus*, the third medico-historical journal of this name, was founded in the Netherlands in 1896. The *Archiv für Geschichte der Medizin und Naturwissenschaften* was founded by Sudhoff in 1907.

104

Singer to Sigerist, London, 7 January 1924

My dear Sigerist,

For the last few days my wife and I have been struggling with old Sudhoff's introduction to the Syphilis tracts. What a silly old fool he is! The difficulty is not with the German but with the confusion of ideas. Do you not think it possible that it could be translated into German first and then we could tackle it? As it is it is really incomprehensible.[1]

It would be useless for me to invoke any one else to do the work. We have of course in London expert German scholars, and I have several colleagues who are this, but they could make no more of it than I can. I think if I worked at it hard enough I could get it into English, but I reckon it would take me some weeks. Would it not be possible for Sudhoff to re-write it under the express condition that no sentence was longer than three lines in length, or could someone do this for him in German? Once this were done I could of course tackle the work right away and finish it off in one day.

I am truly sorry to bother you with this, but the old man is really getting too bad! Have you seen a copy of it?
Yours ever,
Charles Singer

P.S. It is part II from page 9 onward of his stuff that is so awful. The first part is just tolerable, though it is a pity that he has never learnt to write German.

[1] Sudhoff's Syphilis tracts (1924), is indeed written in a difficult German with complex syntax and in a metaphorical style.

105

Singer to Sigerist, London, 8 January 1924

My dear Sigerist,

About your visit to München. There are one or two points which I would like you to attend to.

In the 1493 Ketham there is, as you know, only one coloured plate. I am having a coloured version of this prepared in London.

But there is an interesting coloured copy of the 1495 Latin edition at Leipzig which I have not seen. It might be worth while to prepare coloured figures from it, notably the plague scene. I enclose a letter from Sudhoff in which he says he can have it sent to München. You could arrange to meet it there and to examine it and see whether these figures are worth reproducing. If you see your way to do this would you write direct to Sudhoff himself?

I find there are records of seventeen editions of Ketham of which I have seen only eleven. I append a list of the editions and I should like this list checked off against the editions in the München Library, so that I may ascertain if there are any editions of which I have never heard and also so as to get photographs of editions that I have not seen. If there are editions that I have not seen I should like photographs of the more relevant pages.

Would you investigate the matter for me while there? The editions known to me are:

I.   Venice 1491. Latin. Folio.
II. Venice 1493. Italian. Folio.
III. Burgos 1495 May 25th. Spanish. Folio.

IV.   Venice 1495 Oct. 15th. Latin. Folio.
V.   Pampelona 1495. Spanish. (Stockton Hough). Not seen
VI.   Venice 1500, March 28th. Latin. Folio
VII.   Venice 1501. (Feb. 17th 1500 Old style). Latin. Folio.
VIII.   Venice 1508. Italian. Folio. Not seen.
IX.   Milan 1509. Italian. Quarto.
X.   Milan 1510. Italian. Not seen.
XI.   Antwerp 1512. Latin. Not seen.
XII.   Venice 1513. Latin. Folio.
XIII.   Venice 1515. Latin. Not seen.
XIV.   Seville 1517. Spanish. Folio.
XV.   Venice 1522. Latin. Folio.
XVI.   Venice 1523 (Jan. 17th 1522. Old style). Italian. Not seen.
XVII.   Venice 1668. Not seen.

There is also a point or two in the MS of Dioscorides while you are at München, if I have time to look points up before you go and you have time to do it.

Yours ever,

Charles Singer

P.S. I am also having investigations made for these editions at the Bibliothèque Nationale, Paris and in Leipzig. If after this any editions remain over of which I have no news I shall make a more extended search.

I have ordered your photographs of Harley 4346 and Sloane 1313 to-day.

106

Singer to Sigerist, London, 14 January 1924

My dear Sigerist,

Herewith the photographs which you asked for together with the bill. The photographs are full size.

I think you had better pay me direct, and not Fleming, and allow me to pay Fleming.[1] If you deal with Fleming direct I think he will raise prices still further.

The prices are scandalously high and we are endeavouring to deal with the question in London. There are, however, various technical difficulties in the way.

I have had a letter from Sudhoff this morning in which he says he would gladly let you have any Kethams at München. The only one in question, however, is the coloured 1495 of which I wrote you. Will you write to him direct?

Sudhoff proposes a scheme by which I should buy books for his Institute and partly balance them by the price of photographs etc. that I get from there. I don't see how I can possibly afford it. If his Institute gets hard up and cannot pay the differences between our two accounts I cannot press him for the money and I must be the loser, and it would amount to more than I could afford.

I must think the matter over before I answer him. I expect he has proposed a similar scheme to you.
Yours ever,
Charles Singer

---

[1] A photographer in London.

107

Singer to Sigerist, London, 28 January 1924

My dear Sigerist,

As I wrote to you some time ago I had a visit from Hertzberger of Amsterdam from whom I have now had the enclosed letter.

I have sent him a reply of which I enclose a copy. I hope you are not overdoing it, but I rather fear from the tone of your last letters that you are. Don't be in too much of a hurry – you have all your life before you.

If this isn't too late for your visit to München I wonder if you would look through the illustrated Dioscorides MS there (I mean the one in Beneventan Script) and select for me half a dozen pages for photography, just noting the plants upon them. I won't order them at present as photography is so dear in Germany just now, but if I have the pages I can do so when prices become more reasonable.

Many thanks for the 16/5 safely received.

I hope that my brother and his wife won't give Mrs. Sigerist too much trouble. I fear they are a changeable pair who do not know their own minds. They are naturally very anxious about their daughter who is really a good and clever girl. I don't feel myself much doubt that she has a tuberculous infection of the pleura.

Of course with a girl of her age a sanatorium is not a very satisfactory place. I feel myself that if she could be placed in a doctor's family in Switzerland, – even if the conditions of altitude and so on were less satisfactory, – the ultimate result would probably be better.
Yours ever,
Charles Singer

108

Singer to Sigerist, London, 2 February 1924

My dear Sigerist,

Many thanks for your letters of the 29th and 30th of January. Of course I read German with comfort when, as in your case, the writer takes the least trouble to make himself intelligible. It's only with Sudhoff that I ever have any real difficulty. I enclose his preface to the 'Syphilis Schriften' and I cannot help thinking that there are a good many sentences with which even a German would have difficulty. It is often not the language but the sense that is obscure.

See what you can do with it. Above all break up the sentences! It seems to me that it is in the nature of the human mind that it can grasp one idea better than two and it is therefore better to have one idea in each sentence than more! The rule appears to me to be simple and to apply to every language.[1]

I have to-day sent off a letter to Hardt[2] of which I enclose a copy which please return. The first page concerns business details, with which I think you need not trouble. The second page is more important especially as regards the last paragraph.

I quite accept your criticism about omitting certain figures. Some, such as the theatre of Terence[3] which seem strange were put in because the artist of the Ketham volume was also the artist of that figure. There are certain little details in both which are strikingly like the Ketham and which come out in rather an amusing way. I am quite content, however, to wait to see how prices, etc. go before deciding whether to insert such things. You will, however, naturally wish me to have a small section on the identity of the artist of the 1493 Ketham.[4]

What a splendid audience you must have had at Munich. It was a very great pleasure to me to hear of your success.[5] I hope the effort has not been too much for you.

I see we exactly agree about the form, frequency, format and illustration of the proposed "Archives of Medical History".[6] I have, as you know, written again to Hertzberger, and when he calls here – as he will in a few weeks – I shall be able to go forward with the negotiation.

Again I would say don't hesitate to rule out any of my illustrations for Ketham. The fact is that a reader is a much better judge of what a book ought to be than its author, and I welcome your criticism. In any event it will be a very handsome volume.

Many thanks for having helped my brother.[7] I hope things will go all right with them.

With best regards to your wife and yourself from us both,

Yours ever,

Charles Singer

P.S. I enclose corrected proofs of Thorndike's article.[8]

P.S.S. [sic] I have the negatives of those photographs of MSS in the British Museum which I sent you the other day. I will send them on if you like. In the meantime they are stored among my own negatives at University College, and I can let you have prints of them, if you need them, without charge.

---

[1] Singer on Sudhoff's writings about the history of syphilis; Charles Singer (ed.), *The earliest printed literature on syphilis being ten tractates from the years 1495–1498*. Adapted from Karl Sudhoff (Florence, 1925).

[2] A co-worker at Lier Publishing, Milan.

[3] Publius Terentius (2nd century B.C.), Roman playwright.

[4] Singer (1924a).

[5] In January 1924 Sigerist was invited to give lectures at Munich.

[6] The planned international journal.

[7] See letter 107.

[8] Thorndike (1924).

109

Singer to Sigerist, London, 14 February 1924

My dear Sigerist,

The enclosed letter from Hertzberger.

By this post I have written both to Hertzberger and to Streeter and I enclose my letters to them. I don't doubt that you will agree with both.

It will be a bore having de Lindt [sic][1] but I do not think he will have very much to do with the work. Dutch would not be one of the official languages, and he could hardly intervene in any of the others.

I have written to-day also to Hardt telling him that I quite understand his alarm at the enormous number of figures that I am sending to him and suggesting that he should entirely confine himself at the moment to anatomical figures. We can see when these are printed how things stand.

Yours ever,

Charles Singer

P.S. I should be glad if you would return enclosed letters.

---

[1] Probably Jean-Gérard de Lint (1867–1936), Dutch historian of medicine; see J. J. Tricot-Royer, 'Jean-Gérard de Lint, historien de la médecine', *Bulletin de la Société Française d'Histoire de la Médecine*, 1937, **31**: 197–208.

110

Singer to Sigerist, London, 15 February 1924

My dear Sigerist,

Your letter of Feb. 13th to hand.

Of course I agree that it is impossible for me to go to Geneva, which is in a neutral country, if the Germans are excluded from the Congress.[1] I believe that will be the opinion of all the English. We are now at peace with Germany and this state of affairs is simply impossible.

Now the question is what action shall I take? I will of course write in protest to Cumston. The question is had I better do so at once or had I better wait to receive some notice concerning it? I will do whichever you prefer.

I will also ask other English historians to do the same. I think I can rely upon Withington, Crawford [sic][2] and W. G. Spencer and probably also J. D. Rolleston.[3]

Sir Humphry Rolleston has expressed his views clearly enough by contributing to the Sudhoff volume. They are, I am sure, identical with mine.

As regards ilustrations to Ketham II.[4] Do you not think it better that a good many of them should be distributed in the text? Or do you think it better that they should be all collected together on sheets at the end of the volume? I think a use of both methods is advisable. I repeat, "include only the anatomical figures" and leave out all others for the present. Among the things I should particularly like to have included are the dissection scenes, earlier than the year 1500. There are two more of these to come, both quite easy to reproduce. I realise however the anxiety of Hardt.

As regards the index, we will make that here all right.

That is wonderful news that you are going to Monte Cassino.[5] The critical manuscript for my theory of the History of the Herbal is at Monte Cassino and I very much want a full series of pictures from it. I understand there is no accomodation [sic] for a photographer in the Monastery and it is essential to take a photographer with you. I would gladly pay part of the cost of this. The particular MS which I believe to be the original both of the Rome 1484 Apuleius and of the illustrated Anglo-Saxon Herbal is Cassinensis 97 10th century. I want a full series of let us say 20 figures from it, including the more striking and better pages, the incipit and explicit and specimens taken from all three sections if they exist, i.e. Apuleius, Dioscorides and Sextus Placitus. I should be particularly glad to have a roto-graph of the whole manuscript, but this I expect would be impossible. The photographs should show both script and especially figures. You may rely on me for £ 5.-£7-10-0.

I should of course like to have notes on any other illustrated herbals at Monte Cassino.

I think I have only told you incidentally in a letter to Streeter that my wife and I are adopting two children, a boy and a girl.[6] We are at present engaged in altering our house to accommodate [sic] them. It is a great adventure.

With best regards from us both,

Yours ever,

Charles Singer

[1] Geneva was the site of the Congress of the International Society of the History of Medicine with Cumston as president (see letter 14).

[2] Possibly Raymond Henry Payne Crawfurd (1865–1938), physician and medical historian; see J. D. Rolleston, 'Crawfurd, Sir Raymond Henry Payne (1865–1938)', rev. H. C. G. Matthew, *Oxford dictionary of national biography* (Oxford: Oxford University Press, 2004), vol. 14, 92–93.

[3] John D. Rolleston (1873–1946) British physician and medical historian, brother of Sir Humphry; see *British Medical Journal*, 1946, **i:** 507–508.

[4] Singer (1924a).

[5] A Benedictine monastery in southern Italy, bombed in World War II.

[6] Nancy and Andrew Singer, see letters 113, 135 and 173.

111

Singer to Sigerist, London, 27 February 1924

My dear Sigerist,

I have had another try at Sudhoff's Syphilis work[1] and have made something of it, though it has been more difficult than the Ketham. Apart from the difficulties of language and his naturally involved style, there is an additional and very serious trouble in translating this particular work. He assumes that the reader is familiar with everything that he has previously written. Now it happens that while everything that Sudhoff writes is extremely difficult for an Englishman to understand, his work on Syphilis is even more difficult than most [;] I seriously doubt if there is a single person in this country besides myself who has read his Erstlinge or Frühgeschichte.[2] In both works there are passages which I must confess I do not wholly understand, though I think I am getting clearer on them now.

In order to make his essay intelligible to English readers it is absolutely necessary therefore to summarise all that he has previously written on the subject.

I have now finished making a draft and will let you have a copy of it in a day or two. Would you be careful in looking through it to see if I have got details of general German history accurate? Of course these historical points I could do myself, but they are probably quite familiar school knowledge with you, while with me they have to be looked up.

Yours ever,

Charles Singer

P.S. I notice that Sudhoff says in dealing with the Magdeburg 1498 edition of Grünpeck[3] that it exists in a unique copy in the British Museum – "a reproduction of the title-page has so far not reached me". It seems a pity to leave out this one page, especially in the English edition. Had I not better order a photograph of it?

[1] Sudhoff (1924).

[2] Karl, Sudhoff, 'Graphische und typographische Erstlinge der Syphilisliteratur aus den Jahren 1495 und 1496', in *Alte Meister der Medizin und Naturkunde* (Munich, 1912); Karl Sudhoff, *Aus der Frühgeschichte der Syphilis*. Studien zur Geschichte der Medizin, Heft 9. 175 pages (Leipzig 1912).

[3] Joseph Grünpeck (ca.1473-ca.1532) wrote on Syphilis: *Tractatus de pestilenciali scorra siue mala de Franzos* (Magdeburg, 1498).

112

Singer to Sigerist, London, 1 March 1924 (telegram)

PLEASE SEND FESTSCHRIFT PROBEBOGEN. SINGER

113

Singer to Sigerist, London, 2 March 1924

My dear Sigerist,

(1) I have now quite completed the translation of Sudhoff's Zehn Syphilis Drucke.[1] It really has been a perfectly beastly job. I have had to abstract his earlier works & incorporate much of them in the text. I have done nothing else for the last ten days. There is still

one passage which I do not understand but you will be able to fill that in.

The Introduction is now being typed. This will take two or three days. As soon as it is done I will send it to you.

(2) Of course while I have been doing this I have had to neglect Ketham II.[2] I shall get back to this during the coming week.

(3) My secretary, Miss Anderson, is making an Index of the Authors' and Place names for the Sudhoff Festschrift. Miss Anderson has at present some time free & I therefore wired to you for more proof sheets as she could now go on with them[.]

(4) Some friends of ours – our neighbours here who are spending the summer in Switzerland have asked me if you would or could be so very kind as to give them any information about

(a) the Hotel Pension zum Schweizer Alpenclub in the Maderaner Tal

(b) any Hotel in the Sandalp or region North West of Tödi

(5) I wrote to you that we were adopting children.[3] One of them, a little girl age 9, has arrived two or three days ago. She is settling down very nicely & we are very happy with her. As soon as we feel quite at home with her she will [be] joined by a little brother.

(6) I enclose a photograph of myself which has just been taken. Please let me have one of you.

Yours ever,
Charles Singer

[1] Sudhoff (1924).
[2] Singer (1924a).
[3] See letter 110.

114

Singer to Sigerist, London, 7 March 1924

My dear Sigerist,

Here is this Syphilis translation of Sudhoff at last.[1] You cannot imagine what drudgery it has been preparing it. As you will see it is, in effect, a new work. I had to look up all the references, rearrange the whole material & consign much of Sudhoff's original text to the notes. It is really a disgrace to German literature that a man should be allowed to write in this fashion.

On page 25 of his German text corresponding to page 35 of my translation there is a passage which I do not understand. Perhaps you would be good enough to look into it[.] I have surrounded it by a green mark.

Also on page 28A of his German text, corresponding to page 38 of my translation, is a Latin passage which has to be printed in some special manner that I don't quite understand.

My manuscript can now be printed & we can correct these points in proof.
Yours ever,
Charles Singer

I think my version had best be called frankly an <u>Adaptation</u>. It is really not a translation & the original is untranslatable[.]

[1] Charles Singer (ed.), (1925b).

115

Singer to Sigerist, London, 11 March 1924

My dear Sigerist,
In case matters should change and you are able to get to Monte Cassino after all, I have a friend who very much wants a piece of photography done there. He is Dr. E. A. Lowe of 277 Woodstock Road, Oxford, author of the "Beneventan Script".[1] He will of course pay any expenses; what he is having done together with what I am having done will materially help you to cover the cost of a photographer, if you go.
I enclose the exact directions together with a copy of his letter to me in so far as it bears on the matter.
Yours ever,
Charles Singer

[1] Elias Avery Lowe (1879–1969), palaeographer; see James J. John, 'Lowe, Elias Avery (1879–1969)', *Oxford dictionary of national biography* (Oxford: Oxford University Press, 2004), vol. 34, 563–565. Elias A. Lowe, *The Beneventan Script. A history of the South Italian minuscule* (Oxford: Clarendon Press: Oxford, 1914).

116

Singer to Sigerist, London, 15 March 1924

My dear Sigerist,
Many thanks for your letter of March 12th and for the delightful photograph of yourself which came by the next post together with a number of other documents. It is a great pleasure to have your photograph and we shall include it in our gallery.
In your letter there are a number of points raised:
(1) Title page of the Sudhoff volume. I have carefully corrected Allbutt's dedication but I should think I ought to see another proof of it.
I should have preferred to have seen the names of all the contributors on the title-page with ours underneath them if still practicable; but if not let it be as it is.

(2) I am glad you like the Ketham.[1] I have had to neglect it for the last few weeks by reason of being engaged on Sudhoff's Syphilis tracts[2] and a good deal of University business. The Sudhoff work is now finished and the term is drawing to an end, so that I shall be able to take it up again. Of course I quite appreciate what you say about the cost of illustration and entirely sympathise with it. I am quite content with your judgment.

I have an idea that Baer of Frankfurt is more or less the same firm as Lier & Co. I notice that in their new catalogue they have some beautiful illustrations of precisely the things I want. If this is the case perhaps after all they might be obtained without cost to Lier. It is, however, not worth a great deal of bother.

(3) As regards the Syphilis tracts, I had not written to Sudhoff as I wanted to get your approval of the sheets first. I have, however, by this post despatched a copy to Sudhoff with an explanation of what I have done. I have not, however, another copy of his original typescript with the two obscure passages in it. For them you must deal with him direct. If he would write out what he means in simple German in these two cases I would turn them into English.

(4) Concerning the International Congress at Geneva.[3] I have written a letter to Cumston of which I enclose a copy.

I will gladly also, as a member of the Swiss Society, write to Dr. Maillart,[4] but do you not think it wiser that I should wait until I get a reply from Cumston? If I write to Maillart without having Cumston's reply it almost forces a quarrel on Cumston, and it is at least possible that Cumston may give in. If, however, you still think I should write to Maillart without waiting for Cumston's reply, you have only to send me a line to that effect on receipt of this and I will do so at once.

I think I told you that Krumbhaar[5] was here the other day and that he is acting in a similar sense to what I am doing. I have also written to Walter Spencer asking him to write to Cumston. I am sure he will do so, and I have no doubt that J. D. Rolleston will do likewise. If necessary I daresay we could invoke the aid of Sir Humphry Rolleston. But I hope this will not be necessary as it will put him in a difficult position, though one from which I am sure he will not shrink.

(5) Many thanks for the photographs of Monte Cassino 97.[6] Where are the negatives? Could I not get prints of them? I will of course return them to you later on. I suppose you are not in a hurry for them.

This MS certainly very closely resembles the Anglo-Saxon Cotton Vitellius C3. The curious thing is that the Anglo-Saxon work is much better than the Italian! But there is no doubt that they are intimately related.

(6) You will be interested to hear that I am probably going to America for a few weeks from about the middle of June to the middle of July. Things are not quite fixed: it is probable though not certain. When there I am rather hoping to get across the continent to see the Yellowstone Park which I have always longed to visit.

You will be glad to hear that our little girl is settling down beautifully and seems very happy.

With best regards from all to all,

Yours ever,

Charles Singer

[1] Singer (1924a).
[2] Sudhoff (1924).
[3] The International Congress of 1925.
[4] Louis Maillart (1867–1938), Swiss mathematician and astronomer.
[5] Edward B. Krumbhaar (1882–1966), pathologist, medical historian and founder of the American Association of the History of Medicine. See Esmond R. Long, 'Edward Bell Krumbhaar 1882–1966', *Bulletin of the History of Medicine*, 1967, **41:** 1–4.
[6] Monte Cassino 97, a manuscript.

117

Singer to Sigerist, London, 22 March 1924

My dear Sigerist,

Many thanks for your letter of 18th March. As regards Seldwyla's proposition. I telephoned at once to the Oxford University Press. They are perfectly willing to consider it favourably, but they feel they must see proofs first.

Would you therefore ask Seldwyla to send me as soon as he possibly can a complete set of 2 proofs, one for myself and one to take down to the O.U.P.? It would be convenient if Seldwyla would write to me a clear statement of the kind of terms they would suggest. I would translate it into English and would present it also at the same time.

There is no fear of my staying in America! I am going with a wealthy friend who is elderly and in bad health. We are going to spend a few days in the Rocky Mountains and he has a little business to attend to. After that we shall come straight back. I do not even propose to see any of the medical historians who will all be on vacation.

No, I have not seen anything of the Lucca manuscript.[1] Could you take steps to get some photographs of it?

Yours ever,

Charles Singer

[1] Lucca, a town in Tuscany. The MS is Lucca, Biblioteca Governativa 296

118

Singer to Sigerist, London, 24 March 1924

My dear Sigerist,

Many thanks for your letter of March 20th. Do you know, I find your handwriting rather difficult to read!

(1) I have received the enclosed two letters from Cumston. What would you like me to do? I am entirely at your service.

(2) I received from you this morning the proofs of Withington's article and I sent them off by the same post to him at Oxford, asking him to send them on direct to Seldwyla to save time.[1]

(3) What is happening with the Sudhoff volume. Why is it so fearfully slow? As soon as I get something to take to the Oxford University Press I will go at once.

(4) I am now giving all my time to Ketham,[2] and I hope to be able to get them off in a few days.

(5) Carbonelli wrote to me a few days ago concerning the London Manuscript of Roger of Parma. I have complete photographs of it which I am sending him, but I have been so very busy with the end of term and with University matters and with Ketham that I have not been able to answer his letter yet. Will you write to him apologising for me? You may rely on me to do everything in my power for him. You see I have to write to him in French or Italian and – have to put it off until I get a little time.

Yours ever,

Charles Singer

[1] Withington (1924).
[2] Singer (1924a).

119

Singer to Sigerist, London, 27 March 1924

My dear Sigerist,

I return herewith the corrected proof of Allbutt's Dedication received this morning.[1] There is still, as you see, one letter to adjust.

I cannot get at the bottom of what is the cause of the delay in the Sudhoff volume. You have said hardly a word about it. Can we not do anything to hurry things up?

Two days ago I received Withington's proofs of his Roger Bacon article and I sent them off within half-an-hour of their arrival here. He now writes to me that they are imperfect and only contain half his article.[2]

What on earth is the difficulty? I have always returned my proofs at the very earliest possible moment and the book appears to me to be a fairly straightforward piece of printing.

Seldwyla has sent to me what looked like a complete volume. On opening it I find that all the Middle Ages are missing and that there are no plates and that the modern times are not complete. It is really useless for me to go down to the O.U.P. until I have something to show them. As soon as I can get a complete set of proofs I will act at once.

In addition to all these complaints the pages of the proofs are not numbered. When you wrote to me asking if Miss Anderson would make an index I at once set aside some of her time well in advance and she gave up other work. Unfortunately this was wasted as it is impossible to index a book, the pages of which are not numbered.

Can you not induce Seldwyla to give at any rate a date? It is now four months since Sudhoff's Birthday and apparently the book has not yet completely got through the first set of proofs. At this rate it will be Autumn before it can be out. I have always before my eyes the unpleasant memory of the Festschrift presented to Osler, the advance copies of which arrived on the day of his funeral.[3] This is literally true.

Yours ever,

Charles Singer

[1] T. Clifford Allbutt, 'Letter of congratulation [to Sudhoff]', in Singer and Sigerist (eds), (1924).
[2] Withington (1924).
[3] Singer and Singer (1919).

120

Singer to Sigerist, London, 1 April 1924

My dear Sigerist,

(1) Many thanks for your letter which I have sent on to Withington to explain the delay. We can only hope that it will now proceed as quickly as possible.

(2) As regards the dummy volume of binding which you sent me. I like the look of it very much.

I have a criticism to make of the binding. I do not think we can put on the back

"Singer, Sigerist, Essays on the History of Medicine".

On the back we must surely put Sudhoff's name. Would it not be more appropriate to have this legend on the back?

"Essays on the History of Medicine presented to

Professor Sudhoff. Nov. 1923"

Leaving the legend on the side exactly as it stands.

I feel our names should not appear on the back at all.

(3) I still think that it would be better that the names of all the contributors should appear on the title-page, but it is not very important.

(4) I have just got the figures for my Ketham.[1] They are really a very handsome lot and will go into about 22 very fine plates. I take it I shall be able to include a page containing the figures by Streeter and myself that are to come out in the Sudhoff volume.[2]

(5) I quite agree with your restriction of figures. There are, however, three small line blocks of which I have not sent photographs but which I think should be added to my list to make the selection consistent. I do not suppose there will be any difficulty about this.
Yours ever,
Charles Singer

P.S. (6) I enclose "adaptation" of notice of Sudhoff's Syphilis volume[.][3] To save you time I have, by this post, sent copies of it also to Sudhoff himself & to Hardt.

(7) I enclose also a copy of a letter that I have to-day sent to Laignel-Lavastine.

(8) I enclose copy of draft advertisement of the 1493 Fasciculus. I have sent a copy to Hardt.

[1] Singer (1924a).
[2] Streeter and Singer (1924).
[3] Sudhoff (1924).

121

Singer to Sigerist, London, 4 April 1924

My dear Sigerist,
Would not it be the best thing now for the Swiss Society for the History of Medicine to write to Laignel-Lavastine protesting against the holding of a so-called International Congress on Swiss soil from which Germans as such are excluded? Would it be possible to get French-Swiss to sign such a protest?[1]

Ketham I has arrived and looks extremely handsome.[2] I congratulate you on it.[3] I am hard at work on Ketham II, but it is a bigger business than I had really thought.[4]

I have sent on the second part of Withington's article[5] to him by the same post as it arrived with instructions to send it direct to Seldwyla.

I wrote a leader on Hippocrates in this week's "Times" entitled "The Father of Medicine" which I daresay you saw.[6]
Yours ever,
Charles Singer

[1] The Swiss of the French-speaking part of the country.
[2] Sudhoff (1923);
[3] As editor of the Monumenta Medica series.
[4] Singer (1924a).
[5] Withington (1924).

[6] This was a book review rather than a leader; Charles Singer, 'The father of medicine'. Review of W. H. S. Jones (ed.), *Hippocrates*, vol. i and ii; and R. O. Moon , *Hippocrates and his successors*, in *Times Literary Supplement*, 3 April 1924, 197–198.

122

Singer to Sigerist, London, 8 April 1924a

My dear Sigerist,

I have had a bright idea concerning Ketham II.[1]

Why not bring it out in two volumes, the first containing the facsimile all by itself exactly as originally printed, the second containing my translation and Introduction? This will make it easier to refer to and will make the subscribers feel they are getting more for their money. The increase in the cost of production will be very small indeed.

Yours ever,

Charles Singer

[1] Singer (1924a).

123

Singer to Sigerist, London, 8 April 1924b

My dear Sigerist,

Have you looked at the manuscript Bernensis A 52 12th century Folios 1–20v?

In Diels it is ascribed to Joannes Joannis Alexandrini Discipulus.[1]

The only other manuscript of this text known is British Museum Additional 18201.

It is a commentary on the De usu partium of Galen and is, I think, quoted by Mundinus. It is odd that Mundinus should have used so rare a text.

But the point is that despite the ascription by Diels the British Museum text gives, in fact, not Joannes but Joannitius. It is, I think, a Latino-Arabic and not a Latino-Greek text. The point is of some importance for my purpose as Mundinus uses very few Latino-Greek texts, among the few were Aristotle's De partibus animalium.

Can you tell me therefore whether the Berne MS says "Joannes" or "Joannitius"?

Yours ever

Charles Singer

[1] Hermann Diels, *Die Handschriften der antiken Ärzte* (Berlin, 1905–1907).

124

Singer to Sigerist, London, 14 April 1924

My dear Sigerist,

I have had enclosed letter from Cumston to which I have sent the enclosed answer, of which I hope you approve.

Yours ever,

Charles Singer

P.S. I don't quite know what Seldwyla's note to Withington means, and I don't think he will know. Does it refer to reprints or to the book itself, or to extra copies of the book? Furthermore I don't understand what is the price they mention, whether it is English or Swiss money, or in what coin in either country. I have sent it on to him.

Withington is an excellent German scholar, and they can safely write to him in that language. His address is 4 Polstead Road, Oxford.

Charles Singer

125

Singer to Sigerist, London, 24 April 1924a

My dear Sigerist,

I have sent enclosed letter to-day to Lier.

I am sorry to bother again about the Sudhoff volume but as you know I am leaving for America on June 4th. I cannot possibly undertake any literary work after the third week in May. If, therefore, the Sudhoff volume is to appear before the summer it is absolutely imperative that the final proofs should reach me before then.

Would you perhaps tell Seldwyla of this?

Furthermore until I get these final proofs it is really useless for me to approach the Oxford University Press.

Yours ever,

Charles Singer

126

Singer to Sigerist, London, 24 April 1924b

My dear Sigerist,

You will like to see enclosed. Of course I shall not come if they do not ask the Germans.[1]

Yours ever,

Charles Singer

[1] Regarding the International Congress of the History of Medicine, Geneva 1925.

127

Singer to Sigerist, London, 29 April 1924

My dear Sigerist,

Many thanks for your note of April 26th & enclosed letters. Cumston is a silly old fool. It is all very annoying but I do not really think that it matters a great deal. The Congress won't do much. I shall not go to it – which is after all so much time saved!

Many thanks for the note about Codex Bernensis A 52.[1] It is certainly the same text as our British Museum. The latter is fairly legible so I don't want a photograph. But I should like your opinion as to whether it is really XIIth century. If it is it is interesting as an early and unnoticed Latino-arabic text. It might be worth further investigation. Would you have time for it?

I am hoping to get my proofs to Lier posted to-day.

Yours ever,

Charles Singer

P.S. I enclose a "leader" on Aristotle that I wrote for the British Medical Journal.[2] You might like to see it.

[1] Codex Bernensis, see letter 123.

[2] 'The Master of those that know', review of W. D. Ross, *Aristotle* (London: Methuen & Co., 1923), *British Medical Journal*, 1924, **i**: 757–758.

128

Singer to Sigerist, London, 2 May 1924

My dear Sigerist,

Many thanks for Sanchez de Rivera which I return.[1] I don't see any reason for quoting it and in this I think you will agree.

Who is doing Berengar of Carpi's Isagoge?[2] I have been looking through copies of the book in London lately and I find that, apart from various later editions, there were in fact two issues with different title-pages sent forth by Berengar himself at Bologna in 1522-3.

I have not collated them to see to what extent they differ. This ought to be done, however, before you go to the press. Let me know if you want me to do it.

In the course of my search of early anatomical books I have come across one little one which is I think of unrecognised interest. It is always assumed that Johannes Dryander of Marburg was a mere plagiarist, and so he was. But he did issue an interesting little work at Marburg in 1536, Anatomia capitis humani in Marpurgensi Accademia superiori anno publice exhibita, Marburg 1536.[3] This pamphlet is equipped with a rather interesting preface and it borrows to some extent from Berengar. It has original elements. I find that the whole thing can be photographed on fifteen plates and it might be worth considering whether it would not be appropriate to include it as an appendix to the Isagoge.

I have sent off all my plates and legends for Ketham II[4] to Hardt who is staying at Com. Breganzona (Ticino), Lucino.[5]

Yours ever,
Charles Singer

[1] Daniel Sanchez de Rivera y Moset, *Siluetas de médicos y libros de antaño* .... (Madrid, 1921).
[2] Berengario and his *Isagoge*, see letter 91.
[3] Johannes Dryander (1500–1560) German physician; see Walther Killy (ed.), *Deutsche biographische Enzyklopädie*, vol. 2, 629.
[4] Singer (1924a).
[5] Hardt's temporary address in Switzerland

129

Singer to Sigerist, London, 5 May 1924

My dear Sigerist,

In case it interests you & in case you still have that Berne Johannitius MS at Zurich I enclose rough notes on the London copy which will be enough for you to determine if they are the same text.[1]

I have sent off all my material for the 1493 <u>Fasciculo</u> to Hardt & I expect to have an advance copy to take with me to America.[2]

Yours ever,

Charles Singer

---

[1] Berne Johannitius, see letter 123.
[2] Singer (1924a).

130

Singer to Sigerist, London, 8 May 1924

CONFIDENTIAL

My dear Sigerist,

Enclosed foolish letter from Cumston. I shall not act until I have official information from Laignel-Lavastine. My impression is that by 1925 the action of the Society will appear so ridiculous that they will have to alter it. As soon as I get officially informed of the action of the Committee I shall write to say that under the circumstances I must decline to attend.

You will of course treat this confidentially for the moment. Better not say anything to Klebs. It will only excite him & will do no good.

Yours ever,

Charles Singer

The line that I propose to take in declining to attend is that it appears to me unfair to the Swiss to place them in this position.

C. S.

131

Singer to Sigerist, London, 13 May 1924

My dear Sigerist,

A line to tell you the very sad news that I shall not be going to America after all. The man with whom I was going is not able to travel and this destroys the whole scheme.

The matter has its consolations as I shall be able to put in a little more time at various works which I have on hand, including the <u>Fasciculo di Medicina</u>.[1]

Thanks for the letter of Cumston. I should think in spite of all that has happened, that the French will very likely change their minds before next year.[2]

I certainly think it would be better for Klebs not to intervene, but it is impossible to tell him so!
Yours ever,
Charles Singer

---

[1] Singer (1924a).
[2] The French still insisted on banning Germans and Austrians from participating in international congresses.

132

Singer to Sigerist, London, 18 May 1924

My dear Sigerist,

Last night there arrived the advanced copy (still not quite complete) of the Sudhoff presentation volume. It has not yet got its table of contents, its complete bibliography nor its index.

Would you mind dropping me a line at once whether you still would like my secretary to make an index of proper names?

As regards approaching the Oxford University Press. I do not like to do this until I have the Table of Contents. Of course you cannot expect them to read the entire book and the table of contents give them a short summary of what it contains. I am therefore reluctant to approach them until I receive this.

Would you find out from Seldwyla whether in the event of the Oxford University Press not taking it I have their authority to approach other English firms on the same terms as they have suggested for the Oxford University Press?

There still remains an outstanding point. Owing to the peculiarities of the English market June and July are very bad times for publication. If books are brought out at this period it means that reviews appear in August or September when people are away on their holidays and do not read the papers. The best time for publication is about the middle of September, and as the book has waited so long I suggest that in spite of my reluctance for further delay, we bring out the English edition at that date. For this purpose, however, it must be in the publishers' hands in June or at the very latest in July. (In England publication is a definite ceremony that takes place on an arranged day).

If it does not inconvenience the printer nor delay the book I suggest the enclosed corrections in our article on Salerno.[1]
Yours ever
Charles Singer

---

[1] Singer and Singer (1924).

133

Singer to Sigerist, London, 19 May 1924

My dear Sigerist,

Herewith title-page, Table of Contents and List of Illustrations for the Sudhoff volume.

Miss Anderson is making an index of proper names.[1] It will be ready in a day or two. Unless I hear to the contrary from you I shall not approach the Oxford University Press until I get a printed copy of the new title-page, Table of Contents and List of Illustrations.

I am still definitely in favour of publishing early in September.

Yours ever,

Charles Singer

[1] There is no index in the printed Sudhoff Festschrift.

134

Singer to Sigerist, London, 5 June 1924

My dear Sigerist,

Many thanks for your note on the Berne Manuscript.

I should have sent you the index of names for the Sudhoff Volume long ago, but unfortunately my secretary has had a breakdown without finishing the work, and I am finishing it myself. You shall have it as soon as it is done.

Yours ever,

Charles Singer

135

Singer to Sigerist, London, 10 June 1924

My dear Sigerist,

Cumston is in London & has been sending me letters suggesting that as I am in favour of inviting Germans to the Congress at Geneva I should resign my Vice-Presidency.[1] The fact that Cumston <u>wants</u> me to resign is, of course, a very good reason for <u>not</u> resigning. So I shall not do so for the present but shall wait to see what happens. If I once resign I cannot do anything more & it seems to me better that I should remain for the present. You will agree, I am sure.

I am unfortunate with the Index of names of the Festschrift. Miss Anderson is ill & Miss Moulder is on her holiday. I will try to get it done but I think it would not matter if there were no index.[2]

The title page is satisfactory. Now that I have it I can see what can be done about an English publisher. I am seeing one or two tomorrow.

We go away next Monday June 16th until July 17th to Cornwall. Miss Moulder is coming with us & is bringing a type writer so that I shall be able to work. I am taking the translation of Copernicus with me but expect proofs of the Monumenta & of the Syphilis tractates also.[3]

The enclosed syllabus of a new degree at London University will interest you.[4] I[t] is intended particularly for those who are <u>teaching</u> science & will be given only as a secondary degree to those who have already taken a degree in science.

The drawing up of this syllabus & making arrangements for teaching that it has involved has made great demands on my time this term.

Our little girl gets on beautifully. We have not yet a little boy but are looking hard for one!

I wish we could come to Switzerland this year. But it is impossible on account of the little one.

With best regards to you both from us both

Yours ever,

Charles Singer

My address will be
Wallah Dune
Constantine Bay
Near Padstow
North Cornwall

P.S. That old fool Cumston is getting angrier & angrier with me! With any luck we shall get some fun out of him; I think if only I can keep him as angry as this he is sure to do something outrageous!!

---

[1] Singer was Vice-President of the International Society of the History of Medicine (President in 1922).

[2] The printed Sudhoff Festschrift has no name index.

[3] Copernicus (1473–1543), Polish astronomer; see Edward Rosen, 'Copernicus, Nicholas', *Complete dictionary of scientific biography*, vol. 3 (Detroit: Charles Scribner's Sons, 2008), 401–411; and André Goddu, 'Copernicus, Nicholas', *ibid.*, vol. 20, 176–182; Singer has not published a translation of a Copernicus text. Monumenta, Singer (1924a). Syphilis tractates, Sudhoff (1924).

[4] The new degree is possibly in the history of science.

136

Singer to Sigerist, London, 11 June 1924

My dear Sigerist,

A word of warning. If Cumston or anybody else writes to you about whether I am coming to Geneva to the Congress in 1925 don't answer or at least say that you cannot speak for me.

The situation is this. Old Cumston keeps on writing to me to ask will I come to Geneva, may be remove my name from the list of Vice Presidents & so on.

To each letter I send the same reply "Dr. Cumston has no authority from Dr. Singer to remove his name from the list of Vice Presidents".

At each letter he gets angrier & angrier & sillier & sillier. If only we give him time he will very likely do something that will make the meeting at Geneva impossible. So mind you don't spoil it by letting him or anyone else know you have heard from me!

I do not write to Klebs as I feel sure he would not understand & would do something to spoil it.[1]

Now about the Sudhoff volume of Essays. I am still in some hope that the Oxford University Press will take it. But they think – and I quite agree with them – that no index is necessary. It will make the book a little cheaper for Seldwyla to produce & won't make the least difference to the sales. Do agree.

I return the title page etc[.] which is quite satisfactory. There are only two minute corrections. One is that Rolleston has just been made a baronet, i.e. his title becomes hereditary. Of course this seems to you (and is) a silly business but Rolleston is such a good, kind, generous, liberal[-]minded fellow that one can only be pleased at any honour that comes to him. The way the title is usually written is
Sir Humphry Rolleston Bart.

Also one other correction The Title of Withington's paper is
Roger Bacon "On the Errors of Physicians" (note inverted commas and capital O.
yours ever,
Charles Singer

Address from now on
   Wallah Dune
   Constantine Bay
   Near Padstow
   North Cornwall

---

[1] Klebs too wrote angry letters about Cumston to Sigerist. See Bickel (ed.), (2008).

137

Singer to Sigerist, Constantine Bay, Cornwall, 23 June 1924

My dear Sigerist,

After a long correspondence with Cumston I have elicited the following remark from him

"As President of the Congress I appointed the Vice-President & the vice-presidents of honour. They are all of my making & choice, & I am personally responsible for them".

That is he does not claim to have any Swiss Committee. It is for the Swiss to see that he makes no such claim. If he does make any such claim or if you can produce any evidence that he has made such a claim let me know at once giving me documentary evidence for it. If once I can get this I will see if the attention of the Swiss Ambassador in England can be called to it.

The line I have taken & will continue to take is entirely that of the relation of England to Switzerland. England is & always has been at peace with the Swiss. We have no right to [....] force on the Swiss a departure from neutrality.[1]

Is there in Geneva any one I could write to?

As soon as I get home I will have the whole correspondence typed and forwarded to you but in the meantime regard all this as strictly private. Above all don't say anything to Klebs who is sure to do the wrong thing.

Yours ever,

Charles Singer

Has Cumston behind him <u>any</u> Swiss Society?

[1] This refers to the exclusion of Germans from attending an international congress held in traditionally neutral Switzerland.

138

Singer to Sigerist, Constantine Bay, 25 June 1924

My dear Sigerist,

A point occurs to me in connexion with my article in the Sudhoff <u>Festschrift</u>.

In the Bibliography I did not mention Capparoni's book.[1] It is a mad book & not worth mentioning. Moreover when I had the proofs it was not yet out. Nevertheless I don't want to have too many quarrels at the same time & therefore I don't want to offend Capparoni as I surely would.

Would you therefore tell Seldwyla to do as follows <u>at my expense</u>. Print the name & title of Capparoni's book on separate slips & stick them on at the end of my bibliography.

They can be made nearly as good as though originally printed so, and fortunately there is plenty of room on the page.

Would you be good enough to ask Seldwyla to send me an estimate of the cost of doing this. I expect you have a copy of Capparoni's book & can give him the exact title arranged like my other bibliographical entries.

I think it is just possible that I might come to Switzerland for one week in September. If I did would you come for a few days walk with me, meeting me perhaps somewhere nearer than Zurich? It would be a good thing if we could have a talk together.

I have any number of students for the new course to begin in October of which I sent you the syllabus.[2] I think there will be at least twenty & there may be as many as forty.

I have had a line from Brunn of Rostock who is coming to London in a few weeks. I am looking forward to meeting him.[3]

Yours ever,

Charles Singer

---

[1] Capparoni (1923); there is no Capparoni reference in the Festschrift article.

[2] See letter 135.

[3] Walter von Brunn (1876–1952) German surgeon and medical historian; see Anne Kristin Oommen-Halbach, *Briefe von Walter von Brunn (1876–1952) an Tibor Györy (1869–1938) aus den Jahren 1924–1937: ein Beitrag zum Korrespondentennetz Tibor Györys mit deutschen Medizinhistorikern* (Remscheid: Gardez!, 2004), and 'In memoriam Walter von Brunn', *Deutsche medizinische Wochenschrift*, April 17 1953, **78 (16)**: 613.

139

Singer to Sigerist, Constantine Bay, 29 June 1924

My dear Sigerist,

I expect that by now you are comfortably settled at Beatenberg.[1]

Since I last wrote to you something has happened that has materially altered our plans for the summer. We came down here with our little girl, a nurse, another maid & the little boy of my friend Prof. J. F. Dobson the Greek scholar.[2] While down here it was our idea to leave the children occasionally & to take long walks together sometimes being away for the night. This is the kind of holiday that suits us both best & we are particularly fond of the wild & desolate country of Cornwall.

Gradually, however, we have come to realize that our nurse is not reliable. This means that we cannot both leave the children for more than a few hours – indeed we are not quite happy doing even that. So we must revise altogether our ideas of a holiday.

I have a very hard term beginning next October & I feel I must get away from such worries for a week or two. My wife is also anxious that I should do so.

One of the things that crossed our minds is that I should come to Switzerland for a fortnight in July. What I like most is walking & I am not sure whether you are quite fit for it or whether you yourself are able to leave your family for any time.

Another thing that occurred to me is to bring some English friend or one of my nieces to Switzerland & walk with them, visiting you en route. Of course I should not come to Switzerland without at least visiting you.

I should be so much obliged if you would write me quite frankly what you feel about it & equally frankly – what is more important – what your wife feels about it.

I think you will laugh when you see the Cumston correspondence. It is really too long – & too silly – to copy out. But when my secretary gets back from her holiday you shall have the whole dossier.

Write to me direct to this Cornish address.

With best wishes from all to all.

Yours ever,

Charles Singer

I fear I do not see much chance of my wife getting away[.] Even when the nurse is changed she could hardly leave the child for a few weeks. Her holiday must, I fear be deferred till Christmas.

[1] Beatenberg, a resort village in Switzerland.

[2] John Frederick Dobson (1875–1947), Professor of Greek at Bristol University, was an expert on Greek medicine, and his collections of the fragments of Herophilus and Erasistratus, published in the Proceedings of the Historical Section of the Royal Society of Medicine, long remained useful; see Robert B. Todd, 'Dobson, John Frederick (1875–1947)', in Robert B. Todd (ed.), *The dictionary of British classicists*, 3 vols (Bristol: Thoemmes Continuum, 2004), vol. 1, 245. The boy is probably one of Dobson's younger sons; Mrs Dobson, according to family tradition, was not enthused by her many children (4 sons and a daughter), and to help her, the Singers were glad to offer hospitality in Cornwall, and possibly more. In the 1970s, Mrs Eleanor Scott (née Dobson) told Vivian Nutton of being sent to the Singers 'on approval' with a view to a possible adoption. Only when she returned at the end of summer did she find that she had been rejected as unsuitable. This information was kindly provided by members of the Scott family.

140

Singer to Sigerist, Constantine Bay, 12 July 1924

My dear Sigerist,

Many thanks for your letters. We are still not quite settled about our movements but it is almost certain that I shall be coming to Switzerland. It is possible that my wife will be coming with me after all.

We shall certainly visit you though we want to spend our time walking. We return home on July 17 & I will then write to you about our movements.

I shall, of course, send off the proofs of Ketham II before I leave England.[1]
Yours ever
Charles Singer

We are deluged with students for the new History & Principles of Science Course at London University. It is evident that we shall not be able to take them all. We can hardly have a class of more than 40. It looks most hopeful.

[1] Singer (1924a).

141

Singer to Sigerist, London, 7 August 1924 (postcard)[1]

Would it be better for us to get out at Thun[2] or at Beatenberg on August 20th? Perhaps you would let me have a line on this point.
C. S.

[1] Addressed to Sigerist in Beatenberg.
[2] Thun, a town near the village of Beatenberg in Switzerland.

142

Singer to Sigerist, London, 12 August 1924 (postcard)

Many thanks for your letter of August 10[.] We shall be two men and shall be coming right through from Boulogne. We shall arrive as you say at 10:44 a.m. at Beatenberg on August 20 & shall stay till August 22.

Greatly looking forward to seeing you.
Your
Charles Singer

Please engage rooms for us

143

Singer to Sigerist, London, 26 August 1924

My dear Sigerist,

I got back here comfortably and to time. It is of course a very great disappointment to me that I did not continue my trip in Switzerland, though under the circumstances I feel much happier in my mind at being in my own home.

I am very much obliged to your wife and yourself for all your kindness. Please thank her very heartily for me and tell her what a pleasure it was to see you both. I wish I could have been easier in my mind.

Tell her too with my compliments that tobacco is a poisonous drug and that you are smoking too much! Please take this as a piece of friendly advice from a brother medical historian.

You will be immensely entertained at the turn things have taken with the International Society.[1] The morning after I got back I got from Tricot letters of which I enclose copies.[2] From them it is obvious that he has had some row with Cumston. The row doubtless is on the question of Cumston usurping the authority to appoint officers!

Under the circumstances I thought it best <u>not</u> to send the letter of which I showed you a copy in spite of the temptation to make a joke – which is always hard for me to resist and especially where Tricot is concerned!

I enclose a copy of the reply which I have in fact sent.

I wrote yesterday to my friend, J. de M. Johnson, Secretary to the Oxford University Press to say that he must spend a night with me in London and that we must discuss together the whole question of the possibilities of Lier. I will let you know what happens.

With best regards and again many thanks,

Yours ever,

Charles Singer

I have to-day ordered your photos from the British Museum.

[1] International Society of the History of Medicine.

[2] J. J. Tricot-Royer (1875–1951) French historian of medicine, President of the International Society; see F. A. Sondervorst, 'Le Docteur J. J. G. Tricot Royer', *Annuaire de l'UCL* [Université Catholique de Louvain], 1951–1952 (printed 1962), **99**: 165–172.

144

Singer to Sigerist, London, 29 August 1924

My dear Sigerist,

If you have not sent off the proofs please do so as soon as possible.[1] Term will soon be upon us and I shall not be able to attend to them. I could have done a good deal during the last few days.

I have an appointment with the Oxford University Press this afternoon to talk things over with them. It is rather a pity that I have not either the proofs or the advanced copy with me.

I have arranged for all the British Museum photographs to be taken for you, and they will arrive here next Tuesday. I have told them that they are to be put down to my account as I get a discount and I can send you on the bill.

There are a few remarks to make about them.

Additional 17062 should be written Additional 17063. In it there are two figures of Dracontea and I have included them both.[2]

Additional 21115. is the sister manuscript of 17063 and has also two figures of Dracontea. I have included them also.

Additional 8928 is a very important manuscript to which not enough attention has been given. The figures, however, are extremely faint. I have included Vettonica according to your direction. I could find better figures in this MS if you wish.

Harley 5294 calls for no remark.

Cotton Vit. C.III is a very difficult manuscript to deal with. It is in Anglo-Saxon and one has to translate the Anglo-Saxon terms in order to get the plant. Asfodelus, however, presents no special difficulty in this MS. Paeonia and Peristereon are practically destroyed by fire. The manuscript, as I daresay you know, was partially burnt in the eighteenth century and it happens that the page containing these figures has suffered very greatly. I have therefore included Dracontea, and have not sent you the other two, though I will do so if I hear from you that you still wish for them.

I have in fact a very large number of figures of Cotton Vit. C.III which I have studied more closely perhaps than many other manuscript, and I could lend these to you if you wish.

As regards Ashmole 1431. It is tiresome, slow and expensive at present getting photographs from Oxford. If you want that exact page Vettonica f.3v I think probably you would get it quicker by writing yourself. The Librarian is very fussy and if I get it for you and he comes to hear of it he will be angry with me! I enclose, however, an application form for photographs.

I have in fact ransacked the Bodleian and have taken photographs of all I wanted before I left Oxford, among them Ashmole 1431. These I enclose. They include a coloured figure of Paeonia and of Solago minor and 10 pages of in rotograph. Perhaps you would be good enough to let me have them back when you have finished with them.

I return the photographs of the Monte Cassino manuscript. It is certainly very close to Cotton. Vit. C.III, especially as regards the mandrake figure. I find my man has not had time to re-photograph these. When you can spare them would you be so very kind as to let me have them and I will only keep them for one day.

I get glowing postcards from Dobson who is enjoying himself immensely.

With best regards to you all and love to the children.

Yours ever,

Charles Singer

[1] Proofs of the Sudhoff Festschrift

[2] Dracontea, Asfodelus, Paeonia, Peristereon, Vettonica, Solago minor, and Mandrake are all plant names.

145

Singer to Sigerist, London, 30 August 1924a

My dear Sigerist,

(1) I was at the Oxford University Press yesterday. I was much disturbed to find that, in spite of all that I have said, Seldwyla have still not delivered the Sudhoff Festschrift. This means that the book cannot now get into the September catalogue & there may be difficulties in publishing it before Christmas. In any event it means that the book has missed the best market. Can you wire Seldwyla to send copies of the Festschrift <u>instantly</u>. The matter is made worse by the fact that the official who has charge of this book is getting married this week! I think Seldwyla's delays are really too bad.

(2) I am sorry not to have the proofs of the Fasciculo to hand.[1] Evidently they have been delayed <u>en route</u>. My difficulty is that as soon as term begins I shall be unable to work at them. I hope that they will arrive during the next day or two.

(3) As regards Sudhoff's Syphilis tracts.[2] I have received the proofs from you this morning but unfortunately not my original corrections. As the thing stands in this proof it contains a long excursus on Widmann[3] buried in the section on Grünpeck. Sudhoff's reasons for this burying it seem to me inadequate. His point about the date & proper position of Widmann can be brought out in another & less clumsy way. I had endeavoured to do this in my last draft but Sudhoff has altered my arrangement.

(4) The Oxford University Press are willing to hand over to Lier the entire collection of clichées of Vol I of my studies without any charge. I shall forward a copy of the work to Hardt & tell him this.

(5) I got off your Monte Cassino photos last week. The British Museum MSS are being photographed for you & will follow in a day or two. Poor old Dobson is having dreadful weather. At one place he was snowed up!

With best regards to all
Yours ever,
Charles Singer

[1] Charles Singer (ed.), *The Fasciculo di Medicina Venice 1493*. With translation of Anathomia by Mondino da Luzzi, (Florence, 1925).
[2] Sudhoff (1924).
[3] Johann Widmann (Möchinger) (born *c*.1445) German physician, wrote on syphilis.

146

Singer to Sigerist, London, 30 August 1924b (telegram)

BITTE SCHICKEN SIE MIR KETHAM PROBEBOGEN[1]
SINGER

[1] Please send me Ketham proofs.

147

Singer to Sigerist, London, 31 August 1924 (postcard)

Add. 17063
Add. 21115
Ashmole 1431
One without the Sextus Placitus text.
Cotton Vet. CIII contains it in Anglo-Saxon translation.
    Are there any other English MSS on which you would like this question answered?[1]
Charles Singer

[1] See Letter 144.

148

Singer to Sigerist, London, 1 September 1924

My dear Sigerist,

Herewith corrected proofs of the Sudhoff work.[1]

Note firstly the alteration in title, which I am sure is a good move from the point of view of the English public, for which the work is intended. This alteration would be made both on the title page of the book and in the advertisement.

I have your letter from the Beatenberg[2] of August 29th, explaining the count Rudolf von Hohenburg referred to on page 5. of the proofs.[3] I quite understand what Sudhoff meant to say and I had altered it in that sense in one of the proofs, but he altered it back again. As it now stands in my proof, it is perfectly correct. It is a fact, which I have verified, that both of the 1472 editions of the German "Ordnung der Gesundheit" contain the dedication to Count Rudolf Hohenburg and his wife. Having reached that point and stated it, the passage then turns to previous history.

There in [is?] one rather radical change which I had made in a previous version of the proof, which Sudhoff or the printer have put back again. In viewing the matter from the point of view of the English reader, the last paragraphs of page 13 of the proofs, the whole of page 14 and the first paragraphs of page 15 should be removed bodily and inserted as indicated on page 20. I have tried to indicate this by cutting out these sections, fitting them together, numbering them in red as 1, 2, & 3 and indicating on page 20. where they are to be inserted. No violence will be done by this to Sudhoff's sense because [....] the last paragraph of page 13. He there states specifically that the work of Widmann should be considered along with Grünpeck. The reader has therefore only to turn to the page indicated to understand what has happened. Thus the symmetry of the article will be observed and Sudhoff's meaning also brought out.

As regards the Table of Contents, a difficulty arises in that the contents of the Introduction is not in fact, identical with the contents of the facsimile. I think the simplest way out of this, is to have two tables of contents. Firstly, a table of contents of the book as a whole with references to the Facsimile covered by the one word Facsimile. Secondly, at the end of Introduction, a detailed Table of Contents to the Facsimile itself. I should say that in English books, the Table of Contents invariably precedes a work and never follows it. In this the English usage differs from the Continental.

I bother you with these points as my imperfect German may not make it clear to the printers that the sections from page 13 to 15 must be shifted. Will you also tell them that although I sent them the Table of Contents of the work as a whole, proofs of it have not reached me.

Best regards,

Yours ever,

Charles Singer

[1] Singer (1925b).

[2] Letter to Sigerist's vacation address at Beatenberg.

[3] Rudolf von Hohenburg, Rudolf II, Duke of Austria (13th century).

149

Singer to Sigerist, London, 5 September 1924

My dear Sigerist,

Herewith the photographs. They cost £3 and I have paid for them at once as I get a reduction in this way. I will send you receipt as soon as Fleming sends it to me.

I have pencilled on the back concerning the plants. This information I have already sent to you, but it may be convenient for you to have it written on the photographs.

There is one photograph about which I am doubtful, though you have the information before you. It is concerning Cotton Vitellius C. III - the plant named Wudurofe in the Anglo-Saxon text. This plant I think you will find corresponds to the Asfodelus[1] of Apuleius.

I am glad to say that the Sudhoff Volumes arrived safely last night.[2] They really look very well; the only criticism I have to make is on their enormous price.

I sent off the proofs of the Fasciculo di Medicina to Wolff yesterday.[3]

With best regards,

Yours ever,

Charles Singer

[1] Asphodel.

[2] Sudhoff's *Festschrift*, Singer and Sigerist (eds), (1924), which appeared 10 months after his 70th birthay

[3] Singer (1925a);.

150

Singer to Sigerist, London, 6 September 1924

My dear Sigerist,
Herewith Fleming's bill for £ 3.0.0 paid and receipted-Yours ever
Charles Singer

Sudhoff Festschrift has arrived.[1]

[1] Singer and Sigerist (eds), (1924).

151

Singer to Sigerist, London, 19 September 1924

My dear Sigerist,
Many thanks for the cheque for £ 3.0.0 which arrived safely this morning.
I sent off the final proofs of the Syphilis tractates about four days ago and yesterday I sent off also the "Prospekt".[1]
I hope the photographs are what you wanted.
Yours ever,
Charles Singer

[1] Syphilis tractates, Singer (1925b); Prospekt is probably an advertisement for a book.

152

Singer to Sigerist, London, 10 January 1925

My dear Sigerist,
Many thanks for your letter of January 8th. I heard two days ago that you have been appointed "titular" Professor. It is a very great pleasure to hear. I wish it had not been "titular" but perhaps that will be altered later. [1]
I really have had a dreadfully busy term and everyone is pressing me for writing.[2] I am very sorry for the delay in the proofs but most unfortunately the Registered Post between England and Germany is extremely slow. For instance, on the 5th January Kurt Wolff sent me a postcard saying that "gleichzeitig"[3] he had sent me the last proofs of "The Fasciculo".[4] Nevertheless these proofs have not even yet reached me. I think part of the delay

is also due to Kurt Wolff being just a little meticulous. Thus, in the case of the "Zehn Schriften" I wrote to him that I was quite content that he should make two or three small corrections without sending me proofs again.[5] Nevertheless he insisted on sending them, thus delaying matters some weeks. I have no doubt that when I do get the Fasciculo proofs I shall approve of them right away and will telegraph to that effect to Kurt Wolff.

Last week I sent off a small volume to the printer entitled "The Childhood of Anatomy".[6] It is a history of Anatomy and Physiology to Harvey[7] and is being printed at once. It is the substance of my Fitzpatrick lectures.

I rather think the publishers are coming round a little about the Monumenta medica. I called last week on Benn Brothers[8] who are quite keen on the Fasciculo and have written to Hardt direct with the result that the Oxford University Press is also coming round. I am not at all sure, however, that my suggestion to Hardt to employ a lady as his own agent in London would after all not have been best and more profitable for him.

To give you an idea how my time is occupied I will give you a list of my actual commitments [sic] during the next six months. Quite apart from academic work I am committed to an article in a volume for which Lord Balfour is writing an introduction, on "Science and Religion". I am doing the historical section.[9] I am also committed to a volume for Lier as you know; to a volume on the history of Science for the Clarendon Press; an article on Mediaeval Science in the "Legacy of Israel"[10] as companion volume to Greece and Rome; to a colleague at University College for a translation of Celsus[11] and to the Oxford University Press for a composite volume of Three Centuries of Science.

When I called the Benn Brothers they discussed various projects for publication. One of them was a volume which would include all the illustrations that had been produced by Vesalius. What do you think of the idea? It would not be necessary to reproduce the text but only explanations of the figures. Are you going on with your idea of the Epitome? If so, this Vesalius idea had better be dropped but if not I think Benn Brothers would do it very well.

If Hardt is looking round for a short and cheap volume has he considered Gaspari Aselli "De lactibus"?[12] It is extremely interesting from the point of view of the history of printing. As you know it is the first specimen of real colour printing. It would be quite a small book to do.

Please forgive me for having been so very remiss in corresponding but it has been due to pressure of work.

It was delightful having Senn.[13]

Many thanks for the photographs which arrived safely.

With best wishes for the New Year to you all from us all

Yours ever,

Charles Singer

I had a letter from De Lint asking me to meet him & Sudhoff in Holland. I said I would fall in with their schemes but I could not come over to Holland.

[1] When Sigerist received the call to Leipzig the University of Zurich gave him the title of Professor in order to keep him.

[2] A dreadfully busy term was the reason for the four months' gap since Singer's last letter.

[3] "gleichzeitig" = at the same time.

[4] Singer (1925a).

[5] Sudhoff (1924).

[6] Charles Singer, *The evolution of anatomy* (London, 1925).

[7] William Harvey, (1578–1657) English physician and physiologist; see Roger French, 'Harvey, William (1578–1657)', *Oxford dictionary of national biography* (Oxford: Oxford University Press, 2004), vol. 25, 678–683.

[8] Publishers.

[9] Arthur James Balfour, (1848–1930), British politician; Charles Singer, 'Historical relations of religion and science', in Joseph Needham (ed.), *Science Religion and Reality* (London, 1925), 85–148.

[10] Charles Singer, 'Hebrew scholarship in the Middle Ages among Latin Christians', in Edwyn R. Bevan and Charles Singer (eds.), *The legacy of Israel* (Oxford, 1927), 283–314.

[11] Celsus (1st century A.D.) wrote on medicine

[12] Aselli, Gaspare (1581–1626) Italian physician, Gaspare Aselli, *De lactibus* .... (Milan, 1627).

[13] Gustav Senn (1875–1945), Swiss botanist, President of the Swiss Society of the History of Medicine. See H. Fischer, 'Gustav Senn', *Gesnerus*, 1945, **2**: 168–172.

153

Singer to Sigerist, London, 15 January 1925

My dear Sigerist,

I received the proofs of the Fasciculo[1] the day before yesterday late at night and despatched them in the morning to Wolff. There were two necessary corrections in the entire book. In my letter which went off by Air Mail I begged Wolff not to return the proofs to me. I said I was perfectly content for them to make the corrections and to issue the book at once.

This is a matter in which Wolff are rather troublesome. They insist, however often I make this remark, on returning the proofs to me. At present the Parcel Post between England and Germany takes at least ten days. If they insist on returning these proofs to me it will take three weeks since the proofs have to go back again. Would you instruct them therefore to take me at my word and not return them to me?[2]

I talked to the Clarendon Press yesterday and again with Benn's. I think I am going to advise Lier finally to employ a private agent in this country.[3] There is a competent lady living close be [sic] here who is capable of undertaking the work and employing her would be a fraction of the expense of the Clarendon Press. She would also have the advantage of instruction from me as to whom to send circulars to. The profits of Lier for each copy would thus be much larger.

I am sorry to have taken so long over the book but it is as you know a big bit of work.
Best regards,
Yours sincerely,
Charles Singer

[1] Singer (1925a).
[2] Would you instruct them as editor of the Monumenta Medica series.
[3] The proposed agent was Mrs. Stanton.

154

Singer to Sigerist, London, 27 March 1925

My dear Sigerist,

It was only the day before yesterday that I learned from a letter from Klebb [sic][1] that you had been appointed at Leipzig.[2] In a note from your wife some little time ago she said that you were leaving for Leipzig but we merely thought it was on a visit and did not connect it with this appointment.

Please accept our very heartiest and warmest congratulations on this event. We hope it may bring you every happiness and feel sure that you have a full and useful career in front of you. You know that any help that either my wife or I can give you at any time is at your disposal.

I myself have been laid up with a rather bad attack of influenza which extended over three weeks and it is only this last week that I have been able to attend to my correspondence which has thus fallen a good deal in arrears. I still am not fit as I could wish. I cannot yet do much work. I have however finished & in proof my "History of Anatomy"[.][3]

You will be glad to hear that my own position at University College has been greatly improved and I am now receiving a satisfactory rate of payment.

I take it that you will not attend the Congress at Geneva?[4] I do not propose to go there and so am not anxious that it should be known that I am in Switzerland at the time.

Please give our kind regards to Professor Sudhoff.

With very best regards to your wife and yourself and again all good wishes or [sic] the future.
Believe me,
Yours ever,
Charles Singer

[1] Klebs.
[2] Sigerist was appointed Professor of the History of Medicine at the University of Leipzig, as Sudhoff's successor.
[3] Singer (1925c).
[4] Congress of the International Society of the History of Medicine.

155

Singer to Sigerist, London, 2 April 1925[1]

My dear Sigerist,

I have today written off to von Hardt a letter of which I enclose a copy. I believe that on the lines I indicate a venture might be made not unprofitable. I know a very large proportion of the buyers in England and America and I could circulate them, or rather Mrs. Stanton could circulate them direct, of course under my direction. This will not prevent Von Hardt selling direct from Italy and gaining the complete profits. I hope you will fall in with this idea.

I am hard at work illustrating my "History of Anatomy".[2]

Have you any schemes for a Journal? What is Sudhoff saying about the International Scheme?

With my best regards,
Yours ever,
Charles Singer

P.S. I suppose you have got my letter congratulating you on your appointment?

[1] The letter is addressed to Sigerist on a visit to Leipzig.
[2] Singer (1925c).

156

Singer to Sigerist, London, 8 April 1925

My dear Sigerist,

Many thanks for your letter. I am so glad you are not leaving Switzerland yet. This being so, we shall then have an opportunity of meeting. We leave London on June 2nd and go straight through to Thun, where we put up the nurse and child for the night. Then Mrs. Singer and I are going on to find a place that we like. We think of trying Lake Lungern. As soon as we have a place, we shall go back – probably the next day – for the child and nurse and settle in our holiday quarters.

We shall remain in Switzerland until the 27th July, when we return to England. I shall not be going to the meeting at Geneva.[1] Doubtless, during these two months we can arrange to meet.

I am so glad to hear that you have finished "Apuleius" and are hard at work on "Sextus Placidas"[sic].[2] I wonder if you know the "De animalibus" of Constantine, in the edition published by Petrus of Basel in 1541.[3] It is in a collection entitled "Methodus Medendi Certa" consisting of Albucasis[4] and Constantine for the most part. If you do not know it or have not access to it, I can lend it to you.

As regards your questions about manuscripts, I know all those to which you refer and will gladly have them photographed for you. The Rawlinson Manuscripts are at Oxford.[5]

Let me know whether you would like all in rotograph or in photograph, or only a few pages from each, or whether you would like me to use my discretion.

Yours ever,

Charles Singer

[1] Meeting of the International Society of the History of Medicine.

[2] Ernst Howald and Henry E. Sigerist, *Pseudo-Apulei herbarius* (Leipzig/Berlin, 1927).

[3] *De animalibus* of Constantine the African may be part of Constantinus Africanus, *Medicinae tam simplices ....* (Basel, 1560)

[4] Albucasis (10th century), Arab surgeon at Cordoba, Spain.

[5] The Rawlinson Collection of manuscripts of the 16th and 17th centuries AD.

157

Singer to Sigerist, London, 15 April 1925

My dear Sigerist,

I have had a rather confused letter from Sudhoff in which he says that so far as the Journal is concerned, he would fall in with our wishes.

Does this mean he is going to drop the Archiv and wants[?] to start a new International Journal? If so, what would be your general wishes in the matter? Doubtless we could discuss this when we meet in June or July. Of course he would be "honorary editor".

Do you or he mean to go on with the Mitteilungen[?][1] I suggest that for your own sake it would be better to amalgamate with Sarton. Sarton loves bibliography. Although his principle of selection is a little too drastic there is a good deal in it.

I have had a letter from some Rhenish Association speaking of an Exhibition of Art illustrating the History of the Rhineland. They ask me for the use of my "Hildegard" paintings and I replied I would gladly lend them.[2] I wrote to them also that if they liked they could reprint my article on Hildegard in Volume I of the Studies.[3]

It has occurred to me that Lier might like to do this and he could do so without any great expense. The Clarendon Press are prepared to lend the clichées without charge; the article to be printed as originally written with merely the alteration or correction of two or three sentences. This would give Lier an opportunity of producing a well illustrated piece of work without any great expense to himself, and I feel we owe him something of that sort.

If you think well of this, by all means suggest it to him and I will act accordingly. He has in his possession a copy of a first volume of the Studies which I lent him.

Yours ever,

Charles Singer

[1] *Archiv für Geschichte der Medizin* and *Mitteilungen zur Geschichte der Medizin und der Naturwissenschaften*; both journals founded by Sudhoff

[2] Hildegard von Bingen (1098–1179) German abbess and physician; Charles Singer, 'Allegorical representation of the Synagogue in a twelfth century illuminated MS. of Hildegard von Bingen', *Jewish Quarterly Review*, 1915, **5**: 267–288.

[3] Charles Singer (ed.), *Studies in the history and method of science*, vol. 1 (Oxford: Clarendon Press, 1917).

158

Singer to Sigerist, London, 17 April 1925

My dear Sigerist,

I have received the enclosed letter from Haberling.[1] By "illustrierte und nicht illustrierte" he means of course "Coloured and non-coloured." I send you this in case you are considering anything in connection with "Hildegard" and Lier.

I will order the "Sextus Placitus" Photographs for you at once. I wonder if you know the very interesting manuscript, Bodley 153 (early 12th Century) which contains text closely allied to "Sextus Placitus".

Yours ever,

Charles Singer

[1] Wilhelm Haberling (1871–1940), German medical historian; see Paul Diepgen, 'Wilhelm Haberlings Leben und Wirken', *Mitteilungen zur Geschichte der Medizin, der Naturwissenschaften und der Technik*, 1940, **39**: 90–101,

159

Singer to Sigerist, London, 24 April 1925

My dear Sigerist,

I have been through the British Museum Manuscripts of which you spoke and have been in correspondence with the librarian of the Bodleian Library concerning Rawlinson's Manuscripts. I have ordered rotographs of all of them for you. I am having them sent to me, as I get a rebate of 10% off the London Manuscripts.

There are the following remarks to be made :-

1. Harleian 1585. This is a very beautiful manuscript, some figures of which are reproduced in Figure 2 of Studies.[1] I think you will probably agree that it is of about the year
1200. I have ordered for you folio 59 recto to 62 verso inclusive. It contains only the table
of contents of Sextus Placitus with part of the first chapter.

2. Sloane 1975 is another very beautiful manuscript, fairly closely similar to the Bodleian manuscript, Ashmole 1462. Sloane 1975 I think of the early 13th century. It has been
paginated several times and I have ordered for you the red pagination 74 recto to 77 recto.
This contains the table of contents of Sextus Placitus with the beginning of the chapter on
Cervus.

3. Additional 8928 is an extremely interesting manuscript of the 11th century, in parts
I should think of about the year 1000, though the section of Placitus is a little later. Unfortunately your section, I think you will find, is a little faded. I have ordered for you folios
50 verso to 53 recto. This contains Table of contents and the chapter on Cervus. The entire
text ends on folio 62 verso. I should think it would be an important text for your purpose,
and you might do worse than have the whole photographed.

4. Harleian 5294 is – it seems to me – an exceptionally interesting manuscript. I should
be disposed to date it at about 1100 to 1150. I believe that it is unquestionably connected
with a South Italian Manuscript written in Beneventan script[2] and figures in it are closely
similar to those in the destroyed Turin manuscript KIV 3 (see my Studies, volume 2, page
71). The pages of the Turin are reproduced in Giacosa. I think it might be worth while
enquiring of Giacosa if there exist any other photographs of this lost manuscript besides
those reproduced in his "Magestio [sic] Salernitani."[3] The manuscript Harleian 5294 contains many Anglo-Saxon glosses and is one of the so-called "reserved" manuscripts by the
British Museum, i.e. manuscripts kept in a special safe which can only be examined by
special readers. I should add perhaps that I have much closer parallels than that reproduced in page 71 of Volume 2 of my Studies.

Of Harleian 5294 I have ordered you folio 60 recto to 62 recto. That is all that the
Manuscript contains of Sextus Placitus and it is imperfect – a mere fragment. This manuscript omits a number of page[s] of anti-dotary material. These pages and the pages of
Sextus Placitus are in an early handwriting, but one different from the Herbarium, earlier
in the book containing glosses by Anglo-Saxon glossists.

5. The Rawlinson MS to which you refer in your letter is <u>not</u> Rawlinson <u>C 128</u> but
Rawlinson <u>C 328</u>. The text of Sextus Placitus begins at folio <u>120</u> verso and ends at folio
125 verso. As this is so condensed, I have ordered the entire text for you.

This MS contains drawings in the margins of beasts and birds. Some of the drawings in
the outer margins have been partly pared off by the binder. The size of the leaves is 9 1/2 x
7 inches.

I hope these notes will be of use.
With best regards
Yours ever,
Charles Singer

[1] Charles Singer, 'Greek biology and its relation to the rise of modern biology', in Charles Singer (ed.), *Studies in the history and method of science*, vol 2 (Oxford: Clarendon Press, 1921), 1–101.
[2] Beneventan, a medieval script.
[3] Piero Giacosa, *Magistri salernitani nondum editi* .... (Turin, 1898). Piero Giacosa (1853–1928), Italian pharmacologist and medical historian; see 'Piero Giacosa, M.D.', *British Medical Journal*, 1929, **i:** 328.

160

Singer to Sigerist, London, 7 May 1925

My dear Sigerist,
    Herewith rotographs of Rawlinson 358. Those in the British Museum will follow. I have written again to hurry them up.
Yours ever,
Chas Singer

161

Singer to Sigerist, London, 11 May 1925

My dear Sigerist,
    I have today forwarded the rotographs of the British Museum Manuscripts. They are beautifully done, especially Additional 8928, which is a great deal easier to read in the rotograph than in the original.
    The total bill comes to £1.11.0 I am paying it and will send you the receipt.
Yours ever,
Charles Singer

162

Singer to Sigerist, London, 16 May 1925

My dear Sigerist,
    I have just had a Notice of the Meeting of the Swiss Society, from which I see that you will be in Berne until May 31st.

We leave London on June 2nd and arrive at Thun on the morning of June 3rd. We have already taken our tickets and have booked rooms at the Belle Vue Hotel at Thun. It had been our purpose to leave the nurse and child at Thun for two or three days while we went on at once to find rooms near Lake Lungern. Could not you join us at Thun? If so, we would stay there or near there a few days before going on. It would be delightful if you could manage this.

My niece, Mary Singer, is marrying from this house on May 30th so that my movements are controlled by that.

I have received the last proofs of my History of Anatomy.[1]

Yours ever,

Charles Singer

[1] Singer (1925c).

163

Singer to Sigerist, Thun, Switzerland, 3 June 1925

My dear Sigerist,

We arrived here this morning with nurse and the little girl. The latter bore the journey particularly well & slept right through the night.

We are going to stay here for a few days before we go higher. I have slight sciatica & if it is not better during the next few days I think we shall go to Locarno for a week to get really warm. Warm always cures it. Then we can get up to the Alps. So that our movements are just a little uncertain. But anyhow our letters will be forwarded.

Of course we must manage to meet. I have ordered a copy of my History of Anatomy to be sent to you but you will not get it for a week or two.[1] What about my Mundinus? Is it published yet?[2]

I have written to Klebs to let him know that we are here. I gather that you are at the moment in Leipzig.

Apart from wanting to see you we should much like you and your wife to make the aquaintance of our little girl who flourishes exceedingly.

Let us have a line from you.

Yours ever,

Charles Singer

[1] Singer (1925c).
[2] Singer (1925a)

164

Singer to Sigerist, Ringgenberg, Switzerland, 8 June 1925[1]

My dear Sigerist,

My sciatica has quite disappeared – so much so that yesterday and the day before we went on foot from Sachseln to the Melcher See [sic][2] & back.

We have come on here where we shall remain for a week or two. It is the next station but one on the boat to Interlaken. Let us know definitely by post or wire when you will come & we shall look forward to you being our guest. Do bring your wife with you. It is quite simple here but very comfortable & a most beautiful view.

In about a fortnight's time we shall be moving into the mountains.

I long for us to meet.

Best regards from us both

Yours ever,

Charles Singer

[1] Ringgenberg is on the Lake of Brienz, large enough for steamships.
[2] Melchsee, a small mountain lake.

165

Singer to Sigerist, Ringgenberg, 14 June 1925

My dear Sigerist,

We are settled in this comfortable but very simple hotel until June 27 when we move, I think, to Rosenlauibad. Let us know when, & how many of you, will come & you will be most welcome.

You might bring with you a copy of my Fasciculo which I have not yet seen in its final form.[1] I should like to have just a look at it though doubtless there is a copy waiting for me at home.

Have you by any chance Walter Scott's Hermetica?[2] It has just appeared at the Oxf. Univ. Press. I have the first volume which I have been reading with much interest but have left vol. II in London. If you have vol II you might perhaps lend it to me. If there is anything very special that has recently appeared in German or Italian & you find room for it in your luggage I should be duly grateful.

This hotel is actually on the lake & the most comfortable way to get here is by boat from Brienz. The hotel is on the landing stage. The railway station is almost 10 minutes walk.

Stay with us as long as you can. We are much looking forward to seeing you both [....].

Yours ever

Charles Singer

Klebs is coming over one day. I had a fairly sane letter from him. He says he wants to talk over Congress matters with me. Have you read Capparoni's latest? Poor old thing.

[1] Singer (1925a).

[2] Walter Scott (1855–1925), classical scholar not the Scottish novelist; a new edition of his *Hermetica: the ancient Greek and Latin writings* .... (Boston, 1885), was published in four volumes by Clarendon Press between 1924 and 1936.

166

Singer to Sigerist, Ringgenberg, 20 June 1925 (postcard)

A line to say that on June 29 we move to
    Hotel Victoria
    Reuti Hasliberg
    (Station Brünig)
Yours ever
Charles Singer

167

Singer to Sigerist, Ringgenberg, 25 June 1925

My dear Sigerist,
    Many thanks for your letter of June 20. On Monday June 29 we move to
    Hotel Victoria
    Reuti
    Hasliberg,
where you & yours will be most welcome. There is a postwagon that comes from Brünig station.
    The most convenient week end for us would be from July 3. On the following week end we – i.e. my wife & I – had preferred to go for a few days walking tour. In any event you will be our guests & we hope that you will stay as long as you can. On Sunday next we expect a visit here (in Ringgenberg) from Klebs.
    Let us know which day & by what train and how many of you will come. I shall hope to meet you.
    It is very pleasant here & I get through a fair amount of work.
Yours ever,
Charles Singer

168

Singer to Sigerist, Reuti-Hasliberg, Switzerland, 29 June 1925

My dear Sigerist,

We arrived in this place this morning & find it quite unusually comfortable.

This letter is just to say that Klebs is coming to see us one day in the near future. Of course I don't know how he regards you at the moment! Knowing how mad he is, and seeing that he has not employed Lier for his reproductions of pestilence plates, & considering that you are now a professor, I think it not unlikely that he is very angry with you! But I really have no other ground for this hypothesis except that he has not mentioned you in his letters. Anyhow I shall persuade him not to come on July 4.[1]

Do try & persuade your wife to come. We should love to have you both with us as our guests & it is really unusually comfortable at this hotel.

Yours ever,

Charles Singer

[1] After a promising beginning of a friendship, Klebs in 1923 insulted Sigerist and spread rumors about him; see Bickel (ed.), (2008).

169

Singer to Sigerist, Reuti-Hasliberg, 1 July 1925 (postcard)

All right. We have put Klebs off & told him not to come till next week. We expect you then by the 10:44 Brünig on July 4.

Many thanks for reprints just received.

Charles Singer

170

Singer to Sigerist, Reuti-Hasliberg, 2 July 1925

A line to say that I shall be in Meiringen on the morning of July 4. If I am <u>not</u> at the station at 10:44 when you arrive I shall be coming up from Meiringen by the train arriving Brünig at 11:00 so please wait for me. We are so looking forward to seeing you. Have put off Klebs.

Yours

Charles Singer

171

Singer to Sigerist, Reuti-Hasliberg, 15 July 1925

My dear Sigerist,

I am afraid Sarton won't come after all. He wrote me a day or two ago. I have mislaid his letter at the moment but will come on it presently! He is going straight to the Pyrenees & says he cannot afford the travel more. It is a pity to have nursed him.

Very many thanks for the cigars which are excellent. You very wrongly do not enclose the bill. I assume that they are 40 centimes. You also left about 15 other cigars so I enclose a cheque for 46 francs. Do please let me know if this is not right.

If all goes well we hope to come to Zürich for a day or two on July 29 or 30 if that will be quite convenient to you. Let us have a line if it will not be convenient. We should go straight home from Zürich.

I have had a long & stupid letter from Klebs & I still don't know whether he will come or not.

We have had some splendid walks from here sleeping out several nights. We are going to have another long excursion of three days beginning tomorrow if the weather is good. We have both become remarkably fit. Nancy flourishes.[1]

With best regards from all to all,

Yours ever,

Charles Singer

---

[1] Nancy, the Singers' adopted daughter.

172

Sigerist to Singer, Leipzig?, 1 October 1925[1]

Mein lieber Singer,

Ich bin nun glücklich in Leipzig eingetroffen und möchte nicht versäumen, Ihren Brief vom 25. Juli zu beantworten. Es war mir eine grosse Enttäuschung, dass Sie damals nicht mehr nach Zürich kommen konnten, und ich habe mich umso mehr gefreut, dass ich ein paar schöne Tage mit Ihnen verbringen konnte.

Wann mein Apuleius[2] erscheint, kann ich Ihnen noch nicht mit Bestimmtheit sagen. Es wird wohl Frühling werden. Vor allem möchte ich Ihnen herzlich danken für Ihre Geschichte der Anatomie,[3] die mich natürlich ganz ausserordentlich interessiert. Ich habe angefangen, sie eingehend zu studieren, und ich werde Ihnen nochmals darüber schreiben, wenn ich das Buch fertig gelesen habe.

Wann reisen Sie nach Amerika? Wann kommen Sie zu uns nach Leipzig?

Mit herzlichen Grüssen, auch an Ihre verehrte Frau, bin ich

Ihr ergebener

[Henry E. Sigerist]

Summary: Sigerist has settled in Leipzig. On his *Apuleius* and Singer's *The evolution of anatomy*.

[1] For Sigerist's Leipzig period his letters are preserved, however Singer's are not.
[2] Howald and Sigerist (1927).
[3] Singer (1925c).

173

Sigerist to Singer, Leipzig?, 18 January 1926

Mein lieber Singer,

Nehmen Sie vielen herzlichen Dank für Ihren Brief vom 16. Dezember und entschuldigen Sie, dass ich ihn erst heute beantworte. Ihre Geschichte der Anatomie[1] und Ihren Beitrag zu dem Buch 'Science, Religion and Reality'[2] habe ich gut erhalten und danke Ihnen bestens dafür. Ich habe beides mit grossem Interesse gelesen und werde die Arbeiten in den 'Mitteilungen' besprechen.[3]

Es hat mich sehr interessiert und sehr gefreut, dass Sie ein zweites Kind adoptiert haben. Meine besten Wünsche für ein glückliches Gedeihen der beiden Kinder.

Den Brief von Krumbhaar habe ich mit Interesse gelesen. Wir sind natürlich grundsätzlich gern bereit, die internationalen Beziehungen wieder aufzunehmen. Allein es muss eine Form gefunden werden, die das Empfinden der deutschen Kollegen nicht verletzt. Sie müssen nicht vergessen, dass der jahrelange Ausschluss von den internationalen Veranstaltungen eine Beleidigung gewesen ist, und Sie können nicht von uns verlangen, dass wir jetzt um Aufnahme bitten. Dass ich persönlich in der Sache nichts tun kann, wissen Sie ja, denn ich war ja Mitglied der internationalen Gesellschaft. Man hat mich aber aus der Gesellschaft, wahrscheinlich aus politischen Gründen, ausgestossen, ohne dass man die Höflichkeit gehabt hätte, mir dies mitzuteilen.

Ich hoffe, dass Sie gute Ferien verbracht haben, und mit herzlichen Grüssen, auch an Ihre Frau, verbleibe ich

Ihr sehr ergebener

[Henry E. Sigerist]

(173) Summary: The Singers have adopted a second child. The German standpoint regarding the resumption of cultural relations. Sigerist's exclusion from the International Society of the History of Medicine for political reasons.

[1] Singer (1925c).
[2] Singer (1925d).
[3] *Mitteilungen zur Geschichte der Medizin und Naturwissenschaften*

174

Sigerist to Singer, Leipzig?, 24 February 1926

Lieber Singer,

Herzlichen Dank für Ihren Brief vom 19. Februar. Ich wäre Ihnen ausserordentlich dankbar, wenn Sie mir den Apuleius, Bodley 130 möglichst bald zuschicken könnten. Ich würde ihn nur 2 – 3 Tage behalten. Die Einleitung zu meiner Ausgabe muss nämlich in den nächsten Tagen in Druck gehen, und es wäre mir sehr wertvoll, wenn ich diese Neupublikation vorher einsehen könnte.

Mit hezlichen Grüssen und vielem Dank zum voraus bin ich

Ihr ergebener

[Henry E. Sigerist]

Summary: Request of an Oxford manuscript.

175

Sigerist to Singer, Leipzig?, 25 February 1926

Lieber Singer,

Herzlichen Dank für Ihren Brief vom 23. Februar. Ihre Arbeit über die 'Fünf-Bilder-Serie' des Caius College wird mir für das 'Archiv' sehr willkommen sein.[1] Wenn Sie mir das Manuskript bald schicken, kann ich es gleich im 2. Heft dieses Jahres herausbringen.

Mit herzlichen Grüssen bin ich

Ihr ergebener

[Henry E. Sigerist]

[1] 'Fünf-Bilder-Series of Caius College' did not appear in the *Archiv für Geschichte der Medizin*.

176

Sigerist to Singer, Leipzig?, 19 March 1926

Mein lieber Singer,

Besten Dank für Ihre Briefe vom 8. und 9. März, sowie für den Apuleius-Band,[1] der mich sehr interessiert und den ich Ihnen nächste Woche zurückschicken werde. Es ist eine prachtvolle Reproduktion. Für die Rekonstruktion des Textes hat die Handschrift jedoch wenig Bedeutung. Ich bin aber sehr froh, das Buch gesehen zu haben, denn ich möchte in der Einleitung[2] möglichst vollständig sein.

Ich bin sehr gespannt, was aus dem Wellcome Museum werden wird.[3]

Den Brief von Günther schicke ich Ihnen beiliegend zurück.[4]

Schicken Sie mir Ihren Artikel,[5] sobald Sie ihn fertig haben. Ich werde ihn dann sobald wie möglich publizieren.

In etwa 14 Tagen werden Sie das 1. Heft des neuen Jahrgangs vom 'Archiv für Geschichte der Medizin' bekommen. Sie werden sehen, dass das 'Archiv' sich sehr verändert hat.

Mit herzlichen Grüssen, auch an Ihre Frau, bin ich

Ihr ganz ergebener

[Henry E. Sigerist]

[1] Apuleius-Band, Oxford manuscript
[2] 'Einleitung' of Howald and Sigerist (1927).
[3] Wellcome Museum of the History of Medicine, London.
[4] Günther not identified.
[5] See letter 175.

177

Sigerist to Singer, Leipzig?, 13 April 1926

Mein lieber Singer,

Herzlichen Dank für Ihren Brief vom 7. April. Ich glaube sicher, dass der Verlag der Münchner Drucke Ihnen ein Rezensionsexemplar des ‚Gart' der Gesundheit'[1] schicken wird, und ich würde Ihnen raten, einmal nach dort zu schreiben. Die Adresse ist: Verlag der Münchner Drucke, Ainmillerstrasse 35, München.

Mit herzlichen Grüssen bin ich

Ihr ergebener

[Henry E. Sigerist]

[1] *Gart' der Gesundheit*, one of the early herbals (1485).

178

Sigerist to Singer, Leipzig?, 15 January 1927

Mein lieber Singer,

Nehmen Sie herzlichen Dank für Ihren Brief vom 10. Januar. Es hat mich sehr gefreut, wieder einmal von Ihnen zu hören, da ich seit Monaten ganz ohnne Nachrichten war. Ich hoffte, Sie in Leipzig einmal zu sehen und besonders, da mir Professor Saxl[1] von der

Bibliothek Warburg in Hamburg gesagt hatte, dass Sie dort einen Vortrag halten würden. Aber wie ich nun vernehme, ist auch dies verschoben worden.

Die Photographie habe ich in Cassel sofort bestellt, und ich hoffe, dass ich sie Ihnen bald schicken kann.

Mein Apuleius is immer noch nicht fertig.[2] Es fehlen noch die Register. Vielleicht interessiert Sie aber die Einleitung, von der ich Ihnen beiliegend Korrekturexemplare schicke. Entschuldigen Sie wenn etwa noch einige Druckfehler darin sind. Vom Stammbaum habe ich leider augenblicklich keinen Abzug, aber ich hoffe, dass das Buch in den nächsten Monaten erscheinen wird. Ich bin mit den Indizes noch nicht fertig, die, wie Sie sich wohl denken können, sehr viel Arbeit machen.

Waren Sie schon in Amerika, oder gehen Sie erst hin? Wir werden uns ja dieses Jahr auf alle Fälle in Leiden am Kongress sehen, denn wie Sie ja wohl gehört haben, sind dank des grossen Taktes der Holländer alle formellen Schwierigkeiten überwunden worden.

Dr. Vonwiller,[3] der Privatdozent für Anatomie in Zürich ist, möchte nächstes Frühjahr in London arbeiten und möchte vor allem die Bekanntschaft von Elliot Smith und Keith[4] machen. Ich habe mir erlaubt, ihm Ihre Adresse zu geben und wäre Ihnen dankbar, wenn Sie ihm helfen wollten.

Mit herzlichen Grüssen Ihnen und Ihrer Frau bin ich

Ihr ganz ergebener

[Henry E. Sigerist]

Summary: First exchange of letters after months. The Dutch succeeded in inviting the Germans and Austrians to the International Congress of the History of Medicine in Leyden.

[1] Fritz Saxl (1890–1948), first Librarian of the Warburg Library in Hamburg, and founder of the Warburg Institute, London; see Gertrud Bing, 'Saxl, Friedrich [Fritz] (1890–1948)', rev. Christopher Lloyd, *Oxford dictionary of national biography* (Oxford: Oxford University Press, 2004), vol. 49, 151–152.
[2] Howald and Sigerist (1927).
[3] Paul Vonwiller (1885–1962), Swiss anatomist.
[4] Sir Arthur Keith, (1866–1955), anatomist and anthopologist; see W. E. Le Gros Clark, 'Keith, Sir Arthur (1866–1955)', rev. Harold Ellis, *Oxford dictionary of national biography* (Oxford: Oxford University Press, 2004), vol. 31, 57–59.

179

Sigerist to Singer, Leipzig?, 16 April 1927

Mein lieber Singer,

Beiliegend schicke ich Ihnen die gewünschten Photographien von Cues.[1] Es ist eine ganz kleine Bibliothek, die natürlich nicht recht eingerichtet ist, sodass ich keine besseren Abzüge bekommen konnte.

Sodann danke ich Ihnen bestens für die Zusendung des Kataloges von Mrs. Singer. Ich glaube kaum, dass es möglich sein wird, ihn im "Archiv" zu veröffentlichen,[2] da wir in letzter Zeit sehr viel Stoff haben und uns nur wenig Raum zur Verfügung steht. Sudhoff hat augenblicklich die Arbeit, und ich werde nochmals mit ihm reden, um zu sehen, was sich machen lässt.

Beiliegend schicke ich Ihnen den Brief von Feldhaus zurück.[3] Es hat gar keinen Wert, dass Sie ihm schreiben.

Was nun Ihr letztes Telegramm betrifft, so habe ich sofort nach Cassel geschrieben und eine Photographie der betreffenden Seite bestellt. Es geht dort immer etwas langsam, aber ich hoffe, dass ich Ihnen die Bilder doch bald schicken kann.

Ich sende Ihnen beiliegend die beiden Seiten aus meiner Ausgabe. Das Bild der Herba Asterion stammt aus der Casseler Handschrift.

Mit herzlichen Grüssen bin ich
Ihr ganz ergebener
[Henry E. Sigerist]

Summary: Minor business.

---

[1] Cues is Berncastel, a town in the Mosel Valley of Germany.
[2] *Archiv der Geschichte der Medizin.*
[3] Probably Franz Maria Feldhaus (1874–1957), controversial German historian of science. See letters 233, 234, 338 and 339.

180

Sigerist to Singer, Leipzig?, 22 June 1927

Mein lieber Singer,
Ich weiss nicht, wo Sie augenblicklich sind. Für alle Fälle schreibe ich nach London und denke, dass Ihnen der Brief nachgeschickt wird.

Ich danke Ihnen für Ihren Scheck von M. 18.- als Jahresbeitrag der deutschen Gesellschaft für 1927[1] und danke Ihnen vor allem für Ihre liebenswürdige Einladung nach England. Die Reise wäre jedoch etwas zu weit mit den Kindern, und wir haben nun die Absicht, nach dem Leidener Kongress fünf Wochen in Holland zu verbringen. Wir haben im Hôtel du Rhin in Katwyk Zimmer bestellt, und es wäre sehr nett, wenn Sie mit Ihrer Familie auch dorthin kommen könnten. Katwyk soll einen sehr schönen Strand haben, ist ein ruhiger kleiner Ort, nicht weit von Leiden entfernt. Es wäre wirklich sehr nett, wenn wir dort zusammen sein könnten und unsere Kinder zusammen spielen könnten.

Herzliche Grüsse Ihnen und Ihrer verehrten Frau von
Ihrem ganz ergebenen
[Henry E. Sigerist]

(180) <u>Summary</u>: Sigerist will spend five weeks in Holland after the Leyden Congress and invites Singer for a family gathering there.

[1] Sigerist was the treasurer of the Deutsche Gesellschaft für Geschichte der Medizin.

181

Sigerist to Singer, Leipzig?, 6 July 1927

Mein lieber Singer,

Herzlichen Dank für Ihr Telegramm und für den Brief von Mrs. Singer. Wie ich Ihnen schon telegraphisch berichtete, fahre ich: am 15. Juli mit meinem Wagen hier weg und rechne damit, am Sonntag den 17. Juli nachmittags in Leiden zu sein. Ich wohne im Hôtel du Commerce. Wenn Sie am Sonntag auch schon dort sein könnten, hätten wir den ganzen Nachmittag und Abend, sowie den Montagvormittag für uns. Meine Frau wird am Kongress nicht teilnehmen. Sie kann nicht so früh weg. Sie wird am 25. Juli mit den Kindern direkt nach Katwyk fahren.

Leider kann ich nicht vor dem 15. Juli verreisen, da unsere Vorlesungen offiziell noch bis zum 22. Juli dauern, und ich sowieso schon eine Woche früher schliessen muss.

Mit herzlichen Grüssen und besten Empfehlungen an Ihre Frau bin ich
Ihr ganz ergebener
[Henry E. Sigerist]

<u>Summary</u>: Sigerist will come to Leyden by car; Mrs. Sigerist and the children will join him in Katwyk after the Congress.

182

Sigerist to Singer, Leipzig?, 7 November 1928

Mein lieber Singer,

Ich komme mit einer grossen Bitte zu Ihnen. Einer meiner Mitarbeiter beabsichtigt, die altlateinischen Uebersetzungen der hippokratischen Aphorismen herauszugeben. Wäre es Ihnen möglich, mir aus Ihrem Katalog ein Verzeichnis der in England befindlichen Handschriften der lateinischen Aphorismen herzustellen, wenn möglich mit Angabe des Incipits. Es hat sich herausgestellt, dass die Aphorismen vor Konstantin von Afrika nicht einmal, sondern dreimal übersetzt worden sind.

Dann habe ich die Absicht, die Gynaecia, die unter dem Namen der Kleopatra gehen, einmal kritisch edieren zu lassen. Ich habe Photographien der Handschriften von Florenz und Kopenhagen, und es würde mich natürlich sehr interessieren, zu wissen, ob auch in England solche Handschriften vorhanden sind. Der Text beginnt: Desideranti tibi filia carissima.

Ihr Brief hat mich sehr erfreut. Namentlich war es mir eine Freude zu sehen, dass es Ihnen und den Ihrigen immer gut geht. Dass Sie sehr fleissig sind, haben mir Ihre verschiedenen Bücher gezeigt, die ich alle mit grossem Interesse gelesen habe.[1] Hier in Leipzig geht alles seinen normalen Gang. Das Institut hat sich sehr stark vergrössert, so sehr, dass wir keinen Platz mehr haben und dass wir nächstes Jahr ein eigenes Gebäude bekommen werden.-[2]

Am 26. November feiert Sudhoff seinen 75. Geburtstag. Es wäre sehr nett wenn Sie zu dieser Gelegenheit nach Leipzig kommen könnten. Es wäre namentlich mir eine sehr grosse Freude, Sie hier begrüssen zu können. Ich werde Ihnen auf alle Fälle eine Einladung schicken.

Mit freundlichen Grüssen bin ich

Ihr sehr ergebener

[Henry E. Sigerist]

Summary: Sigerist asks Singer for ancient manuscripts kept in England. He also invites him for Sudhoff's 75th birthday.

[1] Singer's recent books: Charles Singer, *From magic to science. Essays on the scientific twilight* (London, 1928); Charles Singer, *A short history of medicine* (Oxford, 1928); Charles Singer, *Religion and science considered in their historical relations* (London, 1928).

[2] Sigerist's department increased in terms of staff; the planned new building did not materialize.

183

Sigerist to Dorothea Singer, Leipzig?, 21 December 1928

Liebe Frau Singer,

Nehmen Sie vielen herzlichen Dank für die liebenswürdige Zusendung Ihrer Notizen über die hippokratischen Aphorismen und über Kleopatra, die mir beide ausserordentlich wertvoll sind. Einer meiner Assistenten, ein junger klassischer Philologe, schreibt eine Geschichte der Aphorismen im Mittelalter[1] und wird eine neue Ausgabe der frühlateinischen Uebersetzung herausgeben, sodass Ihre Angaben für ihn ganz besonders wertvoll sind. Ich badaure nur, dass es für die Bibliotheken der anderen Länder keine solchen Kataloge gibt, was die Arbeit ja bedeutend erleichtern würde. Die Gynäcia von Kleopatra werde ich gelegentlich durch einen Doktoranden herausgeben lassen.

Es tat mir sehr leid zu hören, dass Sie nicht wohl gewesen sind. Ich hoffe, dass Sie sich alle gut erholt haben und wünsche Ihnen und Ihrer ganzen Familie frohe Feiertage und ein glückliches Neues Jahr.

Mit herzlichen Grüssen bin ich stets

Ihr ganz ergebener

[Henry E. Sigerist]

Summary: Sigerist thanks Mrs. Singer for answering his questions in his letter to Singer of 7 November 1928, and reports on work of his assistant, Ludwig Englert.

[1] Ludwig Englert (1902–1981), assistant from 1928–1934. The only published fruit of his medieval researches seems to be 'Die medizinhistorische Bedeutung des Fragmentum Donaueschingense', *Sudhoffs Archiv für Geschichte der Medizin*, 1931, **24**: 220–224.

184

Sigerist to Singer, Leipzig?, 20 March 1929

Mein lieber Singer,

Nehmen Sie herzlichen Dank für Ihren Brief von 11. März. Ob Hübotters Lexikon[1] gut wird, weiss ich nicht. Ich habe erst in diesen Tagen davon gehört und habe es natürlich auch subskribieren müssen, obwohl der Preis wirklich sehr hoch ist. Ich finde es vollkommen überflüssig dass das Buch illustriert wird; es wird dadurch nur unnötig verteuert.

Wir hatten einen scheusslich kalten Winter. Drei Wochen lang war unsere Wasserleitung eingefroren, sodass wir unter geradezu mittelalterlichen Verhältnissen gelebt haben. Jetzt haben wir aber genug davon, und Ende dieser Woche fahren wir für einige Wochen nach Florenz.

Ich habe die Absicht, die Pfingstwoche in Paris mit meiner Frau zu verbringen und würde mich sehr freuen, Sie beide dort zu sehen.

Es freut mich sehr, dass Sie wieder ein Buch vollendet haben, und ich beglückwünsche Sie dazu.[2] Ich selber habe in diesem Winter nicht sehr viel schreiben können. Ich hatte jede Woche 9 Stunden Vorlesungen und Seminarübungen, was sehr viel Vorbereitung erforderte, und im Augenblick sind 19 junge Leute im Institut, die grössere wissenschaftliche Arbeiten unternommen haben, was mich selbstverständlich auch stark absorbiert.

Der zweite Band unseres "Kyklos"[3] ist im Druck und wird Anfang Mai erscheinen. Er ist ziemlich viel grösser und reichhaltiger als der letzte Band und wird Ihnen sicher gefallen. Auch von den Vorträgen ist ein neuer Band im Druck und ein dritter ist in Vorbereitung, der in diesem Sommer gedruckt werden soll.

Mit herzlichen Grüssen, auch an Ihre verehrte Frau, bin ich

Ihr ganz ergebener

[Henry E. Sigerist]

Summary: News from research, teaching and publications in Sigerist's Institute.

[1] Franz Hübotter (1881–1967), German medical historian; his 'Lexikon' is probably Franz Hübotter, *3000 Jahre Medizin* (Berlin, 1920). See P. Huard, 'Franz Hübotter (1881–1967), *Histoire des Sciences Médicales*, 1968–69, **2–3**: 61, and 'Franz Hübotter', in Peter Voswinckel (ed.), *Biographisches Lexikon der hervorragenden Ärzte der letzten fünfzig Jahre von Isidor Fischer: Berlin und Wien 1932–1933*, Bd.3, (Hildesheim: Georg Olms, 2002-), 681.

[2] Singer's book is probably the American edition of Singer (1928c).

[3] Kyklos, the yearbook of Sigerist's Institute in Leipzig.

185

Sigerist to Singer, Leipzig?, 26 July 1929

Mein lieber Singer,

darf ich Ihnen meinen Assistenten Dr. Owsei Temkin[1] bestens empfehlen. Dr. Temkin ist für einige Tage in London. Er möchte gern Crookshank[2] aufsuchen und das Well-come-Museum. Vielleicht haben Sie die Freundlichkeit, ihm Empfehlungen dorthin zu geben.

Mit herzlichen Grüssen bin ich

Stets Ihr

[Henry E. Sigerist]

Summary: Recommendation for Temkin in London.

[1] Owsei Temkin (1902–2002), Sigerist's first collaborator in Leipzig and later in Baltimore; see Vivian Nutton, 'Owsei Temkin 1902–2002', *Medical History*, 2003, **47**: 100–103.

[2] Possibly the physician Francis Graham Crookshank (1873–1933), see *Britsh Medical Journal*, 1933, **ii**: 848.

186

Sigerist to Singer, Leipzig?, 27 August 1929

Mein lieber Singer,

Ich danke Ihnen bestens für Ihre verschiedenen Briefe. Um dem Komitee keine Schwierigkeiten zu machen, habe ich Mieli geschrieben,[1] dass ich bereit bin, das Amt eines Schatzmeisters zu übernehmen. Viel Arbeit wird es nicht geben, da wir ja kein Geld haben. Es wäre jedoch zweckmässig, wenn für den Kongress[2] ein eigener Schatz-meister, der in London wohnt, ernannt würde, wie Sie das ja selber vorschlagen.

Was die Einsiedelner Handschrift betrifft, möchte ich Ihnen raten, sie in der Zentralbi-bliothek Zürich photographieren zu lassen. Schreiben Sie an den Pater bibliothecarius in Einsiedeln und bitten Sie ihn, die Handschrift nach Zürich zu schicken mit genauer Angabe, welche Seiten Sie photographiert haben wollen. Ich mache das selber immer so. Dass eine Handschrift von Einsiedeln[3] nach England geschickt würde, halte ich für ausgeschlossen.

Unsere Ferien waren durch sehr schlechtes Wetter getrübt, sodass wir sie abgekürzt haben und schon jetzt nach Leipzig zurückgekehrt sind. Anfang September reise ich jedoch mit einer Gruppe von Studenten nach Budapest zum Kongress und werde dann noch einige Tage in Wien und Prag verbringen.

Mit herzlichen Grüssen Ihnen und Ihrer Frau

bin ich stets Ihr
[Henry E. Sigerist]

Summary: Sigerist thanks for several letters, accepts a new treasurer's post, gives advice for photographing manuscripts in Switzerland.

[1] Aldo Mieli (1878–1950), Italian historian of science; see P. Sergescu, 'Aldo Mieli', in *Actes du VIe Congrès international d'histoire des sciences*: Amsterdam, 14–21 Août 1950 (Paris: Académie Internationale d'Histoire des Sciences, 1951–1953), vol. 1, 79–95, and José Babini, 'Aldo Mieli y la historia de la ciencia en la Argentina', *Physis*, 1962, **4**: 64–84.
[2] International Congress of the History of Science, 1931, with Singer as President.
[3] Einsiedeln, a monastery and library in Switzerland.

187

Sigerist to Singer, Leipzig?, 16 September 1929

Sehr verehrter Herr Dr. Singer,
   Als ich gestern vom Budapester Kongress[1] nach Leipzig zurückkerhrte, fand ich Ihren werten Brief, der mir aus London nachgeschickt worden war. Es tut mir sehr leid, dass ich Sie in London nicht angetroffen habe, da Sie ja zur Zeit meines dortigen Aufenthalts gerade verreist waren. Ich bin nur bis zum 29. August in London gewesen, wollte aber nicht von dort wegfahren, ohne Ihnen wenigstens ein Lebenszeichen von mir zukommenn zu lassen und habe Ihnen deshalb den "Kyklos" von London aus zugestellt.
   Haben Sie also vielen Dank für Ihren Brief, dessen Vorschlag sich leider nicht verwirklichen lässt und lassen Sie mich die Hoffnung aussprechen, dass ich doch vielleicht in absehbarer Zeit die Ehre haben werde, Sie persönlich begrüssen zu dürfen.
   Mit vorzüglicher Hochachtung
Ihr sehr ergebener
[Henry E. Sigerist]

Summary: After Budapest Sigerist was in London when Singer was out of town. Hopes to see Singer soon.

[1] The Congress of the International Society of the History of Medicine in Budapest.

188

Sehr geehrter Herr Dr. Singer,

Ich habe Ihren zweiten Brief aus London erhalten und möchte Ihnen nachträglich herzlichst für Ihre freundliche Einladung danken. Sie können sich denken, wie peinlich es für mich ist, dass Sie durch das Missverständnis der nachträglichen "Kyklos- Uebersendung" einen so schlechten Eindruck von mir bekommen mussten. Es würde mich sehr freuen, wenn Sie mir durch eine Postkarte die Gewissheit geben würden, dass Sie mir wegen der Umstände, die ich Ihnen unverschuldet bereitet habe, nicht böse sind.

Mit ergebenstem Gruss
Ihr
[Henry E. Sigerist]

Summary: Sigerist thanks Singer for his invitation and excuses himself for the misunderstanding created by the belated sending of Kyklos.

189

Mein lieber Singer,

Nehmen Sie herzlichen Dank für Ihren Brief vom 13. September. Wir haben Sie in Budapest sehr vermisst. Wissenschaftlich war der Kongress nicht viel wert. Aber Budapest ist eine wunderschöne Stadt. Wir haben viele nette Menschen getroffen. Vor allem Garrison ist ein ganz reizender Mensch. Wir waren fast immer zusammen und haben uns sehr gut verstanden. Aus England war nur Malcolm[1] hier, mit dem ich auch viel zusammen war.

Ich freue mich sehr, dass Ihnen der zweite "Kyklos-Band" gefallen hat. Der dritte Band ist bereits in Vorbereitung. Ein Exemplar des ersten Bandes wird Ihnen vom Verlag geschickt werden.

Dr. Temkin hat sehr bedauert, Sie nicht zu sehen. Er war nur wenige Tage in London.

Mit herzlichen Grüssen an Sie und Ihre Frau bin ich stets
Ihr
[Henry E. Sigerist]

Summary: On the Budapest Congress and Kyklos.

[1] L. W. G Malcolm (1888–1946), conservator at the Wellcome Historical Medical Museum

190

Sigerist to Singer, Leipzig?, 14 December 1929

Mein lieber Singer,

Vor 5 oder 6 Jahren erschien in England eine neue Ausgabe der hermetischen Schriften. Ich habe den genauen Titel nicht. Wäre es Ihnen möglich, mir diesen anzugeben?[1]

Mit herzlichen Grüssen bin ich stets

Ihr

[Henry E. Sigerist]

[1] Request for a copy of a new English edition of *Hermetica*; see letter 165.

191

Sigerist to Singer, Leipzig?, 13 January 1930a

Mein lieber Singer,

Ich danke Ihnen bestens für Ihren Brief vom 16. Dezember und werde die Hermetica bestellen. Ich habe im Augenblick niemand, der darüber arbeiten könnte. Meine Mitarbeiter sind alle anderweitig beschäftigt.

Somerville wird mir sehr willkommen sein, und ich will ihm gern helfen.[1] Voraussichtlich werde ich März und April verreist sein, sodass er besser vor- oder nachher kommt.

Es hat mich sehr gefreut zu hören, dass Sie eine Vortragsreise nach Amerika machen. Kalifornien muss wunderbar sein.

Was nun Ihren Brief vom 20. Dezember betrifft, so muss ich Ihnen sagen, dass ich Dr. Singer in Zürich nicht kenne.[2] Ich weiss nicht, ob er zu meiner Zeit schon in Zürich war. Jedenfalls habe ich keine Erinnerung mehr an ihn. Ich habe aber sofort nach Zürich an einen Freund geschrieben und um vertrauliche Auskunft gebeten. Sowie ich Antwort habe, schreibe ich Ihnen darüber.

Mit herzlichen Grüssen bin ich stets

Ihr

[Henry E. Sigerist]

Summary: Minor business and Singer's forthcoming lecture tour in America.

[1] Somerville not identified.
[2] Dr. Singer in Zurich not identified.

192

Sigerist to Dorothea Singer, Leipzig?, 13 January 1930b

Liebe Frau Singer,

Ich danke Ihnen herzlich für Ihren Brief vom 12. Dezember. Ich finde es ausserordentlich interessant und auffallend, dass Sie eine so grosse Zahl von Handschriften von Roger Bacon in England haben. Im Augenblick habe ich niemand zur Verfügung, der nach kontinentalen Handschriften suchen könnte, aber ich habe mir die Sache notiert, und sowie ich einen geeigneten Schüler habe, werde ich ihn mit der Aufgabe betrauen.

Ich wünsche Ihnen eine glückliche Reise in den Vereinigten Staaten und bin mit herzlichen Grüssen

Ihr ganz ergebener

[Henry E. Sigerist]

Summary: Sigerist has no collaborator to deal with the English Roger Bacon manuscripts.

193

Sigerist to Singer, Leipzig?, 25 February 1930

Mein lieber Singer,

Darf ich Ihnen meinen Mitarbeiter Dr. Tadeusz Bilikiewicz aufs beste empfehlen? Dr. Bilikiewicz macht eine Studienreise durch Holland und England, und ich wäre Ihnen zu grösstem Dank verpflichtet, wenn Sie ihn in seinen Studien unterstützen könnten.

Mit herzlichen Grüssen bin ich

Ihr ganz ergebener

[Henry E. Sigerist]

Summary: Sigerist recommends his Leipzig collaborator Tadeusz Bilikiewicz (1901–1980).

194

Sigerist to Singer, Leipzig?, 27 March 1930

Sehr geehrter Herr Dr. Singer,

Besten Dank für Ihren Brief vom 24. März. Wir haben Herrn Dr. Schmidt, Köln, gebeten, Ihnen eine Mitgliederliste zugehen zu lassen, da wir selbst nicht im Besitz einer vollständigen sind, und wir hoffen, dass Sie sie bald in Händen haben werden.

Mit vorzüglicher Hochachtung
Ihr sehr ergebener
[signed by secretary in absence of S.]

Summary: Dr. Schmidt will send a list of the members (probably of the German Society of the History of Medicine).

195

Sigerist to Singer, Leipzig?, 12 January 1931

My dear Singer,
   I have got the first invitation for the international congress.[1] Of course I shall attend it if ever possible, although the time is rather inconvenient for us. There must have been a misunderstanding. In Germany the summer-term runs from end of April to end of July. So I am afraid that for all the Germans who have academic work it will be rather difficult to leave as early as end of June. Personally I have 10 lectures a week and I must ask for a special permission, if I want to leave my work during the term. Still I hope to make it possible, and if I cannot come for the whole week, then I will come at least for a few days.
   With kindest regards to Mrs. Singer and yourself
Yours very sincerely
[Henry E. Sigerist]

[1] The Second International Congress of the History of Science and Technology, presided over by Singer. Apparently Sigerist had not yet received the invitation for his study tour in the U.S. in 1931–1932.

196

Sigerist to Singer, Berkeley, CA, 21 December 1931[1]

Sehr verehrte Herr und Frau Dr. Singer,
   In Vertretung von Herrn Professor Sigerist, der ja diesen Winter in Amerika weilt, erlaube ich mir, Ihnen bestens für Ihre Wünsche zu danken und Ihnen gleichzeitig auch meinerseits ein glückliches und frohes Neujahr auszusprechen.
   Mit vorzüglicher Hochachtung
   Ihr sehr ergebener
   "On behalf of Dr. Sigerist, who is spending this winter in America, I thank you for your good wishes. At the same time I would like to wish you a happy New Year."

[1] On his study and lecture tour of the U.S., Sigerist went to California in January 1932; this letter was probably written by a (German?) colleague in the Department of History at the University of California, Berkeley. During his tour Sigerist was offered the chair of the History of Medicine at the Johns Hopkins University. He moved from Leipzig to Baltimore in the autumn of 1932.

197

Singer to Sigerist, Berkeley, 20 September 1932[1]

My dear Sigerist,

A line of welcome to you in your new home. I gather that by now your wife & children are with you.[2] Do please give them our united and heartiest wishes. We wish you every success & happiness in your new position. If there is anything that I can do to forward any of your projects, I shall be only too happy to do so.

You will perhaps, like to hear how things go in the University of California[.] I give a general course in the History of Science & I am staying until the end of this semester. Next semester Sarton will be here for at least a month.

The class is a very large one. Last semester it contained 85 sitting "for credit" as they call it here. This semester the number is about 132 "for credit" besides auditors. The quality is mainly low but is much better this semester than last. I give 3 lectures a week in this course.

I have also a seminar course in "Science as Literature" with a membership of 29. Here I am assisted by several members of the department of English & of philosophy.

As things stand at present we leave here in December (or perhaps in January). We cross the Pacific, make short stops in Hong Kong, Singapore[,] Java & Ceylon[3] & arrive in England about the end of March or the beginning of April.

Whether it will be possible to [....] this department after I leave is far from certain. Of course funds are a great difficulty. The original scheme was to invite both Sarton & myself but this, I imagine will be quite impossible & I am not sure that I would care to stay without him. There is a young chemist at Leland Stanford who might be suitable, however.

I have been very hard at work on my "Short History of Science".[4] It will be about 50 per cent longer than my Biology & on about the same lines. The labour involved in writing it is very great, for it means cramming up all the sciences. I am in hopes of getting it finished in December .

I have just received a whole batch of reprints from Leipzig. I congratulate you most heartily on your final burst of energy & I am writing a line also to Temkin.

Germany seems in a perfectly dreadful state. I am simply amazed that so intelligent & instructed a people does not exhibit more political capacity. I received yesterday a letter from an English schoolboy not yet 16 years of age (son of my friend Dobson of Bristol[5]). He is travelling in Germany to learn the language & he write [sic] (age 16 mind you!) that "in politics all Germans seem to be little children". It is a queer world![6]

Again heartiest and best wishes to you all for every happiness & success & health.
Yours ever
Charles Singer

---

[1] Singer spent several months at the University of California in Berkeley while Sigerist moved to Baltimore.
[2] Mrs. Emmy Sigerist, and their daughters Erica and Nora.

[3] Ceylon, today's Sri Lanka.

[4] *A short history of science* appeared much later: Charles Singer, *A short history of science to the nineteenth century* (Oxford, 1941).

[5] See Letter 139.

[6] Singer muses about the confused political situation in Germany in 1932, i.e., just before Hitler's rule.

198

Sigerist to Singer, Baltimore?, 27 September 1932

My dear Singer: [1]

I was delighted to read your letter of September 20th. I heard from Larkey that you were staying in California until January.[2] We arrived in Baltimore a week ago and hope to be settled soon. We rented a nice little house and I expect my furniture and forty some boxes of books to arrive in a few days.

I was interested in hearing about your teaching experience. I am giving a course on the History of Science myself. It will be two hours a week and will be given at the university chiefly for the premedical students. Besides this I give an Introductory course in the History of Medicine for medical students, a seminar on the History of Anatomy and Physiology and during the last quarter a series of lectures on Civilization and Disease. I do not want to give too much advance work in the beginning before I know what kind of students we have, but I hope to be able to give a research seminar in a not too distant future. Did you know that Temkin has been appointed Associate at our Institute? He worked with me for seven years in Leipzig and I did not want to miss his help, so I was glad that he was appointed with me. He is a very promising young fellow, an excellent philologist, and I am sure that he will be very successful in America. He announced a seminar on Galen and especially on Techne iatrike.[3]

I am very glad to know that you are writing a Short History of Science, and I only regret that it is not out yet.[4] I would have liked to recommend it to my students and it would have been a great help to me. Your History of Biology, of course, will be in the hands of all of my students.[5]

Germany is indeed in a perfectly dreadful state. It is worse than you can imagine. During the last weeks I spent there, we had street battles in Leipzig nearly every day and I am really glad to be here. We had a delightful vacation in the Engadine.[6] It was a perfectly wonderful summer and we enjoyed being in the mountains very much indeed. We are thinking of buying a little chalet somewhere in Switzerland for the summer months, but I have to sell my house in Leipzig first, which, at present, is really impossible.

I envy you your trip through China, but regret that this will prevent you from coming East and seeing us in Baltimore. With kind regards to Mrs. Singer and yourself, I am

Very sincerely yours,

Henry E. Sigerist

[1] This letter is addressed to Singer in Berkeley, CA.

[2] Sanford V. Larkey (1898–1969) had studied medicine and history in San Francisco and Oxford, England; he was assistant professor of Medical History and librarian at the Medical School of University of California, San Francisco. See Owsei Temkin, 'Sanford Vincent Larkey, 1898–1969', *Bulletin of the History of Medicine*, 1970, **44**: 80–85.

[3] Galen's treatise "Techne iatrike", physicians' art. According to Temkin's later recollection, as told to Vivian Nutton, the seminar was not a success, as only Sigerist had the linguistic capabilities to follow all that was being discussed.

[4] Singer (1941).

[5] Charles Singer, *A Short history of biology* (Oxford, 1931).

[6] Engadine, a mountain valley in southeastern Switzerland.

199

Sigerist to Singer, Baltimore?, 20 December 1932

My dear Singer:

We just decided to have the Noguchi Lectures printed as independent little books in future.[1] You were the first Noguchi lecturer and therefore I would like to ask you whether you would care to have the lectures, which you and Mrs. Singer delivered here on different occasions, printed as first volume of our Noguchi series. If so, I would like to have your manuscripts.

I am sorry that you are leaving this country, but I hope that we will meet somewhere in Europe next summer.

With kind regards to Mrs. Singer and yourself and with best wishes for Christmas and a happy New Year, I am

Very sincerely yours,

Henry E. Sigerist

[1] Hideyo Noguchi (1876–1928) Japanese bacteriologist; his name was used for a lecture series at the Hopkins Institute of the History of Medicine. See Claude E. Dolman, 'Noguchi, (Seisaku) Hideyo', *Complete dictionary of scientific biography*, Vol. 10 (Detroit: Charles Scribner's Sons, 2008), 141–145.

200

Singer to Sigerist, London, 2 May 1933

My dear Sigerist,

Very many thanks for your letter and for the interesting bulletin. I am very glad indeed that you have started it. It ought to be most useful and I should like to contribute to it.[1]

As regards your question about my Noguchi lectures, I wish you had asked me a few months ago. They are in fact incorporated in my Short History of Science, of which I despatched the manuscript before I left America and of which I received proofs on arrival in Ceylon.[2] It is being produced by the Clarendon Press in England and by Harpers in

America. It is just possible that I might abstract a section from my proofs. To do that I should have to obtain the consent of the Clarendon Press and as it happens I have not been able to get hold of the Secretary, who is not often in London. I cannot get down to Oxford for a week or two, so we must, if you do not mind, leave the matter in that state for the moment.

How glad you must be that you are out of Germany! You are by now thoroughly settled, and I expect Mrs. Sigerist also. Do give her our very kindest regards.

Is there any chance of your being in England this year? If so, do let us put you up.

Yours ever,

Charles Singer

[1] Singer contributed to Sigerist's *Bulletin of the History of Medicine* only occasionally in the 1940s.
[2] Singer (1941).

201

Singer to Sigerist, London, 12 June 1933

My dear Sigerist,

Many thanks for your note of May 25 introducing Pijoan.[1] I shall be delighted to do all I can for him.

I hope all goes well with you. I am staying on here all the summer. We shall be in Cornwall as usual from December till March but are otherwise pretty well settled here.

You are well away from Germany. The situation is hideous & growing worse. The country seems to be led by madmen. Best regards to you all.

Yours ever,

Charles Singer

My History of Science is at last in print[2]

[1] Sigerist's letter is missing. M. Pijoan, a physician at Peter Bent Brigham Hospital in Boston.
[2] Singer (1941).

202

Sigerist to Singer, Baltimore?, 26 October 1933

Dear Singer:

It was a great pleasure to read your letter of October 11th[1] and to hear that in future you will spend part of the year in the country. This is a splendid idea, and you may be sure that I shall visit you some day. I hope to be through with my work on the early mediaeval literature within a few years, but before this will be the case I will have to spend some time in England; and I of course am very anxious to consult your catalogue.[2]

I hope you received a copy of "The Great Doctors", if not, do not hesitate to let me know.[3] I also asked my publisher to send you a copy of my book on American medicine, which is my last German book. I began writing it in Leipzig before I had decided to settle in Amerika [sic], and this is why I wrote it in German. An English edition, however, is being done under my supervision and will be out next year.[4]

Things are developing very nicely here. At the present moment, Castiglioni is with us, giving the Noguchi Lectures.[5] I am working very hard on my mediaeval stuff. There will be three volumes, one a catalogue raisonné of all the Mss. that contain early medical texts; the second volume will be a collection of texts in critical editions, as far as such are possible; and the last volume will give a history of the literature of that period. It is a great burden that I have been carrying for more than ten years. In between, as a passe-temps, I am writing a Latin grammar for medical students, using exclusively the medical terminology. It is great fun. And then I am preparing for a trip to Russia. I am extremely interested in the development medicine is taking there, particularly in the philosophical and sociological background of the whole movement.[6]

So you see I am pretty busy, but this winter will be less strenuous than last winter when we had so many social engagements.

We had a very pleasant summer in Europe, but could not help being extremely depressed by the general poitical situation. Even in Switzerland, there are fascist parties; and there is a general unrest that is very disturbing. We are living through a period of experimental history, which is rather inconvenient for the individual, but certainly very fascinating for the historian.

With kind regards to Mrs. Singer and yourself, I am,

Very sincerely yours,

Henry E. Sigerist

---

[1] Singer's letter is missing.

[2] Catalogue unidentified, possibly Dorothea Singer's catalogue now held in the British Library, see letter 1, note 6.

[3] Henry E. Sigerist, *Great doctors*, English translation, (New York, 1933).

[4] Henry E. Sigerist, *American medicine*, English translation, (New York, 1934).

[5] Arturo Castiglioni (1874–1953), Italian medical historian; see Henry E. Sigerist, 'Arturo Castiglioni', *Bulletin of the History of Medicine*, 1953, 27: 387–389.

[6] Sigerist's three volumes of medieval medical texts did not materialize; in the mid 1930s his interests in sociology and health politics became predominant. His plan for a Latin grammar was given up too.

203

Sigerist to Singer, Baltimore?, 22 December 1933

Dear Singer:

This was a very delightful Christmas card, and Mrs. Sigerist and myself reciprocate your wishes most cordially.

I have a great favor to ask you. We intend to build up a picture gallery of all our Noguchi Lecturers, and as you and Mrs. Singer were the first Lecturers on this foundation, you would oblige me very much by sending me a photo of yourself and one of Mrs. Singer with your signatures and the name Noguchi Lecturer 1930 and 1932.

I am sure that you enjoy being in the country. It must be delightful down there, and I hope that I will be able to visit you some day.

With best wishes and kind regards, I am,

Very sincerely yours

Henry E. Sigerist

204

Sigerist to Singer, Baltimore?, 21 February 1934

Dear Singer:

May I ask you for a great favor? You know the Bulletin for the history of medicine that our Institute is publishing. The first volume has just been completed, and the first number of the second volume will be issued next month, and I think that we did quite well for the first year. The journal, of course, is far from being perfect, but I am trying to make it more and more interesting.

I have a good many Mss. ready for publication, and I think that the second volume promises to be quite good.

We are having some financial troubles at the present time. Due to losses in the endowments, I had to cut down the budget for the current year, and this affects particularly the funds available for publications. There is some hope that we may obtain a grant of about one thousand dollars from the National Academy of Sciences, which, of course, would help a great deal and enable me to go on with the Bulletin as before.

Dr. Raymond Pearl, Chairman of the Committee of Funds for Research Publications of the National Academy of Sciences (School of Hygiene and Public Health, Johns Hopkins University) with whom I had a long talk yesterday thought that a letter from you, addressed to him, would have great influence on the Members of the Committee.[1] I therefore would greatly appreciate if you would be good enough to write to Dr. Pearl what you think of our publication and whether you think it worth being supported.

You know what the conditions in this country are, the "Annals of Medical History" and "Medical Life" are both on a commercial basis, and are not the kind of journal that appeals to me. The Annals have so many Mss. that the writer has to wait two years before his paper is published. There undoubtedly is a strong need for a strictly scientific journal in the field. So far our Bulletin has been issued as a supplement to the Johns Hopkins Hospital Bulletin, but from January 1, 1935 on it will be an independent journal. We are already accepting subscriptions to the Bulletin[,] and the journal, of course, is not only open to Hopkins people but to every serious worker here and abroad.

May I add that the matter is rather urgent, as the Committee will decide on this question towards the end of March.

Thanks for your last letter.[2] I am trying to get a fellowship for Edelstein and have him work with us.[3] I think this would be the best solution. I feel exactly like you about Germany, and in all probability will not attend the Spanish Congress, as it will be too late in October.[4]

I envy you the mild climate of Cornwall. We are having a very cold winter this year.

With kind regards to Mrs. Singer and yourself, I am,

Very sincerely yours

Henry E. Sigerist.

---

[1] Raymond Pearl (1879–1940), American biologist. See Franklin Parker, 'Pearl, Raymond', *Complete dictionary of scientific biography*, Vol. 10 (Detroit: Charles Scribner's Sons, 2008), 444–445.

[2] This letter seems to be missing.

[3] Ludwig Edelstein (1902–1965), German classical scholar and medical historian, dismissed by Diepgen in Berlin 1933, he became Sigerist's co-worker in Baltimore; see Owsei Temkin, 'In memory of Ludwig Edelstein', *Bulletin of the History of Medicine*, 1966, **40**: 1–13.

[4] The Spanish Congress of the International Society of the History of Medicine, Madrid 1935.

205

Sigerist to Singer, Baltimore?, 8 March 1934

Dear Singer:

I know that you will be glad to hear that I have finally succeeded in obtaining sufficient money to provide for a salary for Dr. Edelstein.[1]

The Emergency Committee in Aid of Displaced German Scholars, in New York, has granted our university $1500 for the academic year 1934–1935, and I expect to obtain the same amount from the Rockefeller Foundation in New York, so that I shall be able to appoint Dr. Edelstein as an Associate in our department on July 1.

The grant is for one year, but I am confident that it will be renewed for the second year, and by then I feel sure that the Institute will be able to provide for Dr. Edelstein's salary out of its own funds.

I am very happy over the solution. In Europe there would have been no future for Dr. Edelstein, while I am sure that he will make a career in this country where philologists of his training and ability are rather scarce.

With kind regards, I am,

Very sincerely yours,

Henry E. Sigerist

[1] This letter is a fine example of both Singer's and Sigerist's efforts to help victims of the Nazi rule in Germany.

206

Sigerist to Singer, Baltimore?, 19 March 1934

Dear Singer:

It was very good of you to write to Dr. Pearl. You just said the right things, and I am sure that your letter will have great weight in the decisions of the Academy.[1]

As you know we started our Bulletin as an house-organ, but I intended to develop it gradually. I have accepted outside Mss. already and will do so more and more. From January 1, 1935, on we will be independent, and I intend to increase the number of pages considerably. I need not say that any contribution from you or Mrs. Singer will be extremely welcome at any time. It would be a great help, and would strengthen the authority of the journal to have you among the contributors.

Dr. Welch is doing relatively well.[2] He, of course, is weak and does hardly ever leave the bed, but he is mentally as alert as ever, interested in everything, and I am sure that a letter of yours would please him very much.

You have received our cable in the meantime. Both Dr. Welch and I are strongly opposed to an interim meeting in Berlin. I do not see any necessity for such a congress, and after all we know that the German idea is to make such a congress a big show for the purpose of propaganda.

With kind regards to Mrs. Singer and yourself, I am,

Very sincerely yours,

Henry E. Sigerist

[1] The National Academy of Sciences.

[2] William H. Welch (1850–1934), American pathologist, hygienist and medical historian; first director of the Hopkins Institute of the History of Medicine, i.e., Sigerist's predecessor. See Gert H. Brieger, 'Welch, William Henry', *Complete dictionary of scientific biography*, vol. 14 (Detroit: Charles Scribner's Sons, 2008), 248–250. For a biographical introduction and Sigerist's correspondence with Welch, see Marcel H. Bickel (ed.), *Henry E. Sigerist: Correspondences With Welch, Cushing, Garrison and Ackerknecht* (Bern: Peter Lang, 2010), 15–37.

207

Singer to Sigerist, Kilmarth, Cornwall, 20 March 1934

My dear Sigerist,

Enclosed is a copy of a letter that I have sent Mieli. Many thanks for your cable which I am communicating also to him.[1]

Yours ever,

Charles Singer

I have written separately to Welch, Sarton, Lynn Thorndike & Karpinski[2] all of whom I asked to cable to Mieli.

Kenyon[,] Holmyard & Steele[3] have all written from England protesting against a German meeting.[4]

[1] Sigerist's cable is missing.

[2] Louis C. Karpinski (1878–1956), American historian of mathematics. See Phillip S. Jones, 'Karpinski, Louis Charles', *Complete dictionary of scientific biography*, vol. 15, (Detroit: Charles Scribner's Sons, 2008), 255–257.

[3] Frederic Kenyon (1863–1952), British palaeographer; see H. I. Bell, 'Kenyon, Sir Frederic George (1863–1952)', rev. *Oxford dictionary of national biography* (Oxford: Oxford University Press, 2004), vol. 31, 341–343. Eric J.Holmyard (1891–1959), British historian of science and historian of alchemy; see Trevor I. Williams, 'Holmyard, Eric John (1891–1959)', rev. *Oxford dictionary of national biography* (Oxford: Oxford University Press, 2004), vol. 27, 810. Robert Steele (1860–1944), a member of the International Academy of the History of Science; see Dorothea Waley Singer, 'Robert Steele (1860–1944)', *Isis*, 1947, 38: 107–109.

[4] German meeting on the history of science.

208

Singer to Sigerist, Kilmarth, 26 March 1934

My dear Sigerist,

Many thanks for your letter of March 8th concerning Edelstein. I am greatly relieved to hear that you will be able to take him. It is good of you. As you rightly say, even if we succeeded in finding him temporary work in England, there would be no future for him here.

There is a matter of which, I think, I ought to write to you in confidence. When I cabled to you, I cabled also to Welch, Sarton & Karpinski. Knowing Thorndike to be "difficult", I awaited the other replies before cabling him. When I did cable to Thorndike, I added that you, Welch & Sarton agreed with me. I also added a specially adequate sum for reply so that Thorndike should be put to no possible expense.

At Paris the German suggestion was rejected. Only one person favoured it for Thorndike wired Mieli (in reply to my message & without informing me) "I am in favour of meeting in Germany".

Of course I know that Thorndike is a complicated & crotchetty old batchelor [sic], with a mysterious grievance & that he is "close" with his ideas, his money & his praise but I certainly did not think that he would be quite as mean as this.

I am writing in the same sense to Sarton. I think that you & he ought to know of Thorndike's mental state because it is evident that he might injure one of your projects. But having written it, I shall now make it my business to forget all about it. I certainly don't think that Thorndike carries much influence.

Have just had a very pleasant letter from Pearl. From it I gather that your scheme for a journal will go through. It certainly will be a comfort to have a proper journal of Med. Hist. More power to you!

Best regards,

Yours ever

Charles Singer

209

Sigerist to Singer, Baltimore?, 10 April 1934

Dear Dr. Singer:

Thanks for your letter of March 26. The whole situation is disgraceful. I wrote to Diepgen[1] and tried to make it clear why a congress in Germany is impossible at the present time. I wonder what has happened in Spain? You probably saw that Mieli has discharged the Spanish Committee. At any rate I am not concerned, as I will not attend the congress any way. I am tired of the whole business.

With kind regards, I am,

Very sincerely yours,

Henry E. Sigerist

[1] At this time, Diepgen was chairman of the Berlin Department of the History of Medicine.

210

Singer to Sigerist, Kilmarth, 28 April 1934a

My dear Sigerist

Your Bulletin just received. The Sudhoff material is interesting but your report on the Dark Ages is quite first class.[1] I do most heartily congratulate you on the splendid line of work you are carrying through. It will be a landmark in the history of scholarship. I wish I were younger for I might then hope to see the full results.

If in arranging your summer you could manage to come to us in Cornwall with your wife and family it would give us the greatest possible pleasure. It is a most lovely spot

& we have ample accomodation [sic] for such a party in this house & plenty of amusement for the children in our 16 acres. The bathing is quite perfect & safe for children &
the library is tolerably good & no bad place to work in. We are exactly 5 hours from
London. And we could commune on many things.

Yours ever

Charles Singer

---

[1] Henry E Sigerist, 'The medical literature of the Early Middle Ages. A program and a report of a summer of
research in Italy', *Bulletin of the History of Medicine*, 1934, 2: 26–50.

211

Singer to Sigerist, Kilmarth, 28 April 1934b

My dear Sigerist,

Obviously you ought to know all about this affair.[1]

I enclose copies of

(a) Letter received by me to-day from Diepgen

(b) My reply to Diepgen

(c) Covering letter to Mieli enclosing (a) & (b)

Yours ever,

Charles Singer

---

[1] A planned German congress on the history of science

212

Sigerist to Singer, Baltimore?, 11 May 1934

Dear Singer:

Thanks ever so much for your letter of April 28. I was very interested in reading the
copies of your and Diepgen's letters. I suppose the incident is closed with this. It is quite
obvious that the Congress in Germany is out of question under the present conditions.
I wrote a long letter to Diepgen about it and told him frankly what my position was.

It would have been delightful to spend some time with you in Cornwall, but, unfortunately, it will not be possible this year. We have rented a little house near Lucerne that
will serve as headquarters for the family; I myself have to travel a good deal on account
of my mediaeval work. I intend to spend June and July in France, Belgium, and Holland,
and September in Italy, mostly in Rome at the Vatican Library.

I greatly appreciate what you wrote about my mediaeval work. It was extremely encouraging. Some other summer I will spend several months in England, surveying the Mss. preserved there, and, of course, will start by consulting your catalogue.[1]

You will be interested in hearing that the National Academy of Sciences[2] has granted one thousand dollars to support our Bulletin, I therefore will be able to print about 600 pages this year. I am sure that your letter was very influential in the matter, and I am ever so much indebted to you for your help. I need not repeat that any paper of yours or Mrs. Singer's for the Bulletin will always be highly welcome and will be published within two months.

We are sailing on May 30 on a boat of the Baltimore Mail Line. While in Europe my permanent address will be my mother's residence, 182 St. Albanring, Basel.

With kind regards to Mrs. Singer and yourself, I am,

Very sincerely yours,

Henry E. Sigerist

[1] The months in England did not materialize because the Middle Ages became a minor subject; catalogue unidentified, but possibly Dorothea Singer's catalogue now held in the British Library, see letter 1, note 6.

[2] See letter 204.

213

Singer to Sigerist, London, 13 June 1934

My dear Sigerist,

I have just been reading your Summary on recent Hippocratic research in the Bulletin & I cannot refrain from writing to congratulate you on it.[1] I have seldom read so good an account of so difficult & intricate a subject. It was just what was wanted & is a real aid to scholarship as well as being most readable.

Such a summary is what I have always had in mind as an occasional[?] contribution to a scientific journal of the history of medicine. You have set us all an example.

I have lately been talking to the physiologists in London on a somewhat similar theme. Physiologists, nowadays, hardly understand each other. What a fine thing it would be if severe[?] scientific journals, such as the <u>Journal of Physiology</u> would, say twice a year, insert summaries of the state of knowledge in a particular branch. It might solve the crisis of mutual unintelligibility!

I shall use your article as an illustration of what I mean. But it will be difficult to keep up your standard.

I shall be in London until November. Should chance bring you this way please wire in advance. We are going to have a small flat in town but are not sure where. This house we have for only a few weeks. Cornwall always finds us.

Alas! There was no one to write to concerning Welch. He had a long and happy innings.[2] ??

Yours ever,

Charles Singer

Again I am so glad about Edelstein. It is good of you.

[1] Henry E. Sigerist, 'On Hippocrates', *Bulletin of the History of Medicine*, 1934, 2: 190–214.
[2] William H. Welch had died on 30 April 1934.

214

Sigerist to Singer, Kastanienbaum, Switzerland, 4 August 1934[1]

My dear Singer,

Thanks ever so much for your very kind letter of June 13th. I greatly appreciate your comment on my Hippocrates summary.[2] I am preparing another summary on archaeological contributions to medical history. Such summaries are particularly necessary in America where people do not know the European literature sufficiently.

I just had a very interesting trip through France and Belgium in search of early mediaeval material. I found some very important manuscripts particularly in Vendôme, a small provincial library that is open only on Sundays and Thursdays from 1–3. I had my Leica-camera and photographed myself more than 250 pages.

I am with my family in Switzerland now. We have rented a very nice house with a huge garden right on the lake. I wished you could visit us. We bathe every morning in the lake and I spend much time fishing. We will be here till beginning of September and will go to Italy then, where I will continue my work at the Vatican Library. We are sailing back from Naples on September 22nd.

I am very sorry that I will not be able to see you this year but I intend to be in England next year. I will spend several months in Russia in order to make a survey of Soviet medicine in which I am extremely interested. I will probably take one of the boats that sail from London to Leningrad.[3] Whenever I have a choice between a train and a boat I take the boat.

With best wishes from us all to you all I am

very sincerely yours

[Henry E. Sigerist]

[1] Kastanienbaum, a village near Lucerne.
[2] Sigerist (1934c).
[3] Leningrad, former name of St. Petersburg.

215

Singer to Sigerist, Kilmarth, 10 November 1934

My dear Sigerist,

Would you be so very kind as to pass the enclosed communication on to your gynae-cological colleague. You can refer him to me, if you like.

I understand that Fraenkel is a man of very great distinction & a good lecturer.[1] He is not in any want & his age precludes all question of his seeking a post. It is in this sense only that he is "unsatisfactory from the office point of view"!!

As you will see he already has lecture engagements in USA. He is, I understand, not dismissed but just retired on the ordinary age basis.

On the whole the work of settling the unfortunate Academic refugees goes better than we at first thought. Places of at least a temporary character have now been found for about one third of the Academics. It might be worse. Harder cases than Academics are students. Very young graduates can often be used in tropical or unsettled countries but the position of the student is very hard.

You will be interested to hear that Pagel's son is fairly comfortably settled in England. A tiny salary but just enough to live on & a reasonable hope of permanency – & peace, poor fellow![2]

Very sincerely yours,

Charles Singer

[1] Ludwig Fraenkel (1870–1951) German researcher in gynaecology, dismissed by the Nazis; see H. H. Simmer, 'The first experiments to demonstrate an endocrine function of the corpus luteum. On the occasion of the 100th birthday of Ludwig Fraenkel (1870–1951)', *Sudhoffs Archiv*, 1971, **55**(4): 392–417, note 1, 413–414.
[2] Walter Pagel (1898–1983) was Sigerist's pupil in Leipzig, a pathologist in Heidelberg and England, and a medical historian; see Marianne Winder, 'Pagel, Walter Traugott Ulrich (1898–1983)', *Oxford dictionary of national biography* (Oxford: Oxford University Press, 2004), vol. 42, 336–337. His father, Julius L. Pagel (1851–1912) was a German medical historian; see Walter Pagel, 'Julius Pagel and the significance of medical history for medicine', *Bulletin of the History of Medicine*, 1951, **25**: 207–225.

216

Sigerist to Singer, Baltimore?, 26 November 1934

Dear Singer:

I was glad to receive your letter of November 10, and passed it on to Dr. Cullen, our professor of gynaecology. I do not know what will come out of it. Our lecture funds are rather limited; still there may be a possibility, and I certainly will welcome having Dr. Fraenkel here for a while.

Dr. Edelstein is doing exceedingly well, and I hope that he will feel happy in America. I am trying to make his position at the Institute permanent, and I hope that I will succeed.

I am in touch with Pagel. He just sent me a long paper for publication.[1] I am so glad that he is able to continue his historical work besides the work he is doing in pathology.

With best wishes to Mrs. Singer and yourself, I am

Very sincerely yours,

Henry E. Sigerist

[1] Walter Pagel, 'Religious motives in the medical biology of the XVIIth Century', *Bulletin of the History of Medicine*, 1935, **3**: 97−128, 213−231, 265−314.

217

Sigerist to Singer, Baltimore?, 1 December 1934

Dear Singer:

I just received the enclosed letter of our professor of gynaecology,[1] and I am very sorry that there is no chance of our inviting Dr. Fraenkel at the present time.

However, I have your letter concerning Dr. Fraenkel on file, and will see if I can do something for him in some other place.

Very sincerely yours,

Henry E. Sigerist

[1] Thomas S. Cullen, (1868−1953), Canadian-American gynaecologist; see H. Speert, 'Memorable medical mentors: VI. Thomas S. Cullen (1868−1953)', *Obstetrical & Gynecological Survey*, 2004, 59: 557−63, and Judith Robinson, *Tom Cullen of Baltimore* (London; New York: Oxford University Press, 1949).

218

Sigerist to Singer, Baltimore?, 2 January 1935

Dear Singer:

Your Christmas card was most delightful, and it gave a splendid picture of the region where you are living. I wish I could visit you there.

Please let me know where you will be in May. I am thinking of taking a boat in London for Leningrad on May 25th, and will arrange to spend about a week in England before sailing. I very much hope to be able to see you then.

With kind regards to Mrs. Singer and yourself, I am

Very sincerely yours,

Henry E. Sigerist

219

Singer to Sigerist, Kilmarth, 9 January 1935

My dear Sigerist,

I have to day had the enclosed letter from the Nonesuch Press.[1] As you are doubtless aware the publications of that press are unexcelled for artistic merit. I enclose my answer which explains itself.

I am, of course, anxious to see some such project[2] carried through & would do all I can to help it & to avoid overlapping.

Farrington is, I think, going to settle in England for a year or two.[3] He is a quiet industrious worker & is dissatisfied with Cape Town. I rather think that he means to undertake a major piece of research before looking for another post. (He is professor of classics & is a product of Trinity College, Dublin.)

I need hardly say that I would help him or you or both of you in this matter in any way in my power. My only desire is to see the table[?] brought to a satisfactory conclusion.

Do let me hear how you [....] as regards Vesalius & what you would like me to do with the Nonesuch & with Farrington.

Yours ever

Charles Singer

I have not mentioned in my letter to Meynell the project of William Wright.[4] Much of the translation of the book on the nervous system is, I believe, in type but Wright will never finish it. I am in hopes that he will hand it over to Farrington or, alternatively, join hands with Farrington or you.

[1] Nonesuch Press, London.
[2] A Vesalius edition.
[3] Benjamin Farrington (1891–1974), Professor of Latin at the University of Cape Town; in 1936 he was appointed Professor of Classics at Swansea University. See Yasmina Benferhat, 'Farrington, Benjamin', in Robert B. Todd (ed.), *The dictionary of British classicists*, 3 vols (Bristol: Thoemmes Continuum, 2004), vol. 1, 314–315.
[4] Mr. Meynell from Nonesuch Press. William Wright (1874- 1937), Professor of Anatomy and former Dean of the London Hospital Medical College; see 'William Wright', *British Medical Joural*, 1937, **ii**: 881–882. This letter may be the answer to a missing letter from Sigerist.

220

Singer to Sigerist, Kilmarth, 10 January 1935

My dear Sigerist,

Thanks for your note of January 2. I shall certainly be in London throughout May & entirely at your service. The best place to address me is

The Athenaeum

Pall Mall

London SW1

Telegram <u>Hellenist,</u> <u>London</u>

The Athenaeum will always forward letters or telegrams & I am often staying there & nearly always have lunch there when I am in London.

There are a hundred things that I want to talk to you about & I am very glad indeed to hear that I shall have an opportunity.

Very sincerely yours,

Charles Singer

221

Singer to Sigerist, Kilmarth, 23 January 1935

My dear Sigerist.

Very many thanks for your really splendid packet of reprints. I have never had such a batch of good stuff & so many articles in it that do get things on a bit. I most cordially felicitate you on your success.

Can you ginger up Larkey to write to me? We have written to him several times but don't seem to be able to extract an answer.

Is there any chance of seeing you in London this year? Do let me know in good time if there is. The centenary of London University is to be celebrated in June-July[.] I think perhaps that will bring you. Personally I hate these mobs; & ceremonies merely bore me; but if they bring you, I shall be grateful.

What a gunpowder magazine the world is & in what a rotten state Christianity is. Every evening as I turn on the wireless I expect to hear that the great explosion has taken place! Study is at least a comfort & a refuge.

This place is lovely and peaceful as ever. It will be some explosion that disturbs Cornwall where everyone is asleep and desires only to continue to sleep!

Again congratulations.

Yours always

Charles Singer

I suppose there is no idea of any larger account of Garrison? I have a few interesting letters from him.

222

Singer to Sigerist, Kilmarth, 27 January 1935

My dear Sigerist

Just a line to congratulate you

(a) On the excellent and most readable account of your European journey[1]

(b) On this [....] termination of the Bulletin

(c) On the prospective arrival of the new journal.

I have just read this last issue & cannot put it down without writing you a line of good wishes.

Mind you let me know as early as possible as to the date of your arrival in London & the time you will have free. Appointments accumulate at that time of year but I shall set everything aside for you.

Again best wishes & congratulations.

Yours always

Charles Singer

---

[1] Henry E. Sigerist, 'A summer of research in European libraries', *Bulletin of the History of Medicine*, 1934, **2**: 559–610.

223

Sigerist to Singer, Baltimore?, 28 January 1935

Dear Singer:

I read the letter of the Nonesuch Press and your answer to it with great interest. I quite agree with you that some kind of English edition of Vesalius would be extremely welcome, and should have a good market. I also agree with you that a complete translation of the whole Fabrica is not advisable. It would be a tremendous job to make it, and I do not think that there is anybody who would ever read it.[1]

I have dropped the idea of doing anything in the subject myself as I am busy with other plans, but I know that a great deal of work is being done on Vesalius in this country at the present time.

I would recommend the Nonesuch Press to get in touch, first of all, with the New York Academy of Medicine, which is publishing the Vesalian plates from the original woodblocks preserved in Munich, and which intends to publish some other Vesaliana. Then, I know that Dr. Cushing is considering an English translation of the Epitome. Finally, Dr. Sanford Larkey, at the University of California, has done some work on Nicholas Udall,[2] and I know that he would like to have this translation reprinted some day.

It seems to me very important that overlapping be avoided, and I think that Farrington should get in touch with Larkey, Cushing and Dr. Malloch[3] of the New York Academy so that the different efforts could be integrated. I am sure that all people concerned would greatly appreciate the cooperation of a Press of such high standing as the Nonesuch Press.

I was glad to hear that you will be in London at the end of May. I shall let you know in time when I expect to be there, as I am most anxious to see you.

With kind regards, I am

Very sincerely yours,

Henry E. Sigerist

---

[1] *De humani corporis fabrica*, the main work of Vesalius. See *On the fabric of the human body: a translation of De humani corporis fabrica libri septem*. Books I-VII, [translated] by William Frank Richardson in collaboration with John Burd Carman (San Francisco / Novato: Norman, 1998–2009).

[2] Nicholas Udall (1504–1556) English playwright and schoolmaster; see Matthew Steggle, 'Udall, Nicholas (1504–1556)', *Oxford dictionary of national biography* (Oxford: Oxford University Press, 2004), vol. 55, 851–853.

[3] Archibald N. Malloch (1887–1953) librarian at the New York Academy of Medicine; see Claude Edwin Heaton, 'Archibald Malloch, M.D.–1887–1953', *Bulletin of the New York Academy of Medicine*, 1954, **30**: 399–401.

224

Singer to Sigerist, Kilmarth, 5 February 1935

My dear Sigerist,

When last I wrote to you, I forgot to call you [sic] attention to the fact that London is likely to be very full & uncomfortable in the first week in May. The date May 6th is the jubilee of the King's accession & is a special public holiday.[1] There are great preparations being made to celebrate this event, & the celebrations are of the kind that conduce to academic quiet or to empty hotels!

Thought you would just like to know this.

Yours as always,

Charles Singer

The second week in May will, I think, be quite all right.

---

[1] King George V (reigned 1910–1936).

225

Sigerist to Singer, Baltimore?, 25 February 1935

Dear Singer:

Thanks for your good letters. I was glad to hear that you liked the paper on my last summer's trip. I wrote it on the spot while travelling and had great fun in doing it.[1]

The BULLETIN is now published as an independent journal. It was taken over by the Johns Hopkins Press, and I only regret that I have no complimentary copies to send to my friends.

I had to postpone my sailing until May 25th. We are sailing on the French liner, Champlain, and will be in Paris on June 1st. I am sailing from London to Leningrad on June 8th, so that, in all probability, I shall be in London about June 5th. I shall get in touch with you from Paris where I shall be staying at the Hotel Louvois.

Please tell Mrs. Singer that I will write her soon about the mediaeval Glossary. We are preparing a plan which I shall submit to her.

With kind regards, I am

Very sincerely yours,

Henry E. Sigerist

[1] Sigerist (1934d).

226

Singer to Sigerist, Kilmarth, 19 April 1935

You have not sent me any Prospectus of the new Bulletin – prices etc. I have had one or two enquiries concerning it. Perhaps you can let me have one. Looking forward to seeing you.

Charles Singer

227

Sigerist to Singer, Baltimore?, 2 May 1935

Dear Singer:

I am sorry that we have no Prospectus of the new Bulletin left, but I have a few odd numbers that I am sending under separate cover. You will find there on the second page of the cover all the information you want.

I am looking forward with great pleasure to seeing you soon. I am sailing from London on June 8th, and will arrive there a few days before. I will let you know the exact date from Paris.

You may have heard that Garrison died quite unexpectedly [. . .].[1] His last years were rather pathetic. He was director of the Library[2] but was not interested at all in library administration; and his historical work became more and more superficial. However, he has done a great deal in stimulating interest in medical history in America.

With kind regards to you both, I am
Very sincerely yours,
Henry E. Sigerist

---

[1] Two and a half sentences deleted as Protected Health Information of the Alan Mason Chesney Medical Archive of the Johns Hopkins Medical Institutions.
[2] The Welch Medical Library of Johns Hopkins University.

228

Singer to Sigerist, Kilmarth, 17 July 1935

My dear Sigerist,

I hope that all goes well with you & I am sure that you have had a very interesting Russian trip.

Did you see the biologist Schaxel or Schacksel[1] & has he [....] through his scheme for appointing an [....] of biology?

Yesterday there came to me G.E.Gask who is professor of Surgery at St. Bartholomew's (full time).[2] He has recently been reading your book on American Medicine & admires it greatly.[3] He very much wants to meet you. He and several others are wondering whether it would be possible to tempt you to come to London, if only for one day in September. If you could manage this we would arrange for about $\frac{1}{2}$ dozen people to meet you – all people who are particularly anxious to hear your news on medicine & the history of medicine as a department of Sociology. I think that such a meeting of half a dozen people would be far better than a larger gathering. I said I would write to you to find out if it would be at all possible.

Please do not forget when you are in Zürich to consider the question of the German publication of The Legacy of Israel edited by Bevan and myself.[4] [....] will remember that we discussed it. Orell-Fussli have the MS & the original book which is very beautifully illustrated.[5] The original blocks are of course available. German pressure has evidently been put on Fussli not to produce the book.

Very best regards [to] your wife and family from us all.

Yours ever
Charles Singer

Am very glad to hear that Larkey will join you at Baltimore.[6]

---

[1] Julius Schaxel (1887–1943), German biologist in Soviet Russia; see Christian Reiss, 'No evolution, no heredity, just development—Julius Schaxel and the end of the Evo–Devo agenda in Jena, 1906–1933: a case study', *Theory in Biosciences*, 2007, **126**: 155–164.

[2] St. Bartholomew's Hospital in London. George Ernest Gask (1875–1951), surgeon; see J. P. Ross, 'Gask, George Ernest (1875–1951)', rev. *Oxford dictionary of national biography* (Oxford: Oxford University Press, 2004), vol. 21, 600–601.

[3] Sigerist (1934a).
[4] Bevan and Singer (1927).
[5] Orell Fussli, a publisher in Zurich and Leipzig.
[6] As head of the Welch Medical Library, i.e. as successor to Garrison.

229

Sigerist to Singer, Baltimore?, 15 October 1935

My dear Singer:

I have not reported yet on the correspondence I had with Orell Füssli in Zürich. The situation is this; that they will not consider the publication of a German translation of your Legacy of Israel for the time being.[1] They would be willing to deliver the manuscript for one thousand Swiss francs if another publisher could be found. My general impression is that it will hardly be possible to find a Swiss publisher willing to do the job. The crisis is very serious in Switzerland now, and all the publishers I saw seemed very much discouraged.

We missed you very much in Madrid.[2] Scientifically, the Congress did not amount to much but Spain was lovely at this time of year. I also enjoyed meeting Sir Humphry Rolleston whom I had never seen before.

We came back a few days ago on the Berengaria, and I am starting my courses this week.

With kind regards to Mrs. Singer and yourself, I am
Very sincerely yours,
Henry E. Sigerist

[1] Bevan and Singer (1927).
[2] Congress of the International Society of the History of Medicine.

230

Singer to Sigerist, Kilmarth, 30 October 1935

Personal

My dear Sigerist,

Many thanks for your letter of Oct 15 concerning Orell Füssli of Zürich.

But you do not tell me what I really want to know & perhaps you cannot tell me. Füssli had already written me that they were willing to sell me the MS for 1000 Swiss Francs. And I had already offered them a subsidy for publishing. Therefore their objection to publish is not economic – or not directly so.

What I want to know is whether their objection to publish is the result of Nazi pressure from Germany. I can see that if a firm's publications were boycotted in Germany, no subsidy would recompense them. But what I want to know, in plain English, is whether this is the case or not. I expect you cannot tell me.

I have during the last week received three independent, direct, & 'Aryan' visitors

from Germany, 2 from Berlin, one from Munich. Most presents[?] [....] Germany have not come off but there is no doubt any longer of food shortage. A lady who left Berlin 36 hours ago & is returning next week told me last night that for her household of eleven she could only secure $\frac{1}{4}$ pound of butter a day. All the booksellers tell me that business with Germany is almost impossible owing to exchange difficulties. One obvious difficulty is that a German creditor cannot now sue an English debtor. Other trades are similarly affected & I am pretty confident that the published German Import-Export figures must be faked. Looks as though something dramatic might happen in Germany this winter. But who knows what?

Yours ever,

Charles Singer

231

Sigerist to Singer, Baltimore?, 7 November 1935

Dear Singers:

My friend and colleague, Prof. L. C. MacKinney, hardly needs an introduction.[1] I am sure that you have read his remarkable papers published in our Bulletin, Isis, and quite a few other places. Prof. MacKinney is professor of mediaeval history at the University of North Carolina and is spending his sabbatical year in Europe investigating mediaeval manuscripts.

He is most anxious to meet you and to be able to consult your catalogue.[2] Any assistance you can give him will be greatly appreciated, and I am sure that you will enjoy making his acquaintance.

With kind regards, I am

Very sincerely yours,

Henry E. Sigerist

[1] Loren C. MacKinney (1891–1963), see *Journal of the History of Medicine and Allied Sciences*, 1964, **19**: 73–74.

[2] Catalogue unidentified but possibly Dorothea Singer's catalogue now held in the British Library, see letter 1, note 6.

232

Sigerist to Singer, Baltimore ?, 11 November 1935

My dear Singer:

Thanks for your letter of October 30th. I am sorry that I can not give you any further information as to Orell Füssli's attitude. All they told me was that they could not undertake to publish the book for financial reasons, but I am sure that your guess is correct that they do not want to commit themselves. They are primarily printers; their chief job is to print posters and bank-notes and other commercial prints. They are probably afraid of losing business in Germany if they were to publish a book on a Jewish subject. However, they did not mention this to me at all.

From all I hear the situation in Germany is becoming more and more tense. One interesting symptom is that I am receiving now letters from purely Aryan professors and physicians who want to leave the country as they can not stand it any longer. However, one should not be too optimistic. The German people can stand great hardships, and the opposition seems so disorganized that even open enemies of the régime dread a change. It is a most up-setting situation.

Very sincerely yours,
Henry E. Sigerist

233

Singer to Sigerist, Kilmarth, 1 December 1935

Confidential

My dear Sigerist,

I had a letter from Sarton a few days ago in which he said, incidentally, that Feldhaus had written to him in great distress.[1]

In 1931 De Thierry of Berlin[2] showed me Feldhaus' horrible police record. I don't suppose the record has much improved since! I heard about a year ago that Feldhaus was now a recognised agent of the present German government. So it looks likes rogues falling out.

I therefore cabled to Sarton not to answer Feldhaus & wrote to him explaining the situation.

I find an enquiry that Feldhaus' record is well known in London.

This letter is merely to warn you in case Feldhaus tries to impose on kind hearted people in America.

It appears that Feldhaus' present address is

Sachsenring 27, Berlin-Tempelhof.

I knew that you know Feldhaus' record much better than I do. It is evidently a case of what Kossina[3] calls "an un-Nordic soul in a Nordic body". I have not seen his soul but I never saw a more Nordic looking man!

Best wishes from
Yours always,
Charles Singer

Have just had a letter from young A. W. Franklin who tells me he has been writing you.[4] You have, perhaps, heard of the really dreadful tragedy in which his mother, his aunt & their 2 servants were burnt to death in a fire in their home in the heart of the doctors quarters in London. He enjoyed his visit [....] immensely.

[1] For Feldhaus see letter 179.
[2] De Thierry not identified.
[3] Kossina, possibly Gustav, a (Nazi) archaeologist.
[4] Alfred White Franklin (1905–1984), founder of the Osler Club of London; see 'A W Franklin FRCP', *British Medical Journal*, 1984, **289**: 1082, and 'Alfred White Franklin', in Gordon Wolstenholme (ed.), *Lives of the Fellows of the Royal College of Physicians*, (Oxford: IRL Press, 1982), vol 8, 166–167.

234

Sigerist to Singer, Baltimore?, 19 December 1935

My dear Singer:

I was glad you wrote me about Feldhaus. I know the fellow, and you can be sure that I will keep him off. He is the most disagreeable type of man I have ever met, and I certainly will not have anything to do with him.

I heard of the tragedy that had befallen Franklin's family and was very much upset by it. You would not think that this could happen in our day.

With best wishes for Christmas and the New Year to yourself and family, I am
Very sincerely yours,
Henry E. Sigerist

235

Sigerist to Singer, Baltimore?, 5 February 1936

My dear Singer:

Thanks ever so much for your letter of January 23rd.[1] I greatly appreciate your comments on our work. I have neglected to send out reprints for a long time but now in the future they will be mailed to you regularly three times a year.

I talked to Larkey and he will write you soon. He was terribly busy in the last few months reorganizing the library which was very necessary indeed.[2]

I am going back to Russia and as I found the Soviet boat very pleasant, I will travel by the same route and will spend a few days in London. I do not know the date yet but in all probability it will be in the first part of June. I will let you know the date as soon as I have my reservation.

We intend to devote a number of the Bulletin to the memory of Garrison. This number will contain Garrison's bibliography and a number of papers giving an appreciation of the various aspects of his life and work.[3] It would be very nice indeed if you could contribute a paper in which you could publish the letters you mentioned.

I envy you your country place. We are living in a constant rush here and I can not do any serious work except at night.

With kind regards to Mrs. Singer and yourself, I am
Very sincerely yours,
Henry E. Sigerist

[1] Singer's letter seems to be missing.
[2] Larkey was now head of the Welch Library in Baltimore as Garrison's successor.
[3] Henry E. Sigerist, Fielding H. Garrison Memorial Number. *Bulletin of the History of Medicine*, 1937, 5: 299ff.

236

Singer to Sigerist, Kilmarth, 24 February 1936

My dear Sigerist,

You will be puzzled at my various telegrams, though I dare say you have now worked out their meaning.[1]

What happened was this. The responsible bodies at Oxford and Cambridge decided not to send representatives to Heidelberg. At that time I wired to you to that effect. It then appeared that their decisions needed formal confirmation by the general body of teachers. I was told that it might do harm if it leaked out that I had conveyed the information. I therefore sent my second telegram. There is to be a general meeting of Vice-Chancellors on March 6th. I therefore gave March 7th as the date on which I would write.

Since then the decision of Oxford, Cambridge and Birmingham, the Royal Society and the British Academy have been made known publicly. All have decided against sending a representative. I therefore sent you my third telegram.

The actual history is as follows: -

The first university to decide was Birmingham. This is one of the best of our new universities. The Senate of Birmingham decided that under no circumstances would they send a representative. They were unanimous. They decided, moreover, that they would not alter their decision whatever the other universities would do.

The next body to decide was the Council of the Cambridge Senate. They decided not to send a representative and to await confirmation by the general body of teachers.

The next body to decide was the Royal Society. They decided not to send a representative but to send a message which would in effect be a message of protest.

The next body to decide was the British Academy. They decided not to send a representative and to send a message that they could not send a representative as to do so would
be contrary to their principles and would cause embarrassment alike to Heidelberg & the
representative.

Lastly came the news of Oxford which has now decided both by its Inner Council and
published [....] not to send a representative but to send a message which will express
admiration for what Heidelberg has been and hope for what it will be again. You may
take it that the other universities will follow suit. In fact, not all have been asked.

I enclose a little pamphlet, the proof of which has just reached me, together with a cutting from this week's <u>Nature</u> which may interest you & a letter for next week's <u>Nature</u>.[2]

I will let you have something about Garrison as soon as I can get to it.[3]

With best regards,

Yours always,

Charles Singer

---

[1] This letter explains three telegrams of Singer, hard to understand and therefore left out. The background is the
550th year of the University of Heidelberg, likely to become a Nazi show.

[2] Singer's letter to the editor of *Nature* was published anonymously in 1936 as 'Heidelberg, Spinoza and
academic freedom', *Nature*, 1936, **137**: 303–304.

[3] Singer did not contribute to the Garrison number of the *Bulletin of the History of Medicine*.

237

Sigerist to Singer, Baltimore?, 2 March 1936

Dear Singer:

I wish to thank you for your cables.[1] I am, of course, very pleased with the decision of
the British universities. I spread the news as much as I could and, besides there was a note
in the papers about it the other day. I do not know yet what the attitude of the American
universities will be. I have not heard anything about it, and I do not think that our university has been invited. However, I feel confident that the American universities will adopt
an attitude similar to yours.

I have just booked my passage on the Normandie for May 27th, and I shall be sailing
from London to Leningrad on June 6th. I shall therefore be in London at about the same
time as last year.

With kind regards to you both, I am

Very sincerely yours,

Henry E. Sigerist

---

[1] See previous letter.

238

Singer to Sigerist, Kilmarth, 2 March 1936

My dear Sigerist,

I have to-day addressed a letter of which I enclose a copy to Professors Laistner, Burr & [....] Smith of Cornell University.[1]

Read clause 17 of my letter particularly careful. The whole thing is a swindle!

You are welcome to publish this letter or any part of it, with my name or without it. The more these things are known the better.

I enclose a few recent pamphlets etc.

Yours always,

Charles Singer

If there is anyone to whom you think I ought to write in America, please let me know. You can cable if you like just giving name. My telegraphic address is Singer, Par, England.

[1] M. L. W. Laistner (1890–1959), Professor of ancient history at Cornell University; see Harry Caplan, Ernst H. Kantorowicz and Gaines Post, 'Max Ludwig Wolfram Laistner', *Speculum*, 1960, **35**: 520. George L. Burr (1857–1938), Professor of history at Cornell University, see Roland H. Bainton, *George Lincoln Burr: His life; Selections from His Writings*, edited by Lois Oliphant Gibbons (Ithaca, N.Y.: Cornell University Press, 1943), and Henry Guerlac, 'George Lincoln Burr', *Isis*, 1944, **35**: 147–152. P.[?] Smith not identified. Cornell University agreed to send a representative to Heidelberg. Singer's opposition was based on the fact that a large number of teachers of the University of Heidelberg had been dismissed by the Nazis for racial and other reasons.

239

Singer to Sigerist, Kilmarth, 3 March 1936

My dear Sigerist,

The enclosed extract from the central page of to-days Times is almost too good to be true![1]

And the invitations have only been withdrawn from England!

Just think what it amounts to. "Because all the people that I have invited have refused, therefore I withdraw their invitations". A naughty child of 8 in a bad temper could work up a better story than the rector of Heidelberg. What clumsy creatures the Germans are. They can always be trusted to make a gaff. But I never hoped for anything as good as this. Unbelievable isn't it?

I thought that I would let you know at once.

Yours ever,

Charles Singer

[1] *The Times* printed a letter from the Rector of Heidelberg University to British universities and academies retracting the invitations to the 550th anniversary celebrations; 'The Heidelberg invitations withdrawn from British universities', *The Times*, Tuesday, 3 Mar 1936, p.16.

240

Sigerist to Singer, Baltimore?, 9 March 1936

Dear Singer:

Thanks for your letter of February 24th and for your documents which I read with a great deal of interest. In the meantime, I heard that Harvard and Cornell have accepted the invitation of Heidelberg, and that Yale is hesitating. As far as I know, our university has not been invited.

Yours ever,

Henry E. Sigerist

241

Singer to Sigerist, Kilmarth, 21 March 1936

My dear Sigerist,

I have just been reading your letter to Sarton.[1] Bravo! I am sure you have got to the root of the matter. And most amusing. My wife also read it & enjoyed it very much.

I enclose typed copies of mine of Garrisons [sic] letters. I have probably a few more some where. Make any use that you like of them & print any part of them that you think proper. Obviously you cannot print all or you would be prosecuted for libel!

The proper place for the originals is the Johns Hopkins Library. Ordinarily I should have presented them but it occurred to me that if the Library would buy them, I could present the amount to the Academic Assistance Council & do something to help German scholars. What do you think of the idea? Can you buy them & would you give twenty pounds for them? I do not think that there was anyone else to whom Garrison wrote so intimately.

The situation in Europe looks perhaps a little less black than it did. It is so very difficult to get real information as to the economic state of Germany but the best hope of Europe would be the outbreak of anarchy in Germany. For three years now, however, we have been told that Germany must break down economically but it does not come. Nevertheless the opinion still seems to be that it is really coming. Only last week a responsible man who had seen Hitler was talking at the Institute of International Affairs & said openly that the man was insane. But I wish he would hurry up & declare that he was a poached egg, or Mahomet, or Frederick Barbarossa[2] or something really silly like that.

Your paper is very depressing as well as very amusing.[3]

Yours ever,

Charles Singer

I am to have an Honorary Degree at Oxford – which is quite an honour & heaven knows why!

[1] An open letter to Sarton. Henry E. Sigerist, 'The history of medicine and the history of science. An open letter to George Sarton', *Bulletin of the History of Medicine*, 1936, **4**: 1−13.
[2] Barbarossa, the German emperor Frederick I (1122−1190).
[3] Sigerist (1936), mentioned above.

242

Singer to Sigerist, Kilmarth, 24 March 1936

My dear Sigerist,

I have just received a Dutch newspaper with a passage of which enclosed is a translation. You will be interested.

I cannot read Dutch but it happened that yesterday there came into Par harbour a very small Dutch tramp steamer. I called on the Captain (an educated man) & asked him to translate it. His delight at finding that the Dutch Universities have refused Heidelberg was really quite comic!

I have written to the Presidents of Columbia, Harvard & Yale.

Yours ever,

Charles Singer

243

Sigerist to Singer, Baltimore?, 3 April 1936

Dear Singer:

Thanks ever so much for your letter of March 21st, and for the copies of the Garrison letters.[1] I will make a selection and will submit it to you before it goes to print. This, however, will not be before next winter.

I wished we could purchase the originals but unfortunately this is impossible as we are perfectly broke. We had $8,500 less this year and next year we will have $3,000 less in addition. The grant for Dr. Edelstein will not be renewed and I can only keep him by cutting our salaries which have been cut once before. The situation is very critical, but still we can not complain as we have some money left. The academic division of the University, however, is in a hopeless situation. All the young instructors have been discharged, departments are being closed, and vacancies are not filled. The whole Greek division consists at the present time of one instructor. The University is starting a drive for not less than $10,750,000[?] but I do not think that there is any chance in the world that they will get a fraction of it.

I am glad that you enjoyed my letter to Sarton but you are quite right that it is a depressing story after all.[2]

Congratulations on the honorary degree. You deserve it more than anyone I know.

With kind regards, I am

Very sincerely yours,

Henry E. Sigerist

---

[1] See letter 241.

[2] See letter 241; Sigerist (1936)

244

Singer to Sigerist, Kilmarth, 11 April 1936

My dear Sigerist,

Thanks for your letter of April 3. The Welch Institute is surely the proper resting place for the Garrison letters & I enclose them.[1] Please accept them with all my good wishes for the work[?] of you and your colleagues & for the growing success of the Institute itself. I believe that Garrison himself would wish for this fate of them.

I am looking forward to seeing you as you come through London. I had an idea of putting to you a scheme for publication which is evidently now impossible. J. H. G. Grattan (now professor of Anglo Saxon in Liverpool) has been working with me on the text of Lacnunga (the A.S. text in the 3rd vol. of Cochayne [sic]) for 14 years now![2] We really are bringing it to an end & had thought of offering it to the J. H . Bulletin for publication as a separate work. I suppose this is now out of the question. I had an idea that you had a special publication fund but I expect this too has gone to glory!

I am very sorry indeed to learn the bad news of the state[?] of the JH finances.

I enclosed typed translations of two recent German imbecillities. You may care to have them retyped and circulated. The more widely these things are known the better.

If there is anyone in America to whom you think it would be useful for me to write concerning Heidelberg in particular or concerning the German university situation in general, or who would like literature on the subject, do please let me know. I will gladly do what I can.

Many thanks for congratulations on my honorary degree at Oxford.

With best regards,

Yours ever

Charles Singer

---

[1] The Welch Library or Institute of the History of Medicine. For Garrison letters see letter 241.

[2] John Henry Grafton Grattan (1878–1951), held the Baines Chair of English Language and Philology at Liverpool University from 1930 to 1943. The Lacnunga ('Remedies') is a collection of miscellaneous Anglo-Saxon medical texts; they were published as Charles Singer and John H. G. Grattan, *Anglo-Saxon magic and medicine* (London, 1952).

245

Sigerist to Singer, Baltimore?, 23 April 1936

My dear Singer:

Thanks ever so much for the Garrison letters. They are greatly appreciated.

I wished we could have printed the text of <u>Lacnunga</u>,[1] but at the present time I am sorry to say that it is out of question. We have no special publication fund, and we have to print the Bulletin on the general Institute budget. Fortunately the number of subscribers, although not large, is steadily increasing which reduces the burden gradually. The Noguchi lectures are taken care of by the Noguchi fund, but for printing other publications I have to go around begging.[2] I hope to be able to publish d'Irsay's "History of Physiology" which is a good piece of work, but so far I have not found the money yet.[3]

We are sailing on May 26th on the Normandie. I have to spend a few days in Paris and expect to be in London on June 4th toward evening. On June 6th, the boat for Leningrad will be sailing.

I am sorry that I can not stay longer in England, but the trouble is that the vacations begin in Russia on July 1st, and after that date is is [sic] impossible to find the people. They all go to the country.

I intend to be in Switzerland by the end of July and to spend two quiet months there doing some writing without being constantly disturbed as I am here.

I very much hope that I shall have a chance to see you in London.

With kind regards, to Mrs. Singer and yourself, I am

Very sincerely yours,

Henry E. Sigerist

[1] See previous letter.
[2] See letter 199.
[3] Stephen d'Irsay, (1894–1934), physiologist and medical historian of Hungarian origin, and Sigerist's former co-worker in Leipzig; see Henry E. Sigerist, 'Stephen d'Irsay, 1894–1934', *Bulletin of the Institute of the History of Medicine*, 1935, **3**: (1935), 431–442.

246

Singer to Sigerist, Kilmarth, 5 May 1936

My dear Sigerist,

Thanks for yours of April 23. As you are for so short a time in London would you like me to get you a room near me or, if possible, in the same house?

Please answer me to

15 Palace Court

London W2

which is where I stay. It is conveniently placed, near the tube, 5 minutes from Oxford Circus, quite quiet. Very decent and clean but not luxurious. Hot & cold water in bedroom. I think that it would suit you. I am quite certain to be there at your dates.
Yours ever
Charles Singer

Enclosed article is signed by Sir F. G. Kenyon, late Director of British Museum, Sir F. G. Hopkins O. M., late President of Royal Society & A. V. Hill, Nobel Prizeman & secretary of Royal Society[1]

[1] Sir Frederick Gowland Hopkins (1861–1947), biochemist; see H. H. Dale, 'Hopkins, Sir Frederick Gowland (1861–1947)', rev. *Oxford dictionary of national biography* (Oxford: Oxford University Press, 2004), vol. 28, 52–54. Archibald Vivian Hill (1886–1977), physiologist; see Bernard Katz, 'Hill, Archibald Vivian (1886–1977)', rev. V. M. Quirke, *Oxford dictionary of national biography* (Oxford: Oxford University Press, 2004), vol. 27, 111–113.

247

Sigerist to Singer, Baltimore?, 16 May 1936

Dear Singer:

Thanks for your letter of May 5th and for the reprints on German universities.[1] I will come to London alone. Mrs. Sigerist and the children are going directly from Paris to Switzerland.

I would very much like to stay in the same house as you on 15 Palace Court, and I would appreciate it if you could reserve a room for me for June 4th.

I am very anxious to meet Dr. Gask, who wrote me so very kindly last year, but please do not make arrangements for anything formal. I am travelling in Russia with a minimum of luggage and will not have a dinner jacket with me.

I am looking forward to seeing you soon with the greatest pleasure.

With kind regards to you both, I am
Yours ever,
Henry E. Sigerist

[1] Charles Singer, 'German universities', *The New Outlook*, 1937, **12**: 16–18.

248

Sigerist to Singer, Kastanienbaum, Switzerland, 23 August 1936

My dear Singer:

I still owe you a letter.[1] I preferred to wait until I would have left Russia. I discussed your project[2] with quite a few people and they all agreed that, to have a representative on the spot would accelerate matters very much indeed. The difficulty will be to find the right man. Mr. Habicht, the Open Road representative,[3] whom I suggested and to whom I talked about it, is out of question. He already has three jobs, and is more than busy. I know a young American foreign correspondent, Robert Miller, who might possibly be taken into consideration. He is a Princeton graduate and has been in Russia for two years. I did not speak to him in the matter and just now he is travelling somewhere in Italy.

As I wrote you gefore [sic], I did not see Dr. Rosen,[4] but I called at the office of Agro-joint[5] and had a long talk with Mr. Grower. He suggested that the Council should work in closed cooperation with the Soviet Ambassy [sic] in London. He said that the present ambassador is a very apen-minded [sic] man, who would be willing and able to straighten out difficulties. As you probably heard, Agrojoint succeeded in obtaining visas for quite a number of German physicians.

I realize that this is all very vage [sic] but the matter is delicate and difficult to handle.

I had a most interesting time in the Soviet Union. I completed my material and I am working hard on my book now.[6] I hope to write a good portion of it here in Switzerland, where I intend to stay till the end of September.

I remember with pleasure the days spent with you in London, and with kind regards to you both I am very sincerely yours
[Henry E. Sigerist].

[1] This is probably the first letter after their personal encounter of June 1936.
[2] Pertaining to helping Nazi victims.
[3] Open Road, one of many organizations of this name.
[4] George Rosen (1910–1977), American medical historian, studied in Germany; see Lloyd G. Stevenson, 'George Rosen, 1910–1977', *Bulletin of the History of Medicine*, 1977, **51**: 620–624, and W. L Glenn, 'George Rosen, 1910–1977', *ibid.*, 625–626.
[5] Agro-Joint, a Jewish relief organization
[6] Henry E. Sigerist, *Socialized medicine in the Soviet Union* (New York, 1937).

249

Singer to Sigerist, Kilmarth, 23 November 1937

My dear Sigerist,

A line to introduce you to my friend Dr. Martin Weinbaum.[1]

He is certainly the leading authority on the Growth of English Boroughs. Incidentally he has taught us a good deal about the civic history of the small towns in our own neighbourhood. He has spent some years in England, and has taught at Manchester University for four years. His English is really perfect, and has no trace of a German accent – a most unusual accomplishment in my experience. I believe that you will be interested to meet him.

With all good wishes,
Yours ever,
Charles Singer

[1] Martin Weinbaum (born 1902).

250

Sigerist to Singer, Baltimore?, 20 December 1937

My dear Singer:

Just a line to tell you that it will be a very great pleasure to meet Dr. Martin Weinbaum. He wrote me that he would come to Baltimore early in January. I shall attend the meeting of the History of Science Society in Indianapolis but will be back on New Year's eve.

How are you? It is a long time that I had no news from you but I hope to see you next June. I shall, in all probability, go to Russia again with a group of American public health people[1] and I plan to spend about a week in London with my daughter, Erica.

I instructed my publisher, Victor Gollancz, to send you a copy of my Soviet book and I hope that you received it.[2] I am glad that I am through with this work. It kept me busy for many years. I began working now on a four-volume History of Medicine in which I am trying to approach the subject from a somewhat different angle than has been done so far.[3] It obviously will be an affair of many years but I enjoy working again on ancient history.

With all good wishes for a Happy New Year to Mrs. Singer and yourself, I am
Yours ever,
Henry E. Sigerist

[1] Sigerist's third Russian trip took place in 1938.
[2] Sigerist (1937b).
[3] Sigerist's *History of medicine* was only begun in 1945, as an 8-volume project.

251

Singer to Sigerist, Kilmarth, 8 January 1938

My dear Sigerist,

Many thanks for your letter of Dec. 20 & for the book "Socialised Medicine in the Soviet Union".[1] I have read it & – I assure you, I write with the traditional & conventional compliment – with the utmost interest. It is really a most fascinating piece of work which is far more easily read than I could have hoped for such a theme.

And may I congratulate you also on have [sic] not only acquired English perfectly – that you already had – but on having acquired a distinctive & most attractive English style. The Introduction is a particularly good bit of writing & I appreciate especially the simplicity of your diction. I can only say Well done!

For my own part I am satisfied that you have produced a work which will last longer than we shall, as the first attempt to produce a complete picture of a profession at work in a Socialist state. I have read criticisms of the book with which however, I do not agree. The only criticism that I have to make is perhaps no criticism at all. I could have wished that you had more of a picture of the Russian doctor himself: how his day goes; what he is thinking about; what it must feel like to be a Russian doctor; how he himself, regards the changes that are going on around him; in fact the personal & perhaps the sentimental side.

I should have written to you long ago, but I do assure you that my correspondence has grown beyond all management. I have been overwhelmed with the claims upon me of every kind made & the great German migration of intellectuals. I am very closely in touch with German exiles on the one hand & with Church circles (Fancy!) on the other. I am quite sure that you would never have thought that of me! I do a good deal of writing almost entirely anonymously, on the subject in various journals. I have just issued, however, a pamphlet in my own name which I enclose.[2] I am working in association with the bishop of Chichester, a level headed & humane man who knows perfectly well what is going on in Germany.[3] For various reasons it was considered advisable that this particular pamphlet should not be anonymous. It has, I am told, had a good deal of effect.

Personally I keep very well though beginning to feel older.[4] The events of the last years have made me work much harder than I ever expected to do again. Even my everlasting task of the History of Science has progressed.[5] My partner in it, Daniel [sic] McKie, has just left here after a few days spent on it & we now have it all written except the last chapter.[6]

You will have had news of us from the Larkeys at Prague. I sent him some notes for his work a few weeks ago but I have long ago despaired of ever getting an answer from him!

It is really good of you to see Weinbaum. He is an excellent man & one of the few exiles of whom you can say that his English is perfect. His is a type of scholarship that is rare in America but alas! I fear that the demand for it is rarer still.

I have had a couple of letters from a man named Kagan who is writing a life of Garrison.[7] I gather that he is not much good & has had a row with the Welch Medical Library. However[,] I did not see why I should not write a few lines about poor old Garrison for him & this I have done. I hope that you approve.

I have within the last few hours made an interesting little discovery. You remember the figure of the bees on one Xmas card from Stelluti's <u>Persio Tradotto</u> of 1630.[8] I knew that it was taken from Cesi's single sheet <u>Apiarium</u> of the supposedly unique copy in the Lancisian library at Rome, I have a photo.[9] Well another imperfect copy has just turned up in England and now lies on my table. It belongs to a bee-keepers association. But what surprised me was the degree of magnification – at least 30[?] diameters. I had no idea that it was so much. I am writing an account of the whole story with figures.[10]

With all good wishes to you all – & especially the children – from us all for a happy new year,

Yours ever,

Charles Singer

An American edition of my pamphlet is appearing

[1] Sigerist (1937b).

[2] Charles Singer, *The Christian approach to Jews*, with a foreword by the Rt. Rev. the Lord Bishop of Chichester; and a preface by the Rev. H. W. Fox. (London: [s.n.], 1937).

[3] George Kennedy Allen Bell (1883–1958), bishop of Chichester; see Andrew Chandler, 'Bell, George Kennedy Allen (1883–1958)', *Oxford dictionary of national biography* (Oxford: Oxford University Press, 2004), vol. 4, 927–930.

[4] Singer was 61.

[5] Charles Singer, *A short history of science to the nineteenth century* (Oxford, 1941).

[6] Douglas McKie (1896–1967) British historian of science; see Harold Hartley, 'McKie, Douglas (1896–1967)', rev. *Oxford dictionary of national biography* (Oxford: Oxford University Press, 2004), vol.35, 639–640.

[7] Solomon R. Kagan (1881–1955); Solomon R. Kagan, *Life and letters of Fielding H. Garrison* (Boston: The Medico-Historical Press, 1938).

[8] Francesco Stelluti (1577–1652) Italian scientist; Francesco Stelluti, *Persio/tradotto in verso* (Roma, 1630).

[9] Federico Cesi (1585–1630) Italian botanist; *Apiarium* is his work on bees. See Stillman Drake, 'Cesi, Federico', *Complete dictionary of scientific biography*, Vol. 3, (Detroit: Charles Scribner's Sons, 2008),179–180.

[10] This account by Singer has not been published.

252

Sigerist to Singer, Baltimore?, 31 January 1938

My dear Singer:

Many thanks for your letter of January 8. Dr. Weinbaum was here a week ago and I was delighted to meet him. There is no doubt that he is a fascinating personality and a very fine scholar. I am sure that he will have a good career in this country because he has the type of personality that appeals to the Americans and is very adaptable to new environments. As a matter of fact, I believe that he already has a definite offer for a job in one of the good colleges of the country.

I greatly appreciated your very kind and generous comments on my last book.[1] I have no difficulties in speaking English but writing is a different matter and I still feel tremendously handicapped. It can not be helped, however, and I still have to learn to improve my style.

Dr. Solomon R. Kagan is not known to any of us. He has written not only a biography of Garrison but also one of Dr. Welch and if you or I should die tomorrow, he would probably write our biographies also.[2] We all felt that he was not qualified to write the biography of Garrison as he knew him only very superficially, and most of us refused to give him material as it might forestall a more competent publication. He succeeded, however, in obtaining some material from Mrs. Garrison[3] who is utterly helpless in such matters.

You undoubtedly know that Simon Flexner is writing the life of Dr. Welch and it obviously is absurd for a man like Kagan to try to compete, particularly as Flexner has all the biographical material on Welch in hand.[4]

Do you know J. G. Crowther?[5] He happens to be in America and we hope to have him give a lecture in the Institute. I liked his last books very much indeed.

I just made reservations for sailing on the Statendam on June 3. We shall land in Plymouth and if you happen to be in the country at that time, we would very much like to pay you a short visit.

With kind regards to Mrs. Singer and yourself, I am

Yours ever,

Henry E. Sigerist

---

[1] Sigerist (1937b).

[2] Kagan (1938), and 'William Henry Welch (1850–1934)', in Solomon R. Kagan, *Leaders of medicine*, (Boston: Medico-Historical Press, 1941), 127–161.

[3] Clara Garrison.

[4] Simon Flexner (1863–1946), American pathologist and bacteriologist, disciple of Welch; Simon Flexner and James T. Flexner, *William Henry Welch and the heroic age of American medicine* (New York, 1941). For Flexner see George W. Corner, 'Flexner, Simon', *Complete dictionary of scientific biography*, Vol. 5 (Detroit: Charles Scribner's Sons, 2008), 39–41.

[5] James G. Crowther (1899–1983) British journalist, wrote on science, scientists, and science policy. See Jane Gregory, 'Crowther, James Gerald (1899–1983)', *Oxford Dictionary of National Biography* (Oxford: Oxford University Press, 2006); online edn, May 2007 [http://www.oxforddnb.com/view/article/94975, accessed 27 July 2010.

253

Singer to Sigerist, Kilmarth, 17 February 1938

My dear Sigerist,

Many thanks for your letter of Jan. 31st. I quite agree with you that Kagan is a nuisance. Correspondence with him has already taken up too much of my time. I shall have his letters unaswered.

I am so glad that there is a chance of your having J. G. Crowther with you; he really is a most able, interesting & charming fellow. He is, I think, sure to be a success. He is quite our best scientific journalist & will one day, I hope, be editor of <u>Nature</u>.[1] Incidentally he has a perfectly delightful German wife.

It really ought not to be difficult to place Weinbaum. He has so many qualities that are in demand in the U.S.A.

By the way you write "If you or I die tomorrow Kagan would probably write our biographies". This adds a new terror to death &, incidentally, a motive for trying to out-live Kagan! I, at any rate, mean to do my best.

It is delightful news that we may see you soon after June 3. To judge by the present state of Europe, England & Russia are probably the only states that you will be able to visit. We are normally in London about June 3 but would tremendously like to have you here & shall get back for a few days for the purpose – but of that more later. Do bring the children too.

I write this as the news comes in of the surrender of Austria.[2] Isn't it all beastly & what can our rotten Government be thinking about!

Yours ever,

Charles Singer

[1] Britain's leading science journal
[2] Hitler's incorporation of Austria into the Reich

254

Singer to Sigerist, Kilmarth, 5 April 1938

My dear Sigerist,

You are to be congratulated on being in the United States. The situation here becomes daily worse. I cannot myself see any reason why European civilisation should survive.

I wonder if you are contemplating going to the Historical Congress at Zurich in September? Everything is so uncertain that no one likes to make arrangements six months in advance, and among the uncertain places I suppose that German Switzerland ranks pretty high![1] Of course, if there is a Congress held in Zurich it will be under the most extreme German influence, and will be flooded out by Germans. If you are thinking of going there, it would be well that you should be primed on a number of matters. Perhaps therefore, you would be so good as to let me have a line as to your intentions. In any event we look forward to seeing you in June. We should love to see you either in London or in Cornwall, though, of course, we should prefer the latter.

With all good wishes,

Yours ever,

Charles Singer

[1] Hitler's initial goal was to be ruler of all germanophones, thus, there was fear that after Austria he would seize the German-speaking part of Switzerland too.

255

Sigerist to Singer, Baltimore?, 18 May 1938

Dear Singer:

I postponed writing you until I knew what our definite plans would be. For a while it looked as if I would have to go to Paris first and from there to England. Our present plans, however, are the following:

We sail from New York on June 3 on the Statendam on the Holland America Line and we are due in Plymouth on Friday, June 10, I think in the afternoon. Nothing could give us greater pleasure than to spend the week-end with you in Cornwall. We shall be the four of us – Mrs. Sigerist, myself, and the two girls.[1] I have been looking forward to a visit with you at your Cornwall home for many years and it will be a very great pleasure indeed to have a few quiet days with you in the country. There are so many things that I would like to discuss with you and Mrs. Singer.

I sincerely hope that nothing will interfer [sic] with our plans and I shall confirm the date of our arrival by cable just before we sail. The week of June 13 to 18, we intend to spend in London and we have made reservations in a boarding house. My mother will join us in London for a few days.[2] On June 18 I shall sail from London to the Soviet Union on the Soviet boat with Erica and the group of American physicians and public health people. We are going to have a travel seminar on public health. I am sending you enclosed a copy of the program.

I intend to spend August in Switzerland and in September I am thinking of going to the International Medical History Congress in Jugoslavia.

I do not contemplate going to the historical congress at Zürich. One congress a year is more than I can stand. I think Switzerland is pretty safe, however, and the Nazis are not popular in Zürich. Well, we can talk this matter over.

We made an interesting experiment at the Institute the other day which, I am glad to say, succeeded very well indeed. We gave a one week's post-graduate course in medical history.[3] It was attended by 35 doctors, mostly people who teach medical history in their schools, and also some medical librarians. I am sending you under separate cover the various programs. The whole Week was so successful that we intend to give similar courses regularly, and I think that this is a good way of raising the standard gradually.

I had a frightfully busy winter and I am beginning to feel very tired. I am looking forward with greatest pleasure to a few days of rest and particularly to seeing you and Mrs. Singer again very soon.

With kind regards, I am
Yours very sincerely,
Henry E. Sigerist[4]

[1] His daughters Erica (20) and Nora (16).
[2] Emma Sigerist-Wiskemann, living in Basel, Switzerland.
[3] See Henry E. Sigerist, 'Report of the activities of the Institute of the History of Medicine of the Johns Hopkins University (1937–1938)', *Bulletin of the History of Medicine*, 1938, **6**: 858–881.

[4] The following letter (255A) from Sigerist to Dorothea Singer is held in the Wellcome Library, London (PP/CJS/A.16). Sigerist was then in London to board the boat for Leningrad for his third and last study tour in the USSR. June 18 1938
Hotel Russell, Russell Square, London, W.C.1
Dear Mrs Singer
I hoped to be able to see you once more before leaving but I was so busy with the preparations for the trip that I just could not make it. And—needless to say—the preface for the Neuburger Festschrift will have to be written on the boat.
I wish to tell you what a very great pleasure it was to see you and Dr Singer again and how much we all appreciated your charming hospitality. The reception at the club was delightful and made me realise that some other year I will have to stay much longer in London
With all good wishes to yourself and Dr Singer I am
Yours sincerely
H. E. Sigerist

256

Singer to Sigerist, Kilmarth, 21 November 1938

My dear Sigerist,

Going over some papers today I came upon a long letter from Garrison which I gladly present to be added to the Johns Hopkins collection. It refers to my suggestions for his book but also contains more interesting material.[1] Like everything else it is safer on your side of the Atlantic.

What an awful situation we are in. It is, if anything, more difficult to do any serious work than it was before. I often think that we must add to the direct destruction of civilisation for which Hitler is responsible, the much greater destruction involved in withdrawing the attention of all serious workers from their proper tasks. I had a long talk with Freud three days ago.[2] He says that he is confident that Hitler is insane in the technical sense. He says, however, that his type of insanity is not, unfortunately, likely to lead soon to a state of confusion. Of course if it did it would become obvious to all, even to Germans. But after having seen much of Germans I have at last, arrived at the generalisation that they are, one & all, damn fools!

What a wonderful old man Freud is.
Yours always
Charles Singer

We are not sending out Xmas cards this year. It would be almost indecent.

[1] Fielding H Garrison, *An introduction to the history of medicine* (Philadelphia/London, 1913).
[2] Sigmund Freud (1856–1939) Austrian neurologist and psychiatrist, 1938 exiled in England. see Susan Austin, 'Freud, Sigmund (1856–1939)', *Oxford dictionary of national biography* (Oxford: Oxford University Press, 2004), vol. 21, 3–11.

257

Singer to Sigerist, Kilmarth, 11 January 1939

My dear Sigerist,

Neuburger has written a very distressing letter to the Society for the Protection of Science & Learning. The Society exists, of course, for what its name implies & can only exceptionally give superannuation pensions. Neuburger's own pension in Vienna has been withdrawn & he is destitute. D'Arcy Power & I are trying to do something for him. We are hoping to raise £180 a year to be paid him in England until one of his sons is in a position to support him. We shall give it through the Society.

My first thought was Klebs & Sir D'Arcy agreed to write to him. He got back a letter which (as you would expect) was a model of bad taste!, but I think Klebs will give some-thing. D'Arcy is now writing again to ask him to give 25 pounds a year. D'Arcy is also writing to Cushing, Fulton & St.Clair Thomson. I have undertaken to write to you, H. H. Dale, Chaplin Moon[,] Cawadias & Packard.[1] I am giving five guineas a year & would gladly give more but have for the last 6 years been living far beyond my income by reason of refugee claims & we have guaranteed seven exiles I just simply cannot do more & remain solvent.

I have suggested to Dale that the Wellcome Museum take on Neuburger.[2] It won't get a more learned man. Of course if this should come off and a salary be provided, anything given for Neuburger will be returned to the donors. It is also possible that one of Neuburger's sons may be able to support him. But in the meantime Neuburger cannot wait & something must be done for him.

Do you know whether Mrs. Neuburger is still alive? It makes a difference, of course, because if she is we must manage to find £250 a year instead of £180.

All our time, energy & means has now, for years, been given to helping exiles. The European situation is now so bad that it is very doubtful if we shall, for much longer, be able to do anything at all for them. The general indications seem to point to a war in the spring. This cannot be much worse than the present state.

All good wishes to you all from us all.

Yours ever,

Charles Singer

We felt that we really could not send out Xmas cards this year.

If you think of anyone else for D'Arcy or me to write to, of course we would do so.

---

[1] John F. Fulton, (1899–1960), Yale University physiologist and medical historian; see A. Earl Walker, 'Fulton, John Farquhar', *Complete dictionary of scientific biography*, Vol. 5 (Detroit: Charles Scribner's Sons, 2008), 207–208. St.Clair Thomson, (1859–1943) British laryngologist; see Neil Weir, 'Thomson, Sir St Clair (1859–1943)', *Oxford dictionary of national biography* (Oxford: Oxford University Press, 2004), vol. 54, 553–554. Henry H. Dale (1875–1968), English pharmacologist, Nobel Prize winner; see W. Feldberg, 'Dale, Sir Henry Hallett (1875–1968)', rev. E. M. Tansey, *Oxford dictionary of national biography* (Oxford: Oxford University Press, 2004), vol. 14, 929–932. Chaplin Moon not identified; A. P. Cawadias, British endocrinologist, see 'Alexander Polycleitos Cawadias', in Gordon Wolstenholme (ed.), *Lives of the Fellows of the Royal College of Physicians*, (Oxford: IRL Press, 1982), vol 6, 95–96. Francis R. Packard (1870–1950), Medical historian; see

W. B. McDaniel II, 'Francis R. Packard and his role in medical historiography', *Bulletin of the History of Medicine*, 1951, 25: 66–85.
[2] Wellcome Museum of the History of Medicine in London.

258

Sigerist to Singer, Baltimore?, 3 February 1939

Dear Singer:

I have to thank you for several letters and first for your letter of November 21. The letter of Garrison is most welcome and I am glad to add it to our collections.

The European situation could not possibly be worse and if Spain breaks down, we shall have to take care of an additional number of refugees. It happens that almost all scientists are on the Loyalist side.[1]

You certainly remember Starkenstein, the pharmacologist of Prague?[2] We are just making arrangements for a lecture tour for him, and I am confident that we shall be able to place him in America permanently. He is a very delightful personality and pharmacologists are the easiest to place as there is always some possible outlet in industry.

Castiglioni is also trying to come over. It seems that he has some money abroad but the great difficulty is to obtain a visa for him. He is too old for a regular academic position and visitors' visas are generally refused now.[3]

I would like to recommend you an Italian roentgenologist, Dr. Giuseppe Bertel most warmly. He was a student of Holzknecht[4] and had the best possible training a roentgenologist can have. He then worked for a number of years at the University of Modena where I met him several years ago. I was favorably impressed by him. I hear that he is going to appeal to the Society for the Protection of Science and Learning and I hope that you can do something for him, at least in the beginning. I hope that we can place him in America ultimately but it will take some time as he has no connections of any kind with the United States.

The case of Neuburger is very difficult indeed. Since last spring I had an endless correspondence concerning him. Everybody is most sympathetic but so far no university has been willing to do anything. The chief trouble is his old age and his difficult character.[5] He is embittered and has been so since the war so that he would not be a very pleasant man to have on the staff of a department. I could not possibly take him as I already have three Germans (Temkin, Edelstein and old Neustätter[6]). I cannot possibly crowd my department with refugees but must keep a few places for the training of young Americans.

I shall be very glad to pledge a hundred dollars a year for the support of Neuburger but I am sorry to say that I could not send you this year's contribution before autumn. I am perfectly broke just now. I gave every cent I could spare for refugees, for Spain, China, the Civil Liberties League, International Labor Protection and endless such organizations that do not get any support from rich people.

I have just accepted a visiting lectureship in South Africa for next summer, 25 lectures in ten universities and colleges. They pay expenses and quite a decent honorarium so that in autumn I will be able to send you the money for Neuburger.

I am terribly busy this winter. In addition to my regular work, I am in the middle of the struggle for sickness insurance and have to make endless speeches before all kind of groups.

You will have heard that the two next International Congresses for the History of Medicine will be held in Berlin and Rome so that the International Society is now completely controlled by the Fascist powers. It is a hopeless situation.[7]

I very much hope to see you and Mrs. Singer either on my way to or from South Africa and with kind regards to you both, I am

Yours ever,

Henry E. Sigerist

[1] Spanish Civil War 1936–1939; Loyalists = Republicans, i.e. anti-fascists.

[2] Emil Starkenstein (1884–1942), German pharmacologist, murdered by the Nazis in 1942; see K. E. Senius, 'Emil Starkenstein 1884–1942. The life and work of a German pharmacologist', *Naunyn Schmiedeberg's Archives of Pharmacology*, 1984, **328**: 95–102.

[3] Castiglioni was 65.

[4] Giuseppe Bertel (born 1894). Guido Holzknecht (1872–1931), Austrian radiologist; see Daniela Angetter, *Guido Holzknecht: Leben und Werk des österreichischen Pioniers der Röntgenologie* (Wien: Werner Eichbauer, 1998).

[5] Neuburger was 71.

[6] Otto Neustätter (born 1870), medical historian.

[7] The planned international congresses of medical history in Berlin and Rome did not take place on account of World War II.

259

Singer to Sigerist, Kilmarth, 13 February 1939

My dear Sigerist,

Thanks for yours of Feb. 3. You really are a good & generous fellow.

Improbable as it may seem, I really think there is a good chance of placing Neuburger! Your kind and generous offer may well help but I shall try to use it as a guarantee for I well know of the calls on you & want to lessen them.

As regards Starkenstein. Oddly enough I wrote only yesterday to Miss Layton, the secretary of the Czecho-Slovak Committee offering, if needed, to market parts of his library for him. I am glad to hear that there are prospects for him in U.S.A. You know, do you not, that we have in London fairly good funds for anyone expelled or forced to leave the old Czecho-Slovakia,[1] guaranteed without distinction of race, religion or politics by the British Government. Therefore if you hear of such cases let me know because they ought not to fall on ordinary refugee funds.

I will gladly do all I can for Giuseppe Bertel & have written immediately to the Soc. for the Protection of Science and Learning.

Again as to Neuburger. I <u>think</u> I have persuaded Wellcome[2] to take him on for a year & I am sure they will take him on for 6 months, [sic] As they pay at the rate of £200 for 6 months this should see him through a year. If they take him on for a year the pay (£200) should see him through for 2 years by when, if he (& we) are still alive his sons must care for him. But I will let you know how things go.

We do look forward to a visit from you on your way to Africa.[3] You are always more than welcome. I have reflected a hundred times what a good thing it is that they chose you and not me for Johns Hopkins.[4] For one thing you do it far better than I could. For another you are in a far stronger position to help colleagues than I should have been. More power to you! Of course I fully understand that you cannot take more exiles yourself.

Dorothea & I have now for years done nothing but work for exiles. There is in England a very great shortage of girls as hospital nurses & we have placed about 250 from Germany[.] There have not been 4 failures among the lot. We are now trying to place lads of about 16 as apprentices with farmers with a [....] to emigration at about 18 & are beginning to have some success.

I was asked to lecture on a "Hellenic Travellers Tour" in the Mediterranean this spring & thought of taking Nancy.[5] As the situation deteriorated I refused. I don't think the Eastern Mediterranean is likely to be a very healthy place this April, do you?

The general situation cannot well be worse. I always assume that there will be a European war opening about April or May but have, of course, no other source of information than you have.

With all kind wishes to you all,
Yours ever,
Charles Singer

I wonder if we could have an English Speaking Congress of the History of Medicine & so check mate the other?[6] We can talk of that when we meet on your way to Africa [.]

[1] Just before the German occupation in March 1939.
[2] The Wellcome Museum in London.
[3] To South Africa
[4] Singer was the first to be asked to succeed Welch.
[5] Nancy Singer.
[6] Congresses in Berlin and Rome.

260

Sigerist to Singer, Baltimore?, 27 February 1939

Dear Singer:

Many thanks for your letter of February 13. I was glad to hear that there is a possibility of employing Neuburger at the Wellcome Museum. They should be able to build up a very competent staff under the present conditions. I heard that Walzer is already working there. He is a most competent young scholar; you must have met him.[1]

Your suggestion of an English-speaking congress of the history of medicine to check-mate the Nazi demonstration of 1940 appeals to me very much. As a matter of fact, I discussed the idea last summer already with several people. The International Congress of the History of Science was to be held in Lausanne in September 1940 and I planned to invite a number of people to the First International Conference of the History of Medicine to be held in Kastanienbaum preceding the Lausanne Congress. Kastanienbaum is our summer place on the Lake of Lucerne, and an enchanting spot with a very good and inexpensive hotel. I thought that we should invite a small group of really competent men to meet for a week and to discuss a definite problem from all angles. We then could publish the papers as a volume and I am sure it would infuriate the politicians of the International Society.

I have not done anything in the matter yet because Reymond is dying and the Congress of the History of Science will, in all probability, not be held in Lausanne.[2] But I was delighted to hear that you had the same idea and I think it is time that we do something in the matter. I am sick and tired of these big congresses anyway where you do nothing but eat and drink and listen to nationalistic propaganda. It is time to change the style of these gatherings and to organize some meetings where real work can be achieved.

With kind regards to you all, I am

Yours ever,

Henry E. Sigerist

---

[1] Richard Rudolf Walzer (1900–1975), classical scholar and orientalist; see Luc Deitz, 'Walzer, Richard Rudolf (1900–1975)', *Oxford dictionary of national biography* (Oxford: Oxford University Press, 2004), vol. 57, 231–232.

[2] Arnold Reymond (1874–1958), Swiss historian of science and Professor of Philosophy at the University of Lausanne; see Suzanne Delorme, 'Nécrologie, Arnold Reymond (1874–1958)', *Revue d'histoire des sciences et de leurs applications*, 1958, **11**: 171–174.

261

Sigerist to Singer, Baltimore?, 1 March 1939

Dear Singer:

I just received your letter of December 17.[1] Do not resign from the International Society of the History of Medicine. I think that the liberal members should stay by all means. We may have an opportunity to change the policy of the Society with the help of the Scandinavian members. This is why I accepted to be a vice-president. You will certainly be notified of your election as an honorary member but it takes time because the organization of the Society is perfectly rotten and the Secretary's office most inefficient.

In Sarajewo[2] nothing could be done, but you never can tell. Conditions may change and we may have an opportunity to act sometime.
Yours ever,
Henry E. Sigerist

[1] Singer's letter is missing.
[2] At the International Congress of the History of Medicine in 1938.

262

Singer to Sigerist, Kilmarth, 8 March 1939

My dear Sigerist,
What about this man?[1] I said that I would see him when I am next in London. But the fact that he comes from Diepgen is not the best recommendation in my eyes! But of course he may be all right.
All kind wishes,
Yours ever,
Charles Singer

[1] Singer is referring to Philipsborn, see following letter.

263

Sigerist to Singer, Baltimore?, 29 March 1939

Dear Singer:
I have never met Dr. Alexander Philipsborn.[1] He was recommended to me by the same man who recommended him to you. He is working on a history of the hospital and apparently would like a fellowship that would allow him to continue his research in England or America. I have not succeeded in finding anything for him yet.
We are doing much work for the Spanish refugees now. I hope that South America will absorb most of them but there are a good many who would like to come to the United States. They are now in French concentration camps under appalling conditions.[2]
With kind regards, I am
Yours ever,
Henry E. Sigerist

[1] Alexander Philipsborn wrote on Byzantine medicine.
[2] Concentration camps in the literal, not in the Nazi sense.

264

Singer to Sigerist, Kilmarth, 24 April 1939

My dear Sigerist,

(1) Are you still of opinion that we should try to get an English-speaking Congress of the History of Science for 1940? If so drop me a line to that effect, to the Athenaeum Pall Mall SW. I go to London tomorrow for some weeks. If you agree & if you will support me, I will sound opinion in London. I have little doubt that we could get the hospitality of the Science Museum at South Kensington & I think probably a little government support if we needed it, though we are, perhaps, best without it. I propose it should be a meeting only for "serious" workers & not for all & sundry[?].

(2) Do you know anything of Arcieri who has just started this journal "Alcmeone".[1] Pure propaganda, I suppose. I imagine that he is a little mad. He wrote to the Senate of the University of London asking "What religion is professed by Professor Singer?"!! Of course the Senate made no reply & sent the letter on to me! I did the same. What a mad world.

Yours ever,

Charles Singer

The pathetic little autobiography of Garrison in the Bulletin. Certainly revealing & some fine thoughts in it.[2]

[1] Giovanni Arcieri (born 1897) Italian medical historian; his journal existed from 1939 to 1951; see also letter 268.
[2] F. L. Tietsch, 'Self-portrait of Fielding H. Garrison. Autobiographical excerpts compiled from his letters', *Bulletin of the History of Medicine*, 1939, **7**: 365–373.

265

Singer to Sigerist, London, 8 May 1939

My dear Sigerist

(1) I have been asked by the Society for the Protection of Science and Learning to find out what has become of Starkenstein of Prague. Can you let me have his address and his office if any. I think you said he had found a place somewhere in USA

(2) I saw Adams the other day.[1] He would be willing to be again the Hon. Secretary of an "English Speaking Congress of the History of Science, Medicine and Technology" in London in 1940. But I want your imprimatur & the information that you will support it before I go further.

Yours ever

Charles Singer

[1] Walter Adams (1906–1975), university administrator, then secretary of the London School of Economics; Adams had been the Honorary Secretary of the Second International Congress of the History of Science and Technology held in London in 1931. See James Joll, 'Adams, Sir Walter (1906–1975)', rev. *Oxford dictionary of national biography* (Oxford: Oxford University Press, 2004), vol. 1, 267–268.

266

Singer to Sigerist, London, 10 May 1939

My dear Sigerist,

The second part of the enclosed letter from H. P. Bayon may interest you.[1] (The first part is of no importance.) I should like to have your reaction ct.

Bayon is a very learned & worthy man, extremely honest, endlessly industrious & with a perfect mania for accuracy. He used to have a post in the Pathological department at Cambridge from which he has recently retired – he is about 65 & now devotes himself to history for which he is well equipped. Despite his name, he is, I believe, by birth an Italian. His very clever and charming daughter is married to P.M.S. Blackett the distinguished physicist.[2]

I think, in fact, Bayon would do Garrison's book as well as most people.[3] He would certainly correct the errors! He would need to be restrained from further extending the size of the book but I have always found him willing to take suggestions & amenable to guidance. His worst feature is a wearisome literary style in which every statement is qualified with a qualification to the qualificature! But I think that I could restrain him & if you have no better suggestion, I think Bayon could hardly be bettered for the wearisome task of revising Garrison. Bayon, I should add, is certainly modest & humble minded.

Let me hear from you as soon as you can on the project[?] of an English speaking Congress. I will see if the Wellcome Foundation will support it.

Yours ever,

Charles Singer

[1] Enrico Pietro (Henry Peter) Bayon (1876–1952), pathologist, linguist and medical historian; see 'H. P. G. Bayon', *British Medical Journal*, 1952, **ii**: 1260–1261.

[2] Patrick Maynard Stuart Blackett (1897–1974), physicist see Mary Jo Nye, 'Blackett, Patrick Maynard Stuart, Baron Blackett (1897–1974)', *Oxford dictionary of national biography* (Oxford: Oxford University Press, 2004), vol. 5, 946–949.

[3] Garrison (1913).

267

Singer to Sigerist, London, 23 May 1939

My dear Sigerist,

(1) I have had Bayon (of whom I wrote you) here to-day. I know him well – too well – by correspondence but I had not met him before. I gathered from him that he had had correspondence with you also concerning a new edition of Garrison & that you were unfavourable.[1] After talking with Bayon, I agree with you. He is too pedantic, too limited & too specialised. There is a childish element in him. Also although he has been more than 20 years in England he makes some queer mistakes still in the language.

(2) I gather (only from Bayon) that you are, in principle, opposed to a new edition of Garrison. I know your low opinion of the book & certainly no one can defend its arrangement or its standard of accuracy. Nevertheless it is a most useful reference book & I know of no other that contains so much information about medical history between two covers. I hope therefore that you will reconsider your attitude in this matter – though not to Bayon!

(3) There have been unexpected difficulties over getting Neuburger here. However a few days ago D'Arcy Power & I signed a joint "guarantee" for him (that is a guarantee to the British Government for his support if needed). I just don't see how I can fulfill my side of the guarantee! However I comfort myself with the reflexion that all men must die some time, even medical historians such as Neuburger & Singer.

(4) The human situation grows daily worse, so that I have, at last, reached the point when it seems to me that war is by no means the greatest evil that can come on our world.[2] In that reason I have ceased to fear war or even to regard it with exceptional distaste. On the whole I think I favor it as the least of several great evils.
Yours ever,
Charles Singer

Needless to say Klebs has behaved badly as regards Neuburger. We now expect Neuburger in London daily.

I look forward to your reply concerning the English speaking Congress or Conference on the Hist. of Science, Medicine & Technology.

---

[1] Garrison (1913) was a famous textbook of the history of medicine.

[2] A popular opinion during the turmoil of the 1930s when it was believed that war would be a short affair that would eliminate Hitler's rule in Germany.

268

My dear Singer:

Many thanks for your letters of May 8 and 10. The address of Starkenstein is:

Dr. Emil Starkenstein

11, Albertov 7

Pharmakologisch-Pharmakognostisches Institut der Deutschen Universität

Prague, Czechoslovakia

He has no definite position in America yet. We had invited him to give a series of lectures, but he wrote recently that he was unable to come. I do not know what is behind it but I think you can get more information from:

Professor E. Goldschmid[1]

Villa Richelieu

Chemin de l'Elysée

Lausanne, Switzerland

I am very much in favor or [sic] an English-speaking congress but I think it should be limited strictly to the History of Medicine. Otherwise it will antagonize the International Congress of the History of Science which will be held in 1940 in all probability in Lausanne. The Academy of the History of Science has always had a definitely anti-Fascist tendency so that we should support it and avoid any activity that would handicap its congress. Personally I would prefer a very informal meeting of medical historians in the week preceding the Lausanne Congress to a formal congress. I hope we can talk matters over some time this summer. I am sailing from New York on May 31 and will be in Switzerland until the middle of July where you can reach me at my mother's address:

182 St. Albanring

Basel, Switzerland

I very much like the idea of a revised edition of Garrison's book[2] and from all you say, I should think that H. P. Bayon would very well be qualified for the task. I should advise him to get in touch with Garrison's publisher:

W. B. Saunders Company

West Washington Square

Philadelphia, Pennsylvania

and I would be very glad to recommend the publication most warmly.

Do you know that Krumbhaar is translating Castiglioni's History of Medicine for Alfred Knopf?[3]

With kind regards, I am

Yours ever,

Henry E. Sigerist

P.S. Arcieri, although an American citizen, is an Italian Fascist graduated from the University of Rome. "Alcmeone" is a pure propaganda sheet that intends to prove that all great discoveries have been made by Italians.

[1] Edgar Goldschmid (1881–1957), German pathologist and medical historian in Switzerland; see 'Edgar Goldschmid, M.D.', *British Medical Journal*, 1957, **i**: 1478.
[2] Garrison (1913).
[3] Arturo Castiglioni, *Storia della medicina* (Milan, 1927).

269

Singer to Sigerist, Kilmarth, 24 May 1939 (Telegram)

REGRET OBLIGED TO CHANGE PLANS SHALL BE IN LONDON 15 PALACE COURT FROM MAY THIRTIETH HOPE TO WELCOME YOU THERE
SINGER

270

Singer to Sigerist, Kilmarth, 30 May 1939

My dear Sigerist,
    You had better see the enclosed documents to know what is afoot. I have taken no further action & the simplest thing is to send them to you. No need to return them.
Yours ever
Charles Singer

We expect Neuburger daily but I am very reluctant to write to him to obtain an exact date.

271

Singer to Sigerist, London, 10 June 1939 (Telegram)

WELCOME TO ENGLAND MEETING YOU PADDINGTON STATION EXPECT YOU ALL TO LUNCH
SINGER 15 PALACE COURT W2

272

Sigerist's secretary to Singer, Baltimore?, 14 June 1939

Dear Dr. Singer:

I wish to acknowledge your two letters of May 23 and May 30 to Dr. Sigerist. He left for Europe on May 30 and will not return until December. I have forwarded the entire correspondence to him and wish to notify you of that fact.

Very sincerely yours,

[XY]

Secretary to Dr. Sigerist

273

Sigerist to Singer, Kastanienbaum near Lucerne, Switzerland, 1 July 1939

Dear Singer,

Your letter of May 23 reached me in Switzerland. I am not at all opposed to a new edition of Garrison's book. On the contrary, I am convinced that a revised edition will be very well received in America. The book has weaknesses, but it is a regular mind [sic] of information and it has become a classic in America. I should be very glad to support Bayon's plan with a publisher very strongly.[1]

As to the Congress, I am all in favour of it, but I think I wrote you before, that we should not antagonize the International Congress of the History of Science, that will be held in 1940 in Switzerland or Belgium. The history of science group has always taken a definitely anti-fascist attitude, so that we should support them. Hence I feel, that if we organize a special congress in England, it should be limited to the History of Medicine, so that it will compete with the Berlin Congress.[2]

I had a letter from Neuburger recently, but will not answer it before I hear, that he has landed safely in England. You know that my guarantee of $100 still holds good.[3]

I am in Switzerland for two more weeks, and will sail for South-Africa on July 20.

With kind regards to Mrs. Singer and yourself

I am yours ever

Henry E. Sigerist

---

[1] A new edition of Garrison's book did not materialize before World War II, and the 4th edition of 1929 was reprinted in 1960.

[2] Plans for a congress of the history of science fell victim to World War II.

[3] See letter 258.

274

Singer to Sigerist, Kilmarth, 17 September 1939

My dear Sigerist,

Many thanks for the Bulletin containing your account of the 11th International Congress. I have just read it.[1]

I wish I had known that an invitation for the next Congress was needed. We could easily have had it again in England.

I learn from your excellent & most readable account that I have been elected an Honorary Member of the Permanent Committee. No information to that effect has reached me. Do you suppose that it will? And do you think that if or when it does that I should resign. I don't suppose it matters either way very much.

Anyhow, as the world is now going, 1940 is a very long way off. Anything might happen in that time.[2]

We are getting rather tired – my wife & I. I do not think that we have ever worked so hard as in these last 4 years. The only satisfaction is that we really feel we have successfully planted a few refugees. But it is such an endless task!

Yours always,

Charles Singer

[1] 11th International Congress of the History of Medicine held in Yugoslavia. Henry E. Sigerist, 'Yugoslavia and the XIth International Congress of the History of Medicine', *Bulletin of the History of Medicine*, 1939, **7**: 93–147.
[2] World War II had broken out on 1 September.

275

Dorothea Singer to Sigerist, Kilmarth, 16 November 1939

My dear Professor Sigerist,

This is just a line to assure you that of course we will do everything possible to help Mrs. Sigerist. I have just written to her and begged her to come over and to bring your Mother as well as the children. It will be a real pleasure to us to have them here. I wish it were likely that you could all spend the winter close to us. I am sure we could find you a nice house.[1]

It will be very interesting to hear your reflections on your African experiences.

Many greetings from us both,

Yours very sincerely,

Dorothea Waley Singer

[1] World War II had broken out when Sigerist was in South Africa and his family in Switzerland. The family returned to the U.S. in November, Sigerist in January (see following letter).

276

My dear Singer:

At long last we are all back in America. My family sailed from Genoa at the end of November on an Italian boat and I sailed from Capetown and landed safely in New York on January 4. It was a great worry to me to be separated from my family when the war broke out and you can imagine how happy I am to be reunited with it. Please tell Mrs. Singer how very much we appreciated her kind letters.

What a queer war. It seems that nobody has a plan and that nobody knows what he is fighting for. Hitler must be destroyed, that's obvious but then what? Shall we learn from the past experience or make the same mistakes over again? It seems really hopeless.

I found the Institute in very good shape and it was a pleasure to resume my work after such a long interruption but my trip through South Africa was a most interesting experience.[1]

This year for the first time in my life I shall not go to Switzerland in the summer. We intend to make a motor trip through the continent and visit a few national parks and other places which we have not seen before.

I hope you are all well, as well as one can be under the present circumstances, and I should love to have news from you.

With kind regards to Mrs. Singer and yourself, I am
Yours very sincerely,
Henry E. Sigerist

[1] Henry E. Sigerist, 'A physician's impression of South Africa', *Bulletin of the History of Medicine*, 1940, **8**: 22–27.

277

Dear Dr. Singer:

I wish to take the liberty of requesting a favor of you. Would you be so kind as to send me the latest address of Professor Max Neuburger? Unfortunately I do not have his address in my files and therefore I shall be very grateful to you for your kindness.

Thanking you once more, I am
Sincerely yours
[Hope Trebing?]
Secretary to Dr. Sigerist

278

Singer to Sigerist, Kilmarth, 28 February 1940

My dear Sigerist,

Many thanks for yours of Feb. 6 with the good news that you are safely back in America.

Yes, the whole European situation is very queer with a strange veil of unreality cast over it. As you say, the one thing clear is that Hitler & his group must be destroyed. I find it very difficult to get even a glimpse into the future. But it must, at least, be an interesting future & I want to live, if I can, to see some of it.

Since the war has begun I have felt more fit for work than I have for years. My job is now clear. I just [....] till my medical services are wanted & till then I am a free man & I have nothing on my mind. I have thus made real progress with my history of science.[1] Moreover during the last few days I have sent to the press the articles Medicine, Surgery, Anatomy & Physiology, Botany & Zoology for the Oxford classical dictionary.[2] I suggested Edelstein & Temkin for articles which, I believe, they have delivered. W. D. Ross the acting editor will be here next month & I shall be hearing about them.

By the way I found the articles & reviews on classical themes by the three of you in the 'Bulletin' very useful. I would suggest that you might publish them with very little alteration. They would make a handy collection. You might call them 'Essays on Greek Medicine'. Don't make the better the enemy of the good but get it out. Perhaps you could include a translation of Edelstein's Paul Wissowa [sic] article on Hippocrates.[3]

Incidentally I want to sell my Paul Wissowa [sic]. It really takes up too much room. If you know anyone who wants one I would part with it. It should fetch a good price now.

Poor old Neuburger [....].[4] Financially he is adequately provided for – at the rate of £400 a year which we consider very good indeed for a refugee – and he has the guarantee of D'Arcy Power & myself.

By this post I have a letter from Sarton bringing the bad news of Meyerhof who is in hospital again.[5]

I wonder if we shall ever have an International Congress again. Have you any news of Klebs? I hardly like to write to him. He is such a very uncertain quantity.

Andrew will be 18 this October.[6] He is due to go to an engineering college then & should do very well. His Mathematics, Physics & Chemistry are all good & he is the right type. If the war goes on he will, I think, go into the Navy, where he would be much better than in the army. But everything is dark.

Kindest regards from us all to all the family,

Yours ever

Charles Singer

---

[1] Singer (1941).

[2] Charles Singer, Articles in M. Cary et al (eds), *The Oxford classical dictionary* (Oxford: Clarendon Press, 1949).

[3] Ludwig Edelstein wrote the supplement to the entry 'Hippokrates', in Georg Wissowa (ed.), *Paulys Realencyclopädie der klassischen Altertumswissenschaft* (Stuttgart, 1893-), Supplement Band VI, 1290–1345.

[4] Two sentences deleted as Protected Health Information of the Alan Mason Chesney Medical Archive of the Johns Hopkins Medical Institutions.

[5] Max Meyerhof (1874–1945), German historian of Arabic medicine; see Claudius F. Mayer, 'Arabism, Egypt, and Max Meyerhof', *Bulletin of the History of Medicine*, 1946, **19**: 375–432.

[6] Singer's son.

279

Singer to Sigerist, Kilmarth, 11 March 1940

My dear Sigerist,

Dr. Rhys Jenkins,[1] a distinguished engineer attached for many years to the Patent Office, possesses a manuscript of somewhere towards the end of the reign of Elizabeth – say 1590 – illustrating all kinds of mechanical devices. It is carefully illustrated in colour and has an English text. There are 71 coloured sketches. I enclose a photograph of one, with that of the corresponding text.

Jenkins and Dickinson of the Science Museum regard its contents as unique.[2] The only parallels are the so-called Hausbücher of which several are known in German.[3] It is probably unique also for the skill of the drawing, since draughtsmanship was, at this period, at a very low ebb in England.

The Newcomen Society[4] had thought to reproduce the figures and a page of text in facsimile and the rest of the text in print. The material has been annotated by Jenkins and others. The political situation makes this expenditure very difficult. Is it worth while to seek an American subsidy? It could be well done with two or three coloured plates for $550, and quite satisfactorily but without coloured plates for half that sum. I should be glad to hear your reaction. The project might interest Larkey.

With all kind wishes,

Yours ever

Charles Singer

[1] Rhys Jenkins (1859–1953), engineer and historian of engineering; see R. T. Smith, 'Jenkins, Rhys (1859–1953)', *Oxford dictionary of national biography* (Oxford: Oxford University Press, 2004), vol. 29, 965–966.

[2] Henry Winram Dickinson (1870–1952), historian of engineering and technology; see Arthur Stowers, 'Dickinson, Henry Winram (1870–1952)', rev. *Oxford dictionary of national biography* (Oxford: Oxford University Press, 2004), vol. 16, 93–94.

[3] Hausbücher, literally house books; private sketchbooks by scholars, architects and so on, that were kept at home.

[4] Newcomen Society for the study of engineering and technology.

280

Sigerist to Singer, Baltimore?, 30 March 1940

Dear Singer:

The manuscript sounds most exciting and it should be published by all means. If it were published in America, it would be very easy to get a subsidy but it is rather difficult to find money here to subsidize a publication of a group such as the Newcomen Society. I think the only foundation that could be approached would be the Carnegie Corporation. They have special funds for England and Dominions so that there may be a good chance of getting some money from them.[1]

With kind regards, I am

Yours ever,

Henry E. Sigerist

[1] See previous letter.

281

Singer to Sigerist, London, 14 June 1940

My dear Sigerist,

Just a line to tell you that all is well with us all. Dorothea & I come a good deal to London and never hesitate to undertake the journey when we can be of the least use. We have been in London for the last 10 days but go back to Cornwall next week.

Physically we have both of us never been in better health & the nervous strain of the last years does not seem to have told on us in the least, but, of course, historical work has been almost impossible.

I visited D'Arcy Power today. He is now 85 but well & happy & working well too. I wish I had his wonderful power of abstraction.

About the political situation, I can only say that the change of government has come to us as an immense relief. The resolution & determination in this country is splendid. I have talked to many soldiers back from France.[1] Their attitude is most heartening & beyond all praise. I respect our ordinary soldiers more than I can say & feel that such men cannot fail. Only two days ago I travelled with a trainload of men on leave & it was an inspiring experience.

Love to you all from us all

Yours always

Charles Singer

[1] Winston Churchill had become Prime Minister in May 1940 shortly before France collapsed under the German invasion and the British Army in France escaped at Dunkirk.

282

Singer to Sigerist, Kilmarth, 18 August 1940

My dear Sigerist,

I have just read the review by Agnes Arber in Nature of the Aztec herbal published by the Johns Hopkins[1] and a point[?] occurs to me that you may care to have looked into.

Sir Hans Sloane in his <u>Voyage to Jamaica</u> says that Hernandez was the <u>second</u> botanist to visit America & that the first was "one Codrus an Italian.[2] The discoveries he made were few or not communicated to the world". Sloane's book is a very good one which is undeservedly forgotten. He is normally a most accurate man. I suggest that this Codrus hunting out[?]. Had he anything to do with your[?] herbal?

I hope that you will manage to spare me a copy. It is impossible for me to buy it – even if I could afford it – because as a private buyer I should not be allowed to transmit the foreign currency.

All is well with us & we are pretty comfortable. I have actually sent to the Clarendon Press the very last page of the very last chapter of my <u>History of Science</u>. It is a shortish book.[3]

We are busy here doing all we can to grow food for which our land is particularly suitable. I never thought that I would become a market gardener in my old age. But I like it.

Andrew will try for the Navy or the Royal Engineers this autumn. He is 18 in October & if he is successful, he gets about a year's special training. His whole bias is toward engineering.

We shall stay here whatever happens. We shall go to London a good deal but travelling naturally becomes more difficult & more expensive.

All kind wishes to you all from us all.

Yours ever

Charles Singer

Do you hear from Klebs? I had a rather silly letter from him when I congratulated him on your presentation number[4]

---

[1] Emily W Emmart, *The Badianus Manuscript. An Aztec herbal of 1552* (Baltimore: John Hopkins Press, 1940), reviewed by Agnes Arber, 'An Aztec herbal', *Nature*, 1940, **146**: 81–83.

[2] Hans Sloane (1660–1753), British physician and collector; see Arthur MacGregor, 'Sloane, Sir Hans, baronet (1660–1753)', *Oxford dictionary of national biography* (Oxford: Oxford University Press, 2004), vol. 50, 943–949. Hans Sloane, *A voyage to the islands, Madera, Barbados, Nieves, S. Christophers and Jamaica* (London, 1707–1725). Francisco Hernandez, 16th-century Spanish naturalist; see Juan Vernet, 'Hernández, Francisco', *Complete dictionary of scientific biography*, Vol. 6 (Detroit: Charles Scribner's Sons, 2008), 309–310.

[3] Singer (1941).

[4] Henry E. Sigerist, et al., 'Congratulatory epistle to Arnold C. Klebs', *Bulletin of the History of Medicine* (Arnold C. Klebs Number), 1940, 8: 319–328.

283

Sigerist to Singer, Baltimore?, 14 September 1940

Dear Singer:

I have to thank you for two letters. I meant to write you long ago but I have just been away for two months. Since we could not go abroad this year, we made a motor tour through the country from Coast to Coast, spent nine weeks on the road and made over 10,000 miles. I took advantage of the trip to make a study of new medical service plans and health cooperatives and wrote 25 articles on the subject for a New York paper[1]. It was a most interesting tour. We took four weeks to reach the Pacific at Seattle driving through the Northern states and then followed the Coast down to Los Angeles and came back through the South.

God knows when we shall be able to go to Europe again. I was greatly worried about my Mother who lives a few blocks from the air field in Basel. Fortunately I could persuade her to leave the city and go to the mountains in the critical days of May when all Switzerland was living with the finger on the trigger day and night.[2] It seems that the immediate danger of invasion is over for Switzerland but squeezed in between Italy and Germany with a Fascist France as neighbor, nobody knows what can happen. We get regular news from my Mother and it is amazing that in spite of all, the Clipper service is functioning better than ever.[3]

We are reading the gruesome stories of the bombing of London with much concern. It is horrible to think how many cultural values are being destroyed in a stupid way. What worries me still more is that we have been unable to prevent a catastrophe that every child could foresee. The policy of the great powers, particularly from 1932 on was simply criminal. It was a deliberate suicide. And the trouble is that people do not learn from history. America is probably going to repeat all the mistakes made in the past. We are rearming feverishly but blindly and are fighting fifth colums [sic] activities[4] by persecuting the anti Fascists.

I am glad to send you a copy of the Badianus Manuscript[5] under separate cover and I am very grateful to you for your reference to Sir Hans Sloane's Voyage to Jamaica.[6]

I hope you will be spared in Cornwall. I can well imagine you as a market gardner [sic]. I remember that in Highgate you cultivated not only roses but vegetables as well.

It was excellent news to hear that your History of Science is completed.[7] I have just finished a little book which will be published by the Yale University Press under the title, Medicine and Human Welfare, a series of lectures I gave at Yale some time ago.[8] This winter I am writing an Introduction to Medical Economics, a historical and sociological study based on a series of lectures I gave in South Africa last year.[9]

The family is well. All of them enjoyed the trip very much. Both girls are in College. Erica, the senior, will graduate next spring with history as major subject and Nora is entering college just now. She is particularly interested in social work. It seems that there will be no medical woman in the family.

With all good wishes to you all from us all, I am
Yours ever,
Henry E. Sigerist

[1] Sigerist had 18 articles published in the New York Newspaper PM, 1940.
[2] During the German invasion of the Netherlands, Belgium, and France.
[3] The transatlantic clipper service, with the so-called flying boat planes.
[4] Groups working for the enemy.
[5] Emmart (1940).
[6] Sloane (1707).
[7] Singer (1941).
[8] Henry E. Sigerist, *Medicine and human welfare* (New Haven, 1941).
[9] Possibly Sigerist (1940a).

284

Singer to Sigerist, Kilmarth, 3 November 1940

My dear Sigerist,

Many thanks for the Badianus MS.[1] It is an admirable piece of work and quite a new line. I congratulate you heartily upon it. In studying it[,] several points occur to me, one or two of which may interest you. I have written to Miss Emmart[2] about them and, to save time, I enclose copy of that letter.

Today I enter my 65th year and am surprised and pleased to find myself working well. From the beginning of 1933 till the end of 1939 work was almost impossible for me. My mind was too occupied with the situation and with the fate of my colleagues. Including 1914–18, when I was in the army, the Germans have thus wasted 10 of my years and those the best years. This, should anyone be sufficiently interested, explains the smallness of my output.

I entirely agree with you that the whole situation might have been forseen by a child. I forsaw it clearly enough and the situation has little to teach me that I did not know perfectly well already. Nevertheless two things I have learned. One is the extreme difficulty that even honest men find in seeing things that they do not wish to see. The other is the extraordinary determination, humanity and political intelligence of the British working-class. It is a very great people. The character and composition of our government at the outbreak of war was a world-misfortune from which we cannot hope for an easy recovery. That recovery has begun is due entirely to the good sense, judgement and courage of English working-class leaders who, by a most unfortunate political accident, were and are inadequately represented in Parliament. But the people is all right and would, I am convinced, vote that war is at least less detestable than the peace which preceded it.

We are not infrequently in London. Dorothea spends two or three nights there every fortnight and has been there during the worst bombing nights.[3] It is a plain fact that there is no jitters, no disorder and no panic in London. The self-control of the people is most heartening and impressive. The general feeling might be impressed by saying that it would be better to lose Westminster Abbey and the British Museum than to lose these plus everything else. And the latter would be the effect of a peace with Hitler.

Here, living right on the coast, we are of course in a highly protected area. The improvement in its defences during the last few months has to be seen to be believed. Moreover I feel, as a result of my military experience in the last war, that our troops have improved greatly since then. They appear to be of much better physique and are certainly better educated for English education has gone ahead tremendously in the last twenty years.

We, personally, suffer no privation at all. We are, of course, considerably poorer and for this and other reasons, travelling is more difficult to us. A few articles are rationed but the diet available is excellent and, personally, I prefer it. I think it probable that, as in the last war, the nutrition of the nation as a whole has actually improved. This locality is a grazing and vegetable growing region and has a record crop of vegetable and fruits. Of potatoes alone we ourselves gathered three tons of our own little bit of land so that we are certainly in no danger of starvation! Fuel also is ample – partly, of course, because of the cessation of exports.

The only thing from which we personally suffer is difficulty in getting the books we want. We cannot get any from the continent; we cannot now afford to buy in England as we used; nor do I review as much as I did. The Oxford University Press is very kind and usually sends me anything in my line that they publish but cannot give me things like the Badianus that they publish for others. We cannot buy books from America, – for one thing there would be great diffuculty in obtaining exchange. I was thus particularly glad of the Badianus. I should be very grateful if Americans would send me their works or reprints. I do not yet know whether there will be difficulty in sending subscriptions to American societies.

I was at Oxford a few days ago and spent some time with old friends at the Clarendon Press. Despite war-time difficulties they hope to maintain their programme of learned works. Sales of these actually increased a little during the first year of war. You have, of course, now the complete new Greek Lexicon. The Classical Dictionary should be out soon with articles by Edelstein.[4] By the way I have written to him by this mail. The Dictionary has also several articles by myself.

My Short History of Science should be out early in 1941. I want to call it A sketch of the History of Science – which is what it is – but the Clarendon Press insists on the wider title.[5]

What is happening to Klebs? Is he in U.S.A.? What about Castiglioni and Starkenstein and Meyer-Steinegg?[6] Neuburger survives but has been through a very bad time. He is quite adequately provided for in a financial sense. Isidor Fischer is, I fear, failing. Friedenwald and Kelley sent me two hundred dollars to provide scientific books for Prag who is interned[.][7] For reasons with which I need not trouble you, it has proved difficult to administer this but I hope to do so within the next day or two. Dorothea and I are still burdened with all sorts of work for refugees but, of course, far less than before the war.

I am not sure if I told you that I found in the possession of the Scottish Beekeepers' Association a copy of the huge folio sheet of bees by Federigo Cesi. It is the only copy – so far as I can learn – outside the Lancisian Library. I am working on it with F. J. Cole and am publishing it in full.

Kindest regards to the family,
Yours ever,
Charles Singer

My pupil F. Sherwood Taylor has just been appointed to succeed R. T. Gunther at Oxford. It is, I think, an excellent appointment. F. J. Cole has just retired. Wolf retires at the end of this session. Partington is at Cambridge & comes here sometimes; his wife died a few weeks ago.[8] Dickinson payed us a visit with a new wife – a very charming woman. His work with the Newcomen Society goes on bravely. Have you seen a little work by A. P. Rossiter, The Growth of Science in basic[?] English?[9] Rather good, I thought. H. T. Pledge's Science since 1500 read (or rather cannot be read) like a work of Sudhoff![10] just a muddled [....] ! Sherwood Taylor's Galileo is the best of the recent vintage here.[11]

[1] Emmart (1940).

[2] Emily W. Emmart, (born 1898) medical historian

[3] After the occupation of Norway, Denmark, The Netherlands, Belgium, and France, Germany started the air raids on London and other British cities, apparently as a prelude for an invasion.

[4] *The Oxford classical dictionary* was first published in 1949.

[5] Singer (1941).

[6] Theodor Meyer-Steineg (1873–1936), German historian of medicine; see *Theodor Meyer-Steineg (1873–1936), Arzt Historiker, Sammler*: Ausstellung von Leihgaben des Instituts für Geschichte der Medizin, Naturwissenschaften und Technik (Ernst-Haeckel-Haus) der Friedrich-Schiller-Universität Jena vom 18. Juni bis 4. August 1991 / Katalog bearbeitet von Christa Habrich ; mit Beiträgen von Ernst Künzl und Susanne Zimmermann (Ingolstad: Deutsches Medizinhistorisches Museum, 1991).

[7] Isidor Fischer (1868–1943), German gynaecologist and medical historian; see Arturo Castiglioni, 'Dr. Isidor Fischer, 1869–1943', *Bulletin of the History of Medicine*, 1943, **14**: 114–115. Harry Friedenwald (1864–1950), ophthalmologist and medical historian; see Owsei Temkin, 'Harry Friedenwald', *Bulletin of the History of Medicine*, 1951, **25**: 185–187, and 'The medico-historical writings of Dr. Harry Friedenwald', *ibid.*, 187–190. There are several medical historians named Kelley; Prag not identified

[8] Frank Sherwood Taylor (1897–1956), British chemist and historian of science; see Frank Greenaway, 'Taylor, Frank Sherwood (1897–1956)', *Oxford dictionary of national biography* (Oxford: Oxford University Press, 2004), vol. 53, 884–885. Robert William Theodore Gunther (1869–1940), British zoologist, antiquary and historian of science; see Roger Hutchins, 'Gunther, Robert William Theodore (1869–1940)', *Oxford dictionary of national biography* (Oxford: Oxford University Press, 2004), vol. 24, 261–262. Francis J. Cole (1872–1959), British anatomist and medical historian, see K. J. Franklin, 'Francis Joseph Cole. 1872–1959', *Biographical Memoirs of Fellows of the Royal Society*, 1960, **5**: 37–47. Abraham Wolf (1876–1948), British historian of science, see Jacob Haberman, 'Abraham Wolf: a forgotten Jewish reform thinker', *The Jewish Quarterly Review*, 1991, New Series **81**: 267–304. James Riddick Partington (1886–1965), British chemist and historian of chemistry, see W. A. Smeaton, 'Partington, James Riddick (1886–1965)', rev. W. H. Brock, *Oxford dictionary of national biography* (Oxford: Oxford University Press, 2004), vol. 42, 951–953.

[9] Arthur Percival Rossiter, *The growth of science: an outline history* ([London]: Published for the Orthological Institute by Pitman,1939).

[10] Humphrey T. Pledge (1903–1960), British historian of science; *Science since 1500; a short history of mathematics, physics, chemistry, biology* (London: H.M.S.O., 1939).

[11] F. Sherwood Taylor, *Galileo and the freedom of thought* (London, 1938).

285

Singer to Sigerist, Kilmarth, 27 February 1941

My dear Sigerist,

I want to draw your attention to the work of B. R. Townend, Borrowdale, Many Gates Lane, Sandal, Wakefield, Yorkshire, England (what an address!).[1]

He is a practising dentist but his historical work is <u>sincere</u>, thorough original & incomparably better than most amateur stuff. I do not know him personally but he & I have corresponded regularly for about 6 years & I always encourage him. His work ought to find a wider public than Dental Journals!

I think that you might do worse than ask him to write for the Bulletin, something on rather broader lines. A little encouragement would, I think, do a lot for him. Of course in normal times we should be delighted to ask him to write for the Historical Section of the Royal Society of Medicine but at the present, we are bound to economise print & paper.

My History of Science is going through at last & nearly all of it is now in page proof & revise. I hope & believe that it be actually published this spring.[2]

All well here. Food quite good &, personally, I rather like the war diet with the increased proportion of vegetables. No one has any doubt at all that we shall beat the Germans in the end though it must be a long business. Everyone is prepared for an invasion & all sorts of set backs but we are going to finish the job off this time.[3] As one looks back on what has happened one can almost weep at the misfortune that placed England in the hands of Chamberlain.[4] He was just an inferior manifestation of the human spirit & there is no more & no less to be said of that miserable misfit.

Let me have a line to say that this has reached you.

All kind wishes

Yours ever,

Charles Singer

[1] B. R. Townend, 'The story of the toothworm', *Bulletin of the History of Medicine*, 1944, 15: 37–58.
[2] Singer (1941).
[3] Unlike World War I the goal of World War II would become "unconditional surrender of Germany".
[4] Neville Chamberlain (1869–1940), Prime Minister of the UK from 1937 to 1940; see Andrew J. Crozier, 'Chamberlain, (Arthur) Neville (1869–1940)', *Oxford dictionary of national biography* (Oxford: Oxford University Press, 2004), vol.10, 934–955.

286

Sigerist to Singer, Baltimore?, 27 March 1941

Dear Singer:

Your letter of February 27 just came and reminded me of the fact that I have not written you for a very long time. Many thanks for drawing my attention to Dr. Townend. His paper is very good and I should be glad to have him write for our Bulletin although at present I am swamped with manuscripts. I have enough to fill the journal until next February. I am glad to say that the standard is improving in America, and I am particularly pleased that there are a number of young people like George Rosen – whose articles you have probably seen – who are doing excellent work in the field. I hope you receive the Bulletin of the History of Medicine regularly. Should you have any gaps, please let me know.

The Yale Press has just published a little book of mine, MEDICINE AND HUMAN WELFARE. It is a very unpretentious little book based on three lectures I gave at Yale some time ago. I am sending you a copy under separate cover.[1]

We were very happy to hear that you are all well. The general situation looks infinitely better than last autumn. The African campaign was a splendid military feat and the situation in the Balkans is also infinitely better than it could be.[2] It is stupid to assume as some people here do that Hitler's war machine is invincible. The collapse of Mussolini should have opened their eyes. Once the German Army begins to crack up, I should think that it would collapse as rapidly as it did in 1918, if not more soon.[3]

If Britain, the United States, the Soviet Union, Turkey and China could really stick together and cooperate planfully, I should think the Axis would have little chance to survive.[4]

It was excellent news to hear that your History of Science is in page proof already.[5] Such a book is badly needed, and I should think it would have a very good market in America where so many colleges offer a course and are looking for a good text-book.

With kind regards to Mrs. Singer and yourself from us all, I am
Yours ever,
Henry E. Sigerist

[1] Sigerist (1941a).
[2] African campaign refers to the British victory over Mussolini's troops in Libya. Sigerist could not forsee that the next countries to be invaded by the Germans were Yugoslavia and Greece.
[3] The collapse of the German Army did not occur until 1944/45.
[4] The Axis refers to Nazi Germany and Fascist Italy (plus Japan).
[5] Singer (1941).

287

My dear Sigerist,

Many thanks for yours of Nov. 16 1941 which reached me a few days ago.[1]

I had your letter of August 4 and answered it soon after receipt. I will gladly undertake the notice of D'Arcy Power. My only trouble is that I am now engaged in teaching biology to a group of schools evacuated in this part and find the work very arduous. I do all the practical laboratory work and enjoy it. I took my degree in it many years ago. I love the subject but I am naturally rusty so that my time is very full. The biology master, a young man, was called up into the army. As it is impossible to find another, I have undertaken his job. The work is, in effect, to prepare students for their medical course.

I have been in occasional touch with D'Arcy's son for many years, and I will at once get in touch with him again.

My book was published in June 1941 and is dedicated to you and Sarton.[2] There is some legal difficulty in my sending you a copy because the book is on sale in America on special terms. I have been repeatedly assured by the Oxford Press that you would receive one. It is being distributed in U.S.A. by the American branch of the Oxford University Press. You would do me a service if you would let me know, at once, whether you have received a copy & whether it is yet available in USA.

I was very glad to have your second letter. We are all in it now but nothing whatever has happened that you and I did not know perfectly well for years, was going to happen. What a wretched figure Neville Chamberlain will cut in history.

We are all well. Many American friends have sent us supplies of food, but we really are extremely well off and have enough and to spare. We grow a great deal ourselves[.] There are, of course, certain restrictions on diet but the fact is that they happen rather to suit us. Beyond that Dorothea and I are a bit older – I am now in my 66th year – we are really extremely well. I enjoy sea bathing & hard manual labour, in fact anything except cold! Andrew is in the midst of a course of engineering and it may be that he will be kept on that rather than be sent into the forces. It depends, of course, on where he may be most useful, but for the present he is reserved for engineering. He is in London living with an engineering colleague of mine. In the evenings he helps to train younger boys for the forces. Nancy is teaching at a school near Oxford and likes it greatly. We have had them both home for 3 weeks at Xmas.

The change of public opinion about Russia is, to me, one of the miracles of history.[3] We have learned quite a lot about the nature and formation of public opinion in the last 10 years. But I don't think that even 2 years ago anyone could have guessed that an Archbishop of Canterbury, that the Cardinal of Westminster & the leaders of the Conservative party in England & the Prime Minister and the Foreign Secretary could have been quite so loud in their praises of Stahlin [sic] !

You might ask do we have any hardships. Yes we have. They are all minor hardships and I do not doubt that you in U.S.A. will soon be sharing them.[4] The first hardship is overwork. Everyone really has too much to do. I don't see how that can be helped with all the most active people taken from their work. We must put up with it. The second hardship is the black-out. This is a fatiguing, trying, and depressing nuisance, but it is no more. Third is the difficulty of travel: motoring is greatly limited and is getting more expensive & practically impossible. Train services are naturally curtailed; but worst of all, trains are overcrowded. We all travel as little as possible and I, personally, don't expect to be in London till April at earliest. Fourth is the lack of books and the limitation of contact with scholarship.

To me it seems that probably the worst feature in the situation is, in the long run, that the Roman Catholic Church is pretty consistently on the wrong side and is likely to remain so. This must lead to grim struggles lasting for many years even after the war is ended. The Church is likely to be greatly damaged in the struggle but that is not very much consolation!

I enclose an article which you may like to print in the Bulletin. For your convenience I write of it in an attached separate letter.[5]

I shall send this letter in duplicate, the second a fortnight after the first.

All kind wishes from family to family

Yours ever,

Charles Singer

---

[1] Sigerist's two letters are missing; the last one took two months from the U.S. to the UK
[2] Singer (1941).
[3] Due to the Soviet resistance against the invading Germans.
[4] As a result of the Japanese attack on Pearl Harbor, December 1941, and the U.S.'s entry into World War II.
[5] See following letter (15 January 1942b).

288

Singer to Sigerist, Kilmarth, 15 January 1942b

My dear Sigerist

I enclose an article that you may like for the "Bulletin".[1] No part of it has been published, nor have I offered it before. I gave it as a broadcast in 1932 and have used the material once or twice as a lecture. Archibald Malloch thought it the best thing that I have done. I have often been asked to print it but declined for the excellent reason that I had lost the MS! However[,] I found it a few days ago, and have reshaped it a little.

The Bibliography may be too sketchy for you. If so, omit it. Its completion might be a pleasant & easy student task and Americans seem to like bibliographical work. It is really impossible for me to complete it in England at the moment. Notably I cannot run down the reference to Adams' paper of 1829 On the Nervous System of Galen and other Ancient Authors. I have seen and read it, but cannot find where. I think it is probably in a local Aberdeen medical journal (probably of Aberdeen medical society) but it is 22 years since I visited Aberdeen for the purpose of collecting Adams material![2]

If you decide to print, it will have to be without sending me the proofs. I know how busy you all are but perhaps you or Larkey would correct them for me.

I am sending this letter and its duplicate at intervals of 14 days. Should you get both I suggest that you use the second later copy because I shall have had it a fortnight longer and may have made a few minor improvements.

Yours ever

Charles Singer

This bust of Adams is by the sculptor William Brodie 1815–81 who was well known for his efficiency in work of this kind.[3] It is in Aberdeen University Library & was presented to the University by Dr. A. Leith Adams F.R.S., son of Francis Adams.[4]

If you decide to reproduce it, I suggest that it be enlarged & only the upper half be reproduced. This will partly conceal the ridiculous classical dress.

It is an excellent likeness I have compared it with a photo.

---

[1] Charles Singer, 'A great country doctor. Francis Adams of Banchory 1796–1861', *Bulletin of the History of Medicine*, 1942, **12**: 1–17.

[2] Francis Adams (1796–1861), British physician and classical scholar and historian of science; see Vivian Nutton, 'Adams , Francis (1796–1861)', *Oxford dictionary of national biography* (Oxford: Oxford University Press, 2004), vol. 1, 224–226. *On the nervous system* .... not identified; perhaps part of a book by Adams.

[3] William Brodie (1815–1881), British sculptor, see Helen E. Smailes, 'Brodie, William (1815–1881)', *Oxford dictionary of national biography* (Oxford: Oxford University Press, 2004), vol. 7, 782–783.

[4] A. Leith Adams (1827–1882), British army surgeon and professor of natural history; see Anthony J. Gaston, 'Adams, Andrew Leith (1827–1882)', *Oxford dictionary of national biography* (Oxford: Oxford University Press, 2004), vol. 1, 222–223.

289

Sigerist to Singer, Baltimore?, 23 March 1942

My dear Singer:

Many thanks for your letter of January 15. I received the first duplicate with Adams manuscript. The second duplicate has not arrived so far but may come still. Of course, I shall be delighted to publish the paper in the Bulletin and we shall be very glad to take care of the galley proofs here.[1] I cannot tell you exactly in what number of the Bulletin the paper will come out, but I shall publish it as soon as possible. Just now I am flooded with manuscripts and have enough on hand to fill the next two volumes of the Bulletin. Many more people are working in the field of medical history here, and on the whole are doing quite decent work. In addition to American papers, I have several long ones from England, one from old Neuburger and one from Pagel. Haggis' Paper on Cinchona was very good indeed.[2] He seems to be a good man.

But first of all, I wish to congratulate you most cordially on your History of Science and want to tell you how very much I appreciated your thoughtfulness in having it dedicated to Sarton and myself.[3] The book was issued in America a few weeks ago. It is a splendid piece of work and I am sure it will have a very good reception in this country. A book of that type was badly needed. Many colleges are offering courses in the history of science and I am certain that your book will soon become a required textbook.

At the Institute we are carrying on as well as we can. So far, we have not been greatly affected by the war. Larkey has been in Washington for the last two years and drops in only incidentally but the rest of my staff is still here and I have three new fellows in the history of medicine in addition. Two of them are classical philologists who are working in the field of Greek science. One is a very good botanist and works on Theophrastus[4] and the other is a very good mathematician. These two fellowships are a new experiment financed by the Carnegie Foundation. The idea is to steer young philologists into the field of the history of science. The third fellow is one of my old European students, Erwin H. Ackerknecht, who besides being a physician is a very good social anthropologist and is doing some work on primitive medicine.[5]

We have condensed the medical course from four to three years. The number of courses and hours remains the same but we have sacrificed the vacations. It is going to be very strenuous for the students and I have great doubts as to the results but it is an emergency matter.

I wish I could take a more active part in the war but I am too old for the armed forces and as to an office job, the one I have at the University is probably the best I can do. I am also working with a group of students on health insurance and similar problems. There is no doubt that after the war things will move very rapidly in the medical field and we should prepare for it now. I am, of course, in touch with developments in Britain and in the Dominions. We have two excellent English students in the Medical School; one from Liverpool and one from the University of London. They are doing exceedingly well and are unusually bright and alert young people. They are among my most faithful students. I have also a student from India, a young girl who works at the School of Hygiene and is also extremely promising. We are all watching Sir Stafford Cripps' mission to India with keen interest.[6]

We have no hardships yet. Automobile tires are unavailable but my old ones will run for at least one more year. You cannot buy cars either but since it was the custom to get a new car every two years, there are few old ones around. Sugar will probably be rationed but the rations will be ample, more than we usually consume. There is no doubt, however, that we are going to feel the pinch by the end of the year. The country must have had enormous supplies of everything.

The letter you sent me last summer never arrived and I hope you will let me have some time the obituary note of Sir D'Arcy Power.

The family is well. Erica, the older girl, is studying in the Library School at Columbia and will be a librarian soon. Nora, the younger girl, is at the Conservatory of Music where she is doing very well. She is a good violinist and wants to be a music teacher in a college some day. Of course, life is becoming very expensive. Prices are rising and taxes are increasing very rapidly so that we will have to cut down our expenses very considerably but this is the least we can do, and we certainly have no reason to complain in any way.

Hoping to hear from you soon, I am, with kind regards and all good wishes to Mrs. Singer and yourself

Yours ever,

Henry E. Sigerist

[1] Singer (1942a).

[2] A. W. Haggis, 'Fundamental errors in the early history of cinchona', *Bulletin of the History of Medicine*, 1941, **10**: 417–459. Alec William James Haggis (1889–1946), a member of staff at the Wellcome Historical Medical Museum.

[3] Singer (1941). Singer's dedication reads: "I would like this volume to go as a greeting to two transatlantic colleagues, George Sarton and Henry Sigerist. With the former I have been in fraternal relations for half a lifetime; with the latter for a time shorter only because he has had the advantage of having been born later. I owe much to the work and personality of both."

[4] Theophrastus of Eressos (*c.*371–287 BC) successor of Aristotle.

[5] Israel E. Drabkin and G. Raynor Thompson had Carnegie Fellowships in the History of Graeco-Roman Science; Erwin H Ackerknecht worked from 1942 to 1944 in Sigerist's institute, see Owsei Temkin, 'In memoriam Erwin H. Ackerknecht (1906–1988)', *Bulletin of the History of Medicine*, 1989, **63**: 273–275. For a biographical introduction and Sigererist's correspondence with Ackerknecht, see Marcel H. Bickel (ed.), *Henry E. Sigerist: Correspondences With Welch, Cushing, Garrison and Ackerknecht* (Bern: Peter Lang, 2010), 159–488.

[6] Stafford Cripps (1889–1952), British politician; his Mission to India was to keep India loyal to the British war effort in return for independence after World War II; see Peter Clarke and Richard Toye, 'Cripps, Sir (Richard) Stafford (1889–1952)', *Oxford dictionary of national biography* (Oxford: Oxford University Press, 2004), vol. 14, 200–206.

290

Singer to Sigerist, Kilmarth, 11 May 1942

My dear Sigerist,

Many thanks for various offprints. I was particularly interested in your Paracelsus paper.[1] As you know, I have long hoped that you would do something on him on a larger scale – a general survey of the man & his work. There is nothing on him worth reading in English while nearly everything on him in German is unreadable either from ill-regulated erudition or idiotic mysticism.

I have just spent a fortnight in London but unfortunately missed D'Arcy Power's son. But I go again in a week or two.

I am glad you like my little "History of Science".[2] To me its only merit seems to be its scheme of arrangement. I tried to send you a copy but the Oxford University Press would, unaccountably, not allow this.

I wish you would be so kind as to send me a copy of your Four Paracelsus Treatises.[3] I would buy it but to do so needs a permit to transmit the payment & the formalities for this are really worth while only for major transmissions.

Do you, by any chance, know anyone in America who is an authority on the early European knowledge of America & especially on the use of the word America? I have found what is, I believe, the first matter of course use of the word. It occurs in a pun in the course of a book on music published in Paris in 1509 by one Wollich.[4] It seems very strange that one could make so early the pun between AMERICUS & AMARICUS but so it is & I should like an opinion upon the whole queer story. Who could I write to about?[5]

I am glad that you will print my account of Francis Adams.[6] I did not send you a second copy because I had nothing to alter & I heard from you pretty promptly that you had received it. The posts to & from USA are now fairly rapid.

F. J. Cole's History of Zoology is ready. It is good work. He finds it impossible to get it printed. I am urging him to have it multigraphed & if he does I will see that you get a copy. He is 72 & in poor health & I am very anxious to see it out in some form. Cole is an excellent & [....] scholar.[7]

A few nights ago Clifford Dobell (the authority on Leeuwenhoek) came to see me.[8] He is the literary executor of William Bulloch the historian of biology. He tells me that Bulloch's work on Spallanzani is fit to print. Bulloch often spoke of it to me & wrote me several times about it but I had no idea it was so nearly complete.[9] How goes the publishing trade in U.S.A.[?] Do you think it would be worth putting forward the idea of printing Cole's & Bulloch's work on your side?

I work pretty steadily, so far as school teaching allows. An abstract of my history of Amphioxus is to appear in "Endeavour".[10] Do you think it worth while sending the fuller account to USA?

The war news seems to me distinctly better & there does seem to be at least the dawn of doubt in Germany.

Our Andrew is going into engineering works in a few weeks & I should not be surprised if he remains till the end of the war. But, of course, none of us knows his fate nowadays.

Did you & Miss Emmart get my letter on the Badianus MS. & was it any good. I have had no reply from her.

I saw T. R. Elliott the other day.[11] He told me a story of that quite excellent paper by Haggis on Quinine that you published. It seems that Haggis finished it more than 2 years ago but the first person he showed it to, Johnston Saint[12] of the Wellcome Museum (a most ignorant man) told him it was no good! He just accepted that & put it away! He certainly is a very modest man.

All kind wishes,

Yours ever

Charles Singer

---

[1] Paracelsus (1493–1541), Swiss physician and theologian; Paracelsus paper (Sigerist 1941b). See Walter Pagel, 'Paracelsus, Theophrastus Philippus Aureolus Bombastus von Hohenheim', *Complete dictionary of scientific biography*, Vol. 10 (Detroit: Charles Scribner's Sons, 2008), 304–313; and Dane T. Daniel, 'Paracelsus, Theophrastus Philippus Aureolus Bombastus von Hohenheim', *Ibid*, Vol. 24 (Detroit: Charles Scribner's Sons, 2008), 14–17.

[2] Singer (1941).

[3] Henry E. Sigerist (ed.), *Four treatises of Theophrastus von Hohenheim called Paracelsus* (Baltimore, 1941).

[4] Wollich not identified

[5] Singer (1945a).

[6] Singer (1942a).

[7] Francis Cole published several works on the history of biological themes, however, no history of zoology.

[8] Clifford Dobell (1886–1949), British protozoologist; see Claude E. Dolman, 'Dobell, Cecil Clifford', *Complete dictionary of scientific biography*, vol. 4 (Detroit: Charles Scribner's Sons, 2008), 132–133. Antoni van Leeuwenhoek (1632–1723), Dutch microscopist; see Johannes Heniger, 'Leeuwenhoek, Antoni van', *Complete dictionary of scientific biography*, vol. 8 (Detroit: Charles Scribner's Sons, 2008), 126–130.

[9] William Bulloch (1868–1941), British bacteriologist, pathologist and historian of biology; see Clifford Dobell, 'Bulloch, William (1868–1941)', rev. Claire E. J. Herrick, *Oxford dictionary of national biography* (Oxford: Oxford University Press, 2004), vol. 8, 638–639. Lazzaro Spallanzani (1729–1799), Italian physiologist; see Claude E. Dolman, 'Spallanzani, Lazzaro', *Complete dictionary of scientific biography*, vol. 12 (Detroit: Charles Scribner's Sons, 2008), 553–567. Bulloch's Spallanzani was apparently not published.

[10] Singer's Amphioxus paper was not published in the 1940s.

[11] Thomas Renton Elliott (1877–1961), British physician and physiologist and Trustee of the Wellcome Foundation; see Harold Himsworth, 'Elliott, Thomas Renton (1877–1961)', rev. *Oxford dictionary of national biography* (Oxford: Oxford University Press, 2004), vol. 18, 205–206.

[12] Peter J. Johnston-Saint, conservator of the Wellcome Museum

291

Sigerist to Singer, Baltimore, 17 June 1942

My dear Singer:

I just received your letter of May 11. I take great pleasure in sending you under separate cover the Paracelsus volume that we recently published as well as a few other publications.[1] I think I never sent you the translation of Pettenkofer's lectures on The Value of Health to a City that I made last year.[2] I am also sending a big volume of Edgar Erskine Hume on "Ornithologists of the United States Army Medical Corps".[3] It is an interesting book and shows that some of the old Army doctors in America were keen observers and good scientists. Hume is a very good man, a graduate of both our Medical School and School of Hygiene. At present he is in charge of a training center for Army physicians, but he has such an enormous capacity for work that in spite of his official duties, he still has time for historical research. The Surgeon General's Office bought 500 copies of the book for distribution to the various Army libraries which gave us a subsidy of $2,000 and made the publication possible.

I am also sending a book by Edward H. Hume that we brought out last year, "The Chinese Way in Medicine".[4] Hume is lecturer at the Institute but lives in New York where he is chairman of The Christian Medical Council for Overseas Work. He speaks, reads and writes Chinese perfectly but he is not a very deep scholar as you will notice from the book. I am sending the books, each one separately with a few days' interval so that they will not be all on the same boat.[5]

I was very interested in what you wrote about Haggis. His paper is first-rate and I had many inquiries about it. The Cinchona people were particularly interested in it since it forced them to revise all their propaganda literature.[6]

I am through with Paracelsus, at least for the time being. I read with much amusement the article debunking him in the Proceedings of the Royal Society of Medicine.[7] I found the article rather weak, however. One could make a very good case against Paracelsus but it should be done in a more thorough way. The article contains a good many errors. I will take up Paracelsus again when I come to the Renaissance volume of my History of

Medicine. I do not know whether I ever wrote you that it is going to be an 8-volume book, a rather terrifying thought.[8] However, there are many good one-volume histories available but I feel that we need a thorough and comprehensive book, fully annotated with bibliographies, charts, maps, etc. that will stimulate and aid further research. Laignel-Lavastine's History in four volumes has beautiful illustrations but the text is stupid. Neuburger and Pagel's Handbuch was a flop. Neuburger never finished his History of Medicine so that, since Haeser, there has not been any comprehensive book on the subject.[9] I have been collecting materials for this book for the last 25 years. Next winter I hope to finish the first volume dealing with primitive medicine and the ancient Orient, and I plan to get the eight volumes out in the course of ten years.

My approach to medical history moreover is rather different from the conventional one and this is one more reason why I do not want to make a short book.

Yes, we have an authority on early European knowledge of America here, namely, Leonardo Olschki. I could not think of a better man for you to consult in the matter. His address is: 61 Sparks Street, Cambridge, Massachusetts. The poor fellow has been in this country several years but has not succeeded in getting a decent job. His tremendous knowledge scares the people off. It is very disagreeable to have such a man in a department when the other members all are mediocrities. For a while he made a living teaching elementary Spanish in a girls' school. As you know, he is the son of the book dealer in Florence and I think he must have some money that allows him to live very modestly.

I was very glad to hear about Dobell's book but I have no idea what the chances would be of publishing it in this country.[10] You know what conditions are. We have so-called commercial publishers who will not touch a book unless they can expect good profits, and university presses who will not publish a book without subsidies. Just now I am on a money hunting expedition for two of my associates. Edelstein has just completed a splendid piece of work, a two-volume book on Asclepius which brings a totally new interpretation of the god and his cult.[11] It will cost $3,200 to print and I do not yet know how I shall find the money. Temkin has just finished a History of Epilepsy for the publication of which I also need a subsidy.[12] I am a very poor beggar and there is nothing I hate more than going up and down Fifth Avenue with my hat in hand. I would advise Dobell to write to Dr. Barnett Cohen (Department of Physiological Chemistry, Johns Hopkins University, School of Medicine, 710 N. Washington Street, Baltimore, Maryland). Cohen is archivist of the American Bacteriological Association and in charge of the preliminary studies they are carrying out in view of preparing a history of bacteriology in America. He has a great admiration for Dobell and, I think, has been in touch with him at the time of the Leeuwenhoek centenary. He could possibly mobilize the bacteriologists to do something for Dobell's book.

I should think that your Amphioxus paper would be very suitable for Isis.[13]

Our plans for the summer are still very vague. In all probability we shall stay here until the end of July and go away for a few weeks during the month of August. The academic year is on but I managed to postpone my teaching until autumn. It is really too hot to prepare lectures now when we have 95° and 90% humidity.

I agree with you that the war situation looks much more hopeful. Hitler certainly did not count with the resistance he is finding in Russia, and I doubt if he can survive another winter. With the growing forces of Britain and America, I do not see how Hitler can expect to hold out and the collapse may come sooner than we expect.[14]

With all good wishes to Mrs. Singer and yourself, I am

Yours very sincerely,

Henry E. Sigerist

---

[1] Sigerist (1941c).

[2] Henry E. Sigerist (ed.), *The value of health to a city. Two lectures delivered in 1873 by Max von Pettenkofer*, Translated by H. E. Sigerist, (Baltimore, 1941).

[3] Edgar E. Hume: *Ornithologists of the United States Army Medical Corps* (Baltimore, 1942). For Hume see G. E. Armstrong, 'In memoriam: Major General Edgar Erskine Hume, *Annals of Internal Medicine*, 1952, **36**: 1154–1155.

[4] Edward Hicks Hume (1876–1957), American physican, lecturer in the History of medicine at the Johns Hopkins University School of Medicine, formerly Dean and Professor of Medicine at the medical school and hospital of Yale-in-China; see Jean A Curran, 'Edward Hicks Hume 1876–1957', *Bulletin of the History of Medicine*, 1957, **31**: 575–576. Edward Hicks Hume, *The Chinese way in medicine* (Baltimore: The Johns Hopkins press, 1940).

[5] This refers to the German submarine war in the North Atlantic.

[6] Cinchona, a tree, the bark of which contains quinine. Cinchona people refers to the controversies about Cinchona in the 17th and 18th centuries.

[7] H. P. Bayon, 'Paracelsus: personality, doctrines and his alleged influence in the reform of medicine', *Proceedings of the Royal Society of Medicine*, 1941, **35**: 69–76.

[8] Sigerist's planned 8-volume work was only started in 1945.

[9] P.M. Maxime Laignel-Lavastine (ed), *Histoire générale de la médecine, de la pharmacie, de l'art dentaire et de l'art vétérinaire*, 3 volumes (Paris 1936–1949), this appeared in three volumes only; Max Neuburger and Julius L. Pagel (eds), *Handbuch der Geschichte der Medizin*, 3 volumes (Jena, 1902–1905.1902). Max Neuburger, *Geschichte der Medizin*, 2 volumes (Stuttgart 1906/1911); Heinrich Haeser, *Lehrbuch der Geschichte der Medizin*, 2 volumes.(3rd ed. Jena 1881).

[10] See letter 290.

[11] Emma J. Edelstein and Ludwig Edelstein, *Asclepius; a collection and interpretation of the testimonies* (Baltimore 1945).

[12] Owsei Temkin, *Falling sickness, a history of epilepsy* (Baltimore, 1945).

[13] A journal of the history of science. See previous letter, note 10 for Amphioxus paper.

[14] Hitler's war machine only collapsed in 1945.

292

Singer to Sigerist, Kilmarth, 8 August 1942

My dear Sigerist,

I have several of your letters unanswered. All contain interesting material. You must not think me ungrateful for all this but, as with everyone in the present situation, I am so fully occupied that any task that can be put off, tends to be so. Overwork is, in fact, one of the major evils of war.

First I want to say what an extremely brilliant book your <u>Medicine and Human Welfare</u> is. I am ashamed to say that I have only just read it, but I am very impressed by it indeed. It is, moreover, most beautifully written. You have produced a real work of art.

I should much like to see it published in England in a cheap form. It is, I know, already published in the technical sense in this country. But it ought to be in some very cheap form, 6d or 1/- (10 cents or 20 cents) which is the price at which widely read books are now appearing here. It is also the most lucrative form for I made more out of a 6d book than out of anything else I have written! The most popular is the so called <u>Penguin Series</u> at 6d. I have today written to Sisam, the Secretary of the Oxford University Press, a letter of which I enclose a copy.[1] I hope that he will respond and that you will agree to let me try to get the book into a cheap form and to use my judgement in making the very small changes that I suggest in this letter. I ought to tell you, however, that owing to the shortage of paper, the publication of books is now much restricted here and that the task may prove impracticable. If you and Sisam and the Yale people agree, however, I will do my best. The book should be on to the bookstalls of this country.[2]

I have been to see Air Commodore Power, dear old D'Arcy's only surviving son, whom I have known for years. He has collected all the books and papers of D'Arcy which he thinks of interest for an account of the old man and has sent them to me here. The case has just arrived. I will try to get this work done during the next few months. Air Commodore Power was going abroad and he was glad that this material should be in my possession.

Many thanks for the reprint of my Francis Adams paper.[3] I feel rather bad at loading the post with such slight material. But it was good of you, and I much appreciate the kind thought.

I read with much interest your notes on the <u>Circle of Petosiris</u> in the "Bulletin".[4] I have a few further annotations to make on this queer little bit of Pythagoreanism and I have collected the material for the purpose. I will try to make time to write it up.

There has just turned up in London a late but illuminating new Five Figure Anatomical Series. It has been in the Wellcome Collection for years. Several people got on the track of it but that queerly secretive lunatic Wellcome actually went so far as to write twice that no such manuscript was in his possession![5] However it was all the time and he knew it! I have seen it and it throws quite a lot of light on the series as a whole. It is in the hands of a refugee art-historian, one Otto Kurz, working at the Courtauld Institute for the History of Art in London.[6] He is not medical and is interested chiefly in the art side of certain aspects of the MS that have nothing to do with the anatomy. But he is setting out the anatomical stuff, and I am helping him. We shall probably send it to you for the "Bulletin". I have lent him my photos and transcriptions of other members of the series. Incidentally, like the Caius MS, the Wellcome MS portrays the appendix vermiformis. It is usually said, I think, that this structure was not portrayed till the 16th century.

You have not answered as to whether that letter of mine to Miss Emmart on the Badianus Herbal reached her. There were, I thought, one or two points worth taking up.

It is wonderful news that you have an 8 volumed history of medicine actually in hand. I look forward to it eagerly. If I may make a word of criticism it is that it would be best <u>not</u> to tackle the volumes in chronological order. You write that the vol. on the ancient East and on primitive elements will appear first. This would perhaps be a pity for this aspect alters most rapidly of all, so that when the last of your series appears, the first may be out of date. If it is not too late I would urge that you begin with Renaissance Medicine (on which something is badly needed) and from it as a central point you issue your volumes in the series, one completing the story forwards and the other backwards.

Many thanks for giving me Olschki's name as authority on the early European knowledge of America. I will write my inquiry to him.

Thanks for your hint about Dobell's book. I have told him to write to Dr. Barnett Cohen. As you may perhaps know F. J. Cole's History of Zoology also cannot get published. It is not a very long book and there is about 40 years work in it! It is first class. As Cole is 73 I am urging him to have it multigraphed but I do not think I shall be able to persuade him. The basic difficulties in publication are (a) paper shortage (b) embargo on uses of copper for plate making.

I have been publishing a fair amount but anonymously. I have a couple of long articles under the pen-name Anceps in the Political Quarterly on the decline of Christianity. One is out, the other is in the press. I will send them to you when the second appears but I have had no reprints made.[7]

Andrew has just finished his engineering exam. and his first experience in an Engineering factory. He has a commission and is now in camp training cadets. He will, I think, be sent back to engineering. He comes home next week for a few weeks holiday. Nancy is home for 3 weeks, then she works on the land with a farmer before going back to her teaching.

All kind wishes to you all from us all,

Yours ever,

Charles Singer

[1] Kenneth Sisam (1887–1971), see N. Ker, 1972. 'Kenneth Sisam, 1887–1971', *Proceedings of the British Academy*, 1972, **58**: 409–428.

[2] Sigerist (1941a); no edition has appeared in England.

[3] Singer (1942a).

[4] Henry E. Sigerist, 'The sphere of life and death in Early Medieval manuscripts', *Bulletin of the History of Medicine*, 1942, **11**: 292–303.

[5] Henry Wellcome (1853–1936), U.S.-British pharmaceutical entrepreneur and collector; see Robert Rhodes James, 'Wellcome, Sir Henry Solomon (1853–1936)', *Oxford dictionary of national biography* (Oxford: Oxford University Press, 2004), vol. 57, 999–1001. This refers to Wellcome MS 49; A Seebohm, 'Texts and images in a fifteenth-century German miscellany (Wellcome MS 49)' (Ph.D. thesis, Warburg. Institute 1982), a microfiche facsimile edition of this manuscript has been published as *Apokalypse, ars moriendi, medizinische Traktate, Tugend- und Lasterlehren : die erbaulich-didaktische Sammelhandschrift London, Wellcome Institute for the History of Medicine, Ms. 49* Farbmikrofiche-Edition: introduction to the manuscript, descriptive catalogue of the Latin and German texts and illustrations, index of incipits by Almuth Seebohm (München: H. Lengenfelder, 1995).

[6] Otto Kurz (1908–1975), Austrian art historian in the U.S.; see E. H. Gombrich. 'Otto Kurz', *Burlington Magazine*, 1976, **118**: 29–30.

[7] Charles Singer (Anceps), 'Christianity, science, and the religion of humanity', *Political Quarterly*, 1942, **13**: 280–293 and 414–425.

293

Singer to Sigerist, Kilmarth, 12 August 1942

My dear Sigerist,

Enclosed from Sisam, Secretary of the Clarendon & Oxford University Press explains itself. I hope that you will go on with the matter & hasten things by allowing me to act for you on this side & that the Yale people will be willing.[1]

Yours ever

Charles Singer

[1] Regarding an English edition of Sigerist (1941a). See previous letter.

294

Singer to Sigerist, Kilmarth, 19 August 1942

My dear Sigerist,

(1) Many thanks for "Ornithologists of U.S. Army Corps" which has just come to hand. I am very much obliged.[1]

(2) Thanks for name of Olschki as an authority on early Americana. I have foolishly mislaid his address. Would you be so kind as to send enclosed note to him. And would you put me yet further in your debt by offering to forward his answer by air? Posts are otherwise so very slow and I am anxious to get this note on America published, since it has some minute value for Anglo-American relations.[2]

Yours ever

Charles Singer

[1] Hume (1942).
[2] Singer (1945a).

295

Sigerist to Singer, Baltimore, 23 September 1942

Dear Singer:

I have to thank you for two letters, those of August 8 and August 19. I was very glad to hear that you like my little book MEDICINE AND HUMAN WELFARE and I was perfectly delighted with your idea of having a cheap edition of it brought out in England.[1]

I am very much in favor of the Penguins. Their list of books is excellent and they reach the public all over the English-speaking world better than any other series.

I quite agree with you that the illustrations could be omitted. As a matter of fact, they were forced upon me by the Yale University Press in order to make the book more expensive. It is very difficult to sell cheap books in America. The retail bookdealers will not touch them because the profit per volume seems too small to them– a perfectly foolish point of view.

I also agree with you that the footnotes could be omitted in such an edition and very much like the title that you suggested: Health, Disease and the State. I wish you would write a foreword for the English edition. I think the Penguins would even be better than the Oxford University Press for this type of book.

In the meantime I also had a letter from the Yale University Press informing me that the Oxford Press does not see its way clear to do a special edition but would have no objection to the Yale Press making arrangements with some other publisher. I wrote the Yale Press that I was very much in favor of an English edition and suggested to them to approach the Penguins.

Your papers on the Circle of Petosiris[2] and on the Five Figure Anatomical Series will be most welcome at any time like all the papers you ever cared to send me.

I have finished my book CIVILIZATION AND DISEASE that the Cornell University Press is publishing,[3] and on January 1, I shall begin writing my HISTORY OF MEDICINE. I understand your suggestion to begin with the Renaissance volume very well indeed but I am afraid that I could not follow it. To me, writing a book is like building a house. I have to start it with the foundations. If I began with the second floor, I would feel that the whole is hanging in the air. I am making provisions, however, for having new editions of the individual volumes published periodically so that by the time Volume VIII will come from the press, Volume I should be in the second or possibly even the third revised edition – at least if the book does sell.[4]

I came back to Baltimore a few days ago. We spent a very pleasant month of August in the country where I could finish my book in peace. Then in September I spent a few weeks in Saratoga Springs in the State of New York. The waters there combined with massage, rest, exercises and inhalations for my nose always do me a lot of good, and I try to have such treatment every year before the winter's work begins.

I am going to have a lot of teaching this year. I have lost three of my associates either to the armed forces or to war work in Washington and others may follow soon.[5] Fortunately, I have a German refugee working with me, one of my old European students, Erwin H. Ackerknecht. You may have seen his articles on primitive medicine in the Bulletin.[6] He is an excellent man equally well trained in medicine, history and social anthropology [....][7] I will probably be able to keep him. We are running our departments now with women and cripples.

With kind regards to Mrs. Singer and yourself, I am

Yours as ever,

[Henry E. Sigerist]

---

[1] Sigerist (1941a).

[2] Sigerist (1942).

[3] Henry E. Sigerist, *Civilization and disease* (Ithaca, NY 1943).

[4] Sigerist's estimate of the future of his planned *History of medicine* was optimistic: he died before finishing Vol. II.

[5] Larkey had joined the Army; Temkin had part-time work in Washington.

[6] Erwin H. Ackerknecht, 'Problems of primitive medicine', *Bulletin of the History of Medicine*, 1942, **11**: 503–521; and, 'Primitive medicine and culture pattern', *Bulletin of the History of Medicine*, 1942, **12**: 545–574.

[7] One half sentence deleted as Protected Health Information of the Alan Mason Chesney Medical Archive of the Johns Hopkins Medical Institutions.

296

Singer to Sigerist, Kilmarth, 23 October 1942

My dear Sigerist

I am writing you a short but important letter. Two items of news that concern you have come in today.

The first is a letter from the Oxford University Press telling me that you and the Yale University Press will let me have a free hand with your "Medicine and Human Welfare".[1] I shall go ahead at once and see what can be done about a popular edition. The chief difficulty is paper shortage but I am in good hopes and will act immediately.

The second is a letter from F. J. Cole of Reading University concerning his "History of Zoology to 1800".[2] Cole is 72 and in poor health. He is a most careful and accurate worker and has been on this subject all his working life. There can be no doubt of his qualifications and anything that he produces is always first rate. Schumann [sic] the publisher wrote to me some time ago asking for suggestion of MSS for publication.[3] I told Cole that I would gladly suggest his work. Cole writes me to say that he has written both to you and Schumann [sic] & asks me to write to you both.

If it is possible for you to consider Cole's work, it seems to me that you are hardly likely to find better material in war time. He is sound, recondite, readable and scholarly, and there is nothing effective yet available along the lines on which he writes. It is certainly a real contribution to knowledge. On the point of its medical bearing, I would urge that there was but little zoological writing before 1800 that had not that bearing but I know that this is not a point that will weigh greatly with you personally, though it may with the public with which you have to deal.

We are all well. I am very hard worked and in several different ways but chiefly in teaching biology which I really enjoy.

It is strange how all fear has gone out of us all. This is a general phenomenon throughout the country. We are all confident but also quite ready to face whatsoever may come.

All kind wishes to you and yours from us both,

Yours always

Charles Singer

[1] Sigerist (1941a).

[2] Cole's history of zoology did not appear in the *Bulletin of the History of Medicine* but was published as F. J. Cole, *A history of comparative anatomy: from Aristotle to the eighteenth century* (London: Macmillan & Co., 1944). Singer writes to Sigerist to secure Sigerist's recommendation for help with the publisher.

[3] Henry Schuman (1899–1962) New York publisher and bookseller; see Warner Wells, 'Henry Schuman, 1899–1962', *Bulletin of the Medical Library Association*, 1963, **51**: 152–154.

297

Sigerist to Singer, Baltimore?, 1 December 1942

Dear Singer:

Thanks for your letter of October 23. In the meantime I also received one from Professor Cole and you can be assured that I will do my best in the matter of his book. It will be extremely difficult, however, to bring the book out in America. A book of that size (200,000 words and 200 illustrations) would require a subsidy of a least $3,000 and grants-in-aid of publication are very hard to get for foreign manuscripts.

In my own department we have at the moment manuscripts of ten books ready for the press and I do not know myself yet where to find the money for them.

I have written to Schuman but I doubt very much that he can undertake the job. He is primarily a second-hand bookseller and has very little capital. I have also written Sarton but I should think that he also would need a heavy subsidy in order to bring the book out in OSIRIS.[1] I will write John Fulton and see if he knows of any possibility.

Why does not the Oxford University Press print the book in the United States? They have an American branch and there is no reason why they should not produce their books here for the duration of the war.

I will certainly not fail to keep the matter in mind and will try every possibility, but I am not too hopeful. For the publication of Hume's book on Ornithology, we got $2,000 from the Surgeon General of the Army otherwise we could not have considered it at all and even so, we are losing about $1,500 on the book.[2]

With all good wishes and kind regards, I am

Yours very sincerely,

Henry E. Sigerist

[1] Publication series of the History of Science Society.

[2] Hume (1942).

298

Singer to Sigerist, Kilmarth, 8 June 1944[1]

My dear Sigerist

Somehow or other the number of the Bulletin devoted to VESALIUS has not reached me. I have received the numbers on either side of it. Could you perhaps send me another copy as I am working at him.[2]

I have by this post received your CIVILISATION AND DISEASE for review and am much looking forward to reading it.[3]

I hope all is well with you. I have just returned from a month in London where I was when the exciting news of the landing in France came in.[4]

With all kind wishes,

Yours always,

Charles Singer

Sanford Larkey called on me yesterday.[5]

[1] The gap in the correspondence from January 1943 to May 1944 is most likely due to missing letters, possibly on account of the war, although by then the German submarines were all but wiped out.

[2] *Bulletin* number on Vesalius is December 1943. His article appeared as, Charles Singer, 'Some Vesalian problems', *Bulletin of the History of Medicine*, 1945, **17**: 425–438.

[3] Sigerist (1943a).

[4] The landing of the Allied Armies in Normandy on 6 June, the beginning of the final phase of World War II in Europe.

[5] Larkey was in Britain as a GI.

299

Sigerist to Singer, Baltimore?, 14 August 1944

Dear Singer:

I was sorry to hear that you have not received the December number of the Bulletin and I will see to it that another copy will be sent to you.

I am glad to know that you are reviewing my book, Civilization and Disease.[1] It is a somewhat enlarged series of lectures that I gave at Cornell University some years ago. The book is selling unusually well. The first printing was sold out in a few months. The second printing has just been made and the third printing is being prepared. The paper shortage is not as serious here as it is with you but nevertheless caused a great deal of trouble. Still more serious is the shortage of labor and printing presses. Once a book is in type you have to wait months before you can find a press to print it off. Thus we had a volume of essays presented to old Castiglioni[2] ready for a long time but so far it has been impossible to get it out.

I meant to write you long ago to thank you for your very interesting little book, The Christian Failure.[3] It circulated among the members of the department and we discussed it in great detail. Personally I agree with you in almost every point.

The Institute is still active although everybody is very much overworked. Everyone of us has several extra jobs. I am doing Larkey's work as librarian of the Welch Library and I do not know if you have seen my new journal, The American Review of Soviet Medicine. I am sending it on to you under separate cover. After less then [sic] one year we have 3,000 subscribers which shows that there was a real need for such a journal, but you can readily imagine that it was very difficult to get it launched. I took the editorship because we could not [find?] anybody else and because I was anxious to set the standard and to see that it would be kept free of politics. I will resign the editorship after a few years as soon as the journal is well established.

I am trying desperately to get back to my historical studies but somehow or other I am always driven into other fields. Thus I am just getting ready to spend a month in Canada making a survey of health needs and medical facilities in the province of Saskatchewan. The Cooperative Commonwealth Federation, a farm-labor party, has just taken over the provincial government and they want me to advise them in the reorganization of their medical services. This takes me far away from medieval and renaissance studies but I feel that in times like these we have to help out wherever we seem to be needed.

The war situation looks good and at long last the Nazi machine is breaking down. I cannot help thinking how much better it would have been to prevent the rise of Hitlerism. It could have been done as we both know. I am also not to [sic] hopeful as to our ability to handle postwar situations. The job we have done in Italy so far is not very encouraging. I think a great deal will depend on you in Great Britain. You are so much closer to Europe and your population has been so much more deeply involved in the war that you should have a better understanding of the problems then [sic] the average American who is so far remote from the European scene.

With all good wishes to you both,

I am yours very cordially,

Henry E. Sigerist

[1] Sigerist (1943a).

[2] *Essays in the history of medicine, presented to Professor Arturo Castiglioni on the occasion of his seventieth birthday, April 10, 1944*, Supplement to the *Bulletin of the History of Medicine* no. 3 (Baltimore: Johns Hopkins Press, 1944).

[3] Charles Singer, *The Christian failure* (London, 1943).

300

Singer to Sigerist, Kilmarth, 29 September 1944

My dear Sigerist,

You would, I think, like to see the enclosed "leader" which appeared in this week's British Medical Journal.[1] You will see that it treats largely of your excellent Vesalius number.[2]

My fascicule in the <u>Tabulae sex</u> is finished & has gone off for final typing. I see no reason why it should not be in print early next year.[3] The war with Germany, at least, will then be over.[4]

All kind wishes

Yours always

Charles Singer

The leader is anonymous of course

[1] There are three short articles by Singer in the *British Medical Journal* of 1944; this refers to [Charles Singer], 'Vesalius the man', *British Medical Journal*, 1944, **ii**: 407–409.

[2] Vesalius number of the *Bulletin for the History of Medicine* December 1943.

[3] Charles Singer and Chaim Rabin, *A prelude to modern science. Being a discussion of the history, sources and circumstances of the 'Tabulae anatomicae sex' of Vesalius* (Cambridge, 1946).

[4] The war with Japan would last longer.

301

Sigerist to Singer, Baltimore?, 17 October 1944

My dear Singer:

Many thanks for your note of September 29 and for the splendid editorial on Vesalius.[1] I am very glad that you refuted some of Mr. Ivins arguments.[2] For over ten years he has been going around lecturing on Vesalius and picturing him as a plagiarist. I finally succeeded in getting a manuscript from him and now that his thesis is published, we are able to show how weak his arguments are. He is a very witty old devil and a good speaker but he does not know the history of anatomy.

I returned from Canada a week ago and I am just getting ready to leave for a short trip to India. The Government of India invited me to participate in the work of their Health Survey and Development Committee. Professor J. A. Ryle will be there too and I am looking forward to meeting him.[3] The trip will undoubtedly be an interesting experience, very different from the one I just had in the Canadian Province of Saskatchewan where the general death-rate is 7 and the tuberculosis death-rate 25.

I expect to be back in America early in January and will then resume my historical studies.

I was very sorry to hear of the death of Sir Humphry Rolleston. He was an Honorary Member of our American Association of the History of Medicine and I would like to publish an obituary. Would you be willing to write it for us? You could make it as long as you like. It would also be advisable to add a bibliography of his historical writings and one or two good portraits. The obituary would be published in the July number of 1945 of the <u>Bulletin of the History of Medicine</u> and it would be early enough if I had the manuscript in hand by the end of April so that it could be presented at the Annual Meeting of the Association in May.[4]

My love to you both,
Yours very sincerely,
Henry E. Sigerist

[1] See previous letter.
[2] W. M. Ivins, 'A propos of the Fabrica of Vesalius', *Bulletin of the History of Medicine*, 1943, **14**: 576–593.
[3] John Alfred Ryle (1889–1950), British physician and professor of social medicine at Oxford; see Dorothy Porter, 'Ryle, John Alfred (1889–1950)', *Oxford dictionary of national biography* (Oxford: Oxford University Press, 2004), vol. 48, 485–486.
[4] No obituary appeared in the *Bulletin of the History of Medicine*.

302

Singer to Sigerist, Kilmarth, 20 December 1944

My dear Sigerist,

I have just been going through the American Review of Soviet Medicine & I feel that I really must write to congratulate you. It really is a most impressive series of publications & makes one feel that we are living in a very wonderful age. Well done.

How you manage to maintain so many activities & to do them all so well has always been a puzzle to me. And now it is more of a puzzle than ever.

You will be glad to hear that not only has my study of the Tabulae sex gone to press but galley-proofs are just beginning to come in.[1] It is my first really solid publication for I do not like to think how many years. Only a few months ago did I properly recover from the shock that all these beastly events had on me. It is maddening to think of all the years that I have lost by these detestable wars. The last word should, of course, be in the singular for it is all one war. But one cannot feel much doubt any longer that civilisation really will survive, though we may not yet quite see its pattern. But for some years I really was doubtful in my inner self.

When do you start for India?[2] The Wellcome Foundation is at last coming to its senses and will, I think, open out properly as soon as the war is over.[3]

All best & kindest wishes to you & yours for 1945 from us all.

Yours always,
Charles Singer

[1] Singer and Rabin (1946).
[2] India see previous letter.
[3] The Wellcome Foundation in London, Wellcome's pharmaceutical firm, was at that time legally responsible for the Wellcome Collection and Library for the history of medicine (see letter 332). But letter 310 suggests that Singer was making the common mistake of giving the name to the Wellcome Trust (or the Trustees of Sir Henry Wellcome), which was responsible for funding in the history of medicine. For the complicated story of the Wellcome Trust, see A.R. Hall and B.A. Bembridge, *Physic and philanthropy: a history of the Wellcome Trust, 1936–1986* (Cambridge: Cambridge University Press, 1986), and Roy Church and E. M. Tansey, *Burroughs, Wellcome & Co.: knowledge, trust, profit and the transformation of the British pharmaceutical industry, 1880–1940* (Lancaster: Crucible, 2007).

303

Singer to Sigerist, Kilmarth, 18 January 1945

My dear Sigerist,

This may reach Johns Hopkins after you have left for India. Therefore, I address the envelope to the 'Editor of the Bulletin'. You may care to have the enclosed article.[1] The Bulletin seems to me the most suitable place for it, because it has had most on the subject of Vesalius.

As regards the one figure, that of a dissection scene in Paris in 1531. The photograph I enclose is of the original size. It is of a panel at the foot of a title-page. The rest of the title-page is filled with the usual silly Renaissance portraits of Hippocrates, Galen etc. As regards the dissection scene it will need a whole page of the Bulletin and will, I suppose, have to be little reduced. But do please have it reproduced in line (that is as a zincograph) and not as a half-tone. Also please delete the words ASCLEPIAD and DIOSCORID on the top of the scene because they refer to the portraits above which are not to be included. If left they will give rise to misunderstanding. For your own eye I would point out that there is the mysterious Cross of Lorraine at the foot of the picture itself.[2] I wish we could find out what it means. It occurs in a lot of French illustrations of the period. No one seems to understand it. It must. I think, be a guild-mark.

I am proposing to continue the subject of this article from time to time as points arise. A number have arisen already. There is no reason why you should take the other numbers.

I have begun to get proofs of my edition of the Tabulae sex.[3] It would be a comfort to get such points as those in the enclosed article cleared from the main body of the work. I can thus refer to this article on these points.

I have completed the first draft of a translation of Vesalius on the Brain. This, I suppose, will be the second number of the series.

The Wellcome trustees are at last moving, though still very slowly. I have had a look at the Library. The incompetence in this management is almost unbelievable. There is plenty of first class material but the system of collection has been on a childish level and the system of arrangement merely idiotic. The so-called "Reference Library" seems at first to be a bad joke! It is not easy to guess even an approximate number for the books, but I would make a vague shot at a quarter of a million. So far as organisation goes an intelligent child of 13 could have done better! There are tens of thousands of books that would seem never to have been taken out of the boxes in which they arrived![4]

However, I must not grumble for the Wellcome Trustees are subsidising my Vesalius generously enough. Moreover, they have at last appointed a good Director.[5] Unfortunately he can neither take up the job nor get released from his present one until the war effort slackens. But things do look better.

I am sure you will have a very interesting time in India. Do let me hear from you from there.

With best regards to the family from my wife and myself.

Yours always,

Charles Singer

I think that I might correct proofs of the enclosed article. I suggest that you send me proofs by air mail & I will return them in the same way. C.S.

[1] Singer (1945b).
[2] Cross of Lorraine: A heraldic cross.
[3] Singer and Rabin (1946).
[4] For a history of the Wellcome Library see John Symons, *Wellcome Institute for the History of Medicine: a short history* (London, The Wellcome Trust, [1993]).
[5] Probably E. Ashworth Underwood; see letter 306.

304

Sigerist to Singer, Baltimore?, 7 February 1945

My dear Singer:

I am back from India. It was a short trip of only two months but it was well organized and took us all over the country so that we actually saw a great deal. It was a great pleasure to travel in the company of John A. Ryle of Oxford and Janet Vaughan who is a very remarkable woman.[1] Sir Weldon Dalrymple-Champneys was also a member of our delegation representing the Ministry of Health.[2] I had met him before the war in Belgium once at a congress of social medicine. We were a most congenial group.

On the way to India, I spent a few days in Cairo and saw old Meyerhof. [....].[3] In spite of all this, he is very cheerful and is still working hard on some problems of Arabic medicine. Kraus, who was at the University of Cairo and was doing some very important medico-historical work also, has recently committed suicide; nobody knows why. In other words, very soon there will not be anybody left in the field of Arabic medicine.[4]

Flying through Egypt, Palestine and Mesopotamia was a great experience. There is no better way of studying the geography of the ancient Orient.

I was delighted to hear that your work on the Tabulae sex[5] is progressing so beautifully and I was particularly happy to know that you have resumed your historical studies. We have missed you for all these years and we are so few who are doing serious work in the field. You know that the Bulletin of the History of Medicine is always open to you and whatever you may send will be published immediately.

You probably heard that Schuman in New York is publishing an English translation of the Epitome.[6] The translation was made by a philologist in Kansas City. As I understand, the format will be slightly smaller than the original.

You do not mention the obituary of Sir Humphry Rolleston that I asked you to write for us for the July number of the Bulletin. Rolleston was an honorary member of the American Association of the History of Medicine. I very much hope that you can do this for us.

I have resumed the work at the Institute and things are going their normal way except that we are very much handicapped by the shortage of paper. It is not as serious as it is in England but bad enough and our Hopkins Press is not very efficient. At the moment, I am working with Genevieve Miller on a series of documents to the early history of vaccination that we hope to publish soon.[7] It includes many letters of Edward Jenner. The Cornell

University Press will probably publish a little volume of essays and addresses that I wrote on university education and similar problems.[8] It will consist mostly of articles that I had written for the Bulletin but will include also a few unpublished essays. The circulation of the Bulletin is rather limited and some people felt that these essays should be made available to a wider audience.

I am also working on a new edition of my book on Soviet medicine.[9] The book is out of print and there is much demand for it, particularly also for translation into foreign languages. A Spanish translation was published some time ago in Cuba and a Portuguese translation is in preparation.

I have not quite given up the idea of writing a comprehensive History of Medicine and plan to make an attempt to write it next summer but I do not know yet whether I shall succeed because I have to do all my research and writing at night after an 8 to 10-hour day spent with stupid administrative work. I still have to do Larkey's job as librarian of the Welch Library. While I am writing you, the Russians are a few miles from Berlin and at long last it looks as if the slaughter in Europe might be over soon. This time the Germans cannot expect any pity, and the Russians will see to it that they will receive the punishment that they deserve. We are so stupid that we still talk of "re-educating" the Nazis. Our Army has actually set up a school for educating some of the most hardboiled Nazi policemen in Aachen. The same brutes who only yesterday slaughtered women and children are now given instruction in military courtesy.

I can anticipate the kind of letters that our German colleagues will write us after the war assuring us that they were never Nazis at heart, but you cannot fool the people twice, at least not me and I know not you.[10] I am sure that many of our American colleagues will be only too ready to cooperate with the German medical historians after the war, but I will use all the influence I have to prevent this. I know them and am through with them once and for all.

With all good wishes to Mrs. Singer, I am

Yours very cordially,

Henry E. Sigerist

---

[1] Janet Vaughan (1899–1993) British physiologist, principal of Somerville College, Oxford, England; see Richard Doll, 'Vaughan , Dame Janet Maria (1899–1993)', *Oxford dictionary of national biography* (Oxford: Oxford University Press, 2004), vol. 56, 183–185.

[2] Sir Weldon Dalrymple-Champneys (1892–1980), British veterinarian; see *British Medical Journal*, 1981, **282**: 159.

[3] Two and a half sentences deleted as Protected Health Information of the Alan Mason Chesney Medical Archive of the Johns Hopkins Medical Institutions.

[4] Max Meyerhof (1874–1945) and Paul Kraus (1904–1944) German historians of Arab medicine; see 'Max Meyerhof', *British Journal of Ophthalmology*, 1946, **30**: 498–499.

[5] Singer and Rabin (1946).

[6] L. R. Lind and C. W. Asling (eds), *The Epitome of Andreas Vesalius* (New York, 1949).

[7] Genevieve Miller (born 1914), Sigerist's research secretary, later professor of medical history; Genevieve Miller (ed.), *Letters of Edward Jenner and other documents concerning the early history of vaccination* (Baltimore, 1983).

[8] Henry E. Sigerist, *The university at the crossroads. Addresses and essays* (New York, 1946).

[9] Henry E. Sigerist, *Medicine and health in the Soviet Union*, new edition (New York, 1947).

[10] Sigerist predicts exactly what would happen.

305

Sigerist to Singer, Baltimore?, 13 February 1945

My dear Singer:

I just received your manuscript and was delighted with it.[1] The points you raise are very interesting and contribute a great deal to the subject. I am sending the manuscript to the press right away and will let you have galleys soon.

I was very interested in what you wrote about the Wellcome Museum.[2] They certainly have the material to make it a first-rate research institute and I hope they will see their way clear to disentangle the whole mess.

Yours very cordially,

Henry E. Sigerist

[1] Singer (1945b).
[2] See letter 303.

306

Singer to Sigerist, Kilmarth, 13 March 1945

My dear Sigerist,

Many thanks for your two pleasant letters of Feb. 7th and Feb. 13th, which tell me that you are back from India. How delightful it must have been to travel with Ryle. He is really a most charming man. I know him pretty well, and I knew his father who was a general practitioner and one of the most charming men I have ever met. He was the sort of character of whom one could write a novel. A sort of Francis Adams in his way.

I am in correspondence with Meyerhof and had a letter from him, or rather from his wife, last week. Poor fellow. He seems to like to have scientific questions sent to him. As it happens he is able to help me with my work on Alum which is now approaching completion. Meyerhof is making a sad ending to a distinguished life.

I was sorry to hear of the death of Kraus. We have in England a young refugee Arabist, one Walzer, of whom I had considerable hopes. Have you yet received his translation of that newly discovered text "Galen on Medical Experience"?[1] As a piece of translation I am sure it is excellent, but as a piece of common sense it is really hopeless. It is a specimen of the usual idiotic German scholarship which has no consideration whatever for the public for which it is intended. He says nothing at all of the importance of the Arabic version, nothing at all of the schools of Medicine which the work illustrates, nothing at all of Galen, and nothing at all that would interest any reader who has not had precisely the same training as Walzer himself. It is, in fact, a display of the worst type of German scholarship. It happens that a fragment of the work survives in the Greek and Walzer simply

231

gives the Greek text without translating it. What can one do with such people? And the worst of it is that he is really a decent fellow and not conceited.

My <u>Tabulae sex</u> is in the press allright but the difficulty is to get it out again![2] I have received the first proofs of about a quarter of it, and the rest is promised by Easter. But war-time promises are liable to be broken.

Your letter brings me news that Schuman is publishing an English translation of the <u>Epitome</u>.[3] I shall certainly write to him about it. I have, as you perhaps know, written yet another introductory essay to <u>Choulant-Frank</u> which Schuman is producing.[4] By the time they are finished with that book it will be composed almost entirely of introductions. It is, however, certainly a very useful volume.

Concerning the obituary of Humphry Rolleston, I have had that much on my mind as well as an obituary of D'Arcy Power. I would like to give you my frank thoughts on the matter. I am now in my sixty-ninth year and owing to circumstances which you know too well I have wasted so many years that I feel that I must give the rest to writing. There is such a mass of material that I have to get out which will die with me if I cannot publish it. I feel that I cannot spend these precious years on work which others can easily do. Of course I would not mind "writing up" someone else's work, and if I can find a younger man to prepare all the records of D'Arcy and Rolleston I would give a few days to touching it up. I think you will agree with me, however, that I ought not to spend my own time on such work. I am writing to Rolleston's brother to see if he can make any suggestions, and I am also writing to D'Arcy Power's son. There is a special difficulty concerning D'Arcy Power. His son is a Flying Officer with high rank but is not very bright and anyhow he is out of England. The family is represented [....] by his daughter-in-law who is an extremely stupid and rather vulgar woman, who has got it into her head that people want to make money by writing an account of her father-in-law! Of course the idea is idiotic but it is difficult to get rid of. However[,] I will see what I can do. What I really want them to do is to subsidise some young man of their own choice who could put together the D'Arcy material and allow me or someone else, conjointly with him to publish the result.

We are beginning to open up correspondence with our French friends. I have not written to Laignel-Lavastine nor do I even know if he is alive, though I note that his name has disappeared from the lists of French Committees that reach me. I know you do not approve of him and I know that he is a silly ass, but was he really cooperating with the Germans? Is there evidence against him? Delarnay [sic] of Le Mans is, I suppose, quite allright?[5] Perhaps you would answer these two questions without delay. One line would do.

I don't know how it will be in America but I really do not think there will be much co-operation with German Medical Historians from England. One reason, though not the only reason, is that there are hardly any Medical Historians in England.

As to the Wellcome appointment their man is, as I think I told you, E. Ashworth Underwood and he is the best appointment that was available.[6] Everything considered I think it is a good appointment. Underwood is enormously energetic and works almost too hard. He is well educated, enterprising, very keen, and perfectly willing to learn and to take advice. His main handicap is that he begins rather old. He is forty and of course has little historical work hitherto. All that he has done, however, is excellent and scholarly. His wife is helpful, modest, well-educated and will help him in every way. They have been married for some years and have no children. My chief anxiety about them is that they will over-work and earn rather the reputation for being too "aggressive", but these are good faults and I have great hopes for them. However[,] mystery follows the Wellcome foundation as shadow follows substance and, for some reason, I am not supposed to announce the appointment except to a selected band of some fifty people of whom you are one! You can guess how long it will be secret. Until the old officials of the Wellcome are either bombed or die a natural death we shall have to put up with this silly making of mysteries where there is no mystery.

My son, who is now an official in the Royal Engineers, is home on his embarkation leave. He leaves us to-morrow and is, we believe, going to the East. He is a fine fellow and if he survives should do well.[7]

This has been an interminable letter and I hope you have had the patience to read it all.

With very best wishes from us both to you and your family,

Very cordially yours,

Charles Singer

Glad you liked my Vesalius notes. I look forward to proofs[8]

[1] Richard Walzer, *Galen on medical experience* (New York, 1944).
[2] Singer and Rabin (1946).
[3] Lind and Asling (1949).
[4] Charles Singer, 'Beginnings of academic practical anatomy'. Historical essay in the reissue of L. Choulant, *History and bibliography of anatomic illustration"*, trans. and annotated by M. Frank (New York: Schuman's, 1945), 21A-21R.
[5] Paul Delaunay (1878–1958) French medical historian.
[6] Edgar Ashworth Underwood (1899–1980), British historian of medicine; see M. E. Rowbottom , 'Dr. E. Ashworth Underwood (1899—1980)', *Medical History*, 1980, **24**: 349–352.
[7] Andrew, Singer's son.
[8] Singer (1945b).

307

Sigerist to Singer, Baltimore?, 27 March 1945

Dear Singer:

Your letter of March 13 just arrived and I am delighted to see that mail services are improving. As long as letters took months to arrive, we felt very much isolated from the world.

You are perfectly right. It would be stupid for you to waste your time writing obituary notes when there is much more important work to be done. I wrote you in the matter because I felt that the obituaries of Humphry Rolleston and D'Arcy Power should come from England and should be written by people who actually knew them. I would therefore very much appreciate it if you could find somebody who could write these two articles. Walter Pagel might possibly be considered if you find nobody else.

I have also resumed relations with our French colleagues. Laignel-Lavastine seems to be definitely out. I never liked him. He was a militant Catholic, fascistically inclined, and I would not be astonished if he had cooperated with the Germans and the Vichy crowd.[1] I do not know anything positive but it also struck me that he is not included among the officers of the French Society[2] and it rather confirms my suspicion. Neveu, who was elected president, is a delightful old gentleman.[3] Delaunay used to be all right but I do not know how he acted during the war.

I had lunch with Pasteur Vallery-Radot a few weeks ago. He came through here on his way to South America where he is being sent by the French Government to re-establish cultural relations. He did a superb job during the war as director of the medical services of the Resistance [sic]. They had their headquarters in the basement of the Institut Pasteur, and the Germans never found them. He lived underground in Paris for a long time and it is a miracle that the Germans never caught him.[4]

The galley proofs of your article have been mailed to you some time ago and the article will be published as soon as you return the proofs.[5]

In the February number of the <u>Bulletin</u> you will find an excellent article on the School of Salerno by Paul Oskar Kristeller. It is a beautiful piece of work.[6]

I also just read a long manuscript for the University of Chicago Press. It is a very comprehensive study of the life and work of Ugo Benzi by a man who is professor of Latin in one of our smaller colleges, Dr. Dean Putnam Lockwood. It is also an excellent piece of work.[7]

With all good wishes from house to house, I am

Yours very cordially,

Henry E. Sigerist

---

[1] During World War II the unoccupied Zone of France was ruled by a French puppet government in Vichy.

[2] French Society of the History of Medicine.

[3] Raymond Neveu, French medical historian

[4] Louis Pasteur Vallery-Radot (1886–1970), French physician, grandson of Louis Pasteur

[5] Singer (1945b).

[6] Paul Oskar Kristeller (1905–1999), German scholar; 'The School of Salerno', *Bulletin of the History of Medicine*, 1945, **17**: 138–194. For Kristeller see, see John Monfasani,'Paul Oskar Kristeller, 22 May 1905 · 7 June 1999', *Proceedings of the American Philosophical Society*, 2001, **145**: 207–211.

[7] Dean P. Lockwood, (born 1883) classical philologist; Ugo Benzi (1376–1439), medieval philosopher and physician . Dean P. Lockwood, *Ugo Benzi; Medieval philosopher and physician* (Chicago, 1951).

308

Singer to Sigerist, Kilmarth 19 April 1945

My dear Sigerist,

Enclosed proofs contain, I fear, more corrections than I (or you) would wish.[1] Nevertheless I need not see them again. I am sure that Miss Miller, or someone on your staff, will read the revises with care.

By the time this gets into print another batch of "Vesalian problems" will probably be ready for you, if you have not become sick of my writing by then![2]

The news is wonderful.[3] I will write you more fully later but in the meantime, many thanks for further hints about Laignel-Lavastine.

I have some hopes of getting to Rome for a few weeks but in any event, I hope to be in London for all May & June.

All best wishes & good cheer,

Yours always,

Charles Singer

---

[1] Proofs of Singer (1945b).
[2] Singer did not publish new "Vesalian problems" in the *Bulletin of the History of Medicine*.
[3] Probably of the collapse of the Nazi empire.

309

Singer to Sigerist, Kilmarth, 23 April 1945

My dear Sigerist,

I am not sure whether I wrote to you the suggestion that my article on Vesalian problems should be dedicated to Meyerhof.[1] If you see any way of doing this and if it is in accord with the policy of the Journal do please insert something of the kind. Some phrase as

"dedicated in affection and respect to Max Meyerhof of Cairo" would meet the case. I should have liked to have dedicated something to him on the oriental terms in the Tabulae but my article on that will take me several more weeks to complete and several more months for your [sic] to publish.[2] Therefore in view of his very precarious hold on life you will agree, I am sure, that if anything of the sort is to be done it has best be done at once.

Yours ever,

Charles Singer

P.S. The proofs of the article on Vesalian problems is on its way. It was posted several days ago.[3] It was, however, too heavy to send by Air Mail and this letter may reach you before the proofs.

I do not think I have thanked you for that interesting translation of Arthus.[4] Your output is really wonderful.

---

[1] Singer (1945b).
[2] Singer and Rabin (1946).
[3] Enclosed with previous letter.
[4] *Maurice Arthus' Philosophy of scientific investigation: preface to De l'anaphylaxie à l'immunité, Paris, 1921*, translated from the French, with an introduction by Henry E. Sigerist; foreword by Warfield T. Longcope (Baltimore: The Johns Hopkins press, 1943), reprinted from *Bulletin of the History of Medicine*, 1943, **14**:

366–390. Maurice Arthus (1862–1945), French physiologist, see Sigerist's, 'Introduction to 'Maurice Arthus' Philosophy of Scientific Investigation', *ibid*, 368–372, and 'Nicolas Maurice Arthus', in Allen G. Debus et al. (ed.), *World who's who in science* (Chicago: Marquis-Who's Who, Inc., 1968), 67.

310

Singer to Sigerist, Kilmarth, 26 April 1945

My dear Sigerist,

I am very sorry indeed to bother you yet again with that article on Vesalian problems.[1] The matter is really not my fault. As you know I am at last succeeding in getting the Wellcome Foundation to do something for which it was founded. It has very large funds for the History of Medicine – large even on the expansive American standards. You know how these funds have been wasted. But the old wasters are gradually dying off or being cleared out and prospects are now brighter.

I need not trouble you with details but a condition under which I persuaded them to give grants for the expense of researches was that the recipient should write on each article "The author has to thank the Trustees of the late Sir Henry Wellcome for having made possible the research on which this paper is based". <u>Possible</u> is the operative word. The statement is obviously false in most cases and certainly in mine. But I did not think it worth while to quarrel about a word and I let it be. You will find that offending sentence at the very end of my article.

However[,] I have just had a discussion with the stupidest, most conservative, and most influential of the Trustees, T. R. Elliott. He fully agrees that the term <u>possible</u> is intolerable and must go since it makes the work appear written <u>in forma pauperis</u>. He therefore agrees that it should be altered to the form which I originally used namely – "The preparation of this article has been aided by a grant from the Trustees of the late Sir Henry Wellcome".

Perhaps you will see that it is thus altered. The whole thing is a mere irritating triviality. I apologise for occupying your time with such nonsense.

All May and June I shall be in London and in those months letters will reach me quickest addressed to the Athenaeum, Pall Mall, London. S.W.1.

Yours ever,

Charles Singer

[1] Singer (1945b).

311

Singer to Sigerist, London, 15 May 1945

My dear Sigerist,

There are a number of things to write to you about.

The new British Consul in Baltimore is the son of a very old and dear friend of mine. His name is Harold Braham, and he will be in Baltimore with his family – a wife and two children – in about six weeks. His younger and only brother was killed as a flying officer early in the war. His father, now retired, was for years Foreign Editor of the Times. I am giving him a line to you, and feel sure that you and your wife will like them.

As you doubtless know, the Consular Service of Britain is being amalgamated with the Ambassadorial Service.

I am also giving a line to a very charming French girl who has been staying with us – Geneviève Noufflard – who, before the war stayed with us au pair with Nancy, who went to Paris.[1] Geneviève has behaved magnificently and very bravely. She was a member of the Underground Movement in Paris from the first, and acted as secretary of one of its leading organisers. She has suffered very great hardships, including long periods of semi-starvation, and many dangerous situations. On the arrival of the Americans, she joined the American forces for a time, and was then taken into the French Army (F.F. L.)[2] with a Commission, and has acted as interpreter. Together with several other girls who speak English well, she is being sent on a goodwill mission to America, and will lecture on her experiences. She is a pretty and attractive girl, and a good speaker, and I think should be a very great success.

That is a jolly good article of Kristeller on the School of Salerno.[3] I have written to congratulate him, and to ask for a reprint. It really does clear up a number of points.

You have doubtless heard that a scheme is being drafted for having a proper department in the History of Science in the University of London. The situation there has never been satisfactory. Wolf was not a suitable man, and the Chair itself was divided between two colleges, and was combined with the teaching of Logic. However, the University has now quite made up its mind to put the matter on a proper basis and have a real department.

The chief difficulty is to find a suitable holder of the chair. The field is not a large one, and of the various possibilities none of them seems to be exactly right. You know the names as well as I. The best, I think, is Partington, an exceedingly learned man whose abilities have not been nearly well enough recognised. Against him is that he is very near retiring age, and his activities have been mainly chemical. Anyhow I greatly doubt if he would take it.

Then there is Holmyard. He has gone off of late years, and has become rather involved in industry. He is a very talented and pleasant man with wide teaching experience but he too is at the old side.

The man who has most obvious claims is McKie, who is running the skeleton of a department. McKie's writings are good, especially his Lavoisier,[4] and his journal, "Annals of Science," admirably conducted. He deserves every encouragement. Against him are his health and his personality. He was a regular officer in the last war, and was badly shell-shocked. This has left him very nervy, and he shows no real signs of recovery. I very much doubt if he would stand the strain of directing a department. This, however, is the only thing against him. A good fellow, a good colleague & a good scholar – but ever so nervy.

Another name is Sherwood Taylor, who is perhaps the most talented of them all. Against him is that he is unreliable and a poor administrator. He is also a militant Catholic, with St. Thomas Aquinas on the brain.[5] I do not really visualise him as a possibility.

The only other name that has been mentioned is H. H. Dingle.[6] His philosophical bent would be very useful, and he is a most attractive writer. He has no great affection for History, but he is a good scholar, and would do it well. I do not think for a moment, however, that he would give up his experimental work.

Now for my reason for writing you all this. Your name was mentioned to me as a possibility both by the Provost of University College, Dr. D. R. Pye, and by one or two others. To all of them I said it was a very good idea, but that I did not for a moment believe that you could be persuaded to leave Johns Hopkins. Quite frankly, I do not think the English post as good as that which you hold, but, of course, it is susceptible of very great development. For one thing, it is Science and not Medicine. For another thing, it is in the centre of libraries which cannot be matched. For yet another thing, University College is three minutes' walk from the Wellcome Institute, which has enormous funds, and which might be developed if the present staff could be assassinated ! It has now a good director but he cannot get released from his present post.[7]

I need hardly tell you that were there to be the least indication that you would accept it, you would get any support of which I am capable in starting and running the place. I am sure you would get it, if you would like it.

The other day I saw for a moment Saxl,[8] who was just starting for America, and from whom I gathered he would sound you on the subject. I thought perhaps this letter might get to you before he did, and might prepare your mind a little bit. I should love to have you in England, and perhaps we might do something good together.

Yours ever,

Charles Singer

P.S. I am here in London until the end of June, and possibly later. Anything urgent had better come here (i.e., to Brown's Hotel) and anything else to Cornwall.

Brown's Hotel, Albemarle St., London W.1.

[1] Geneviève Noufflard (born 1920); Nancy, Singer's daughter.

[2] Forces Françaises Libres.

[3] Kristeller (1945).

[4] Douglas McKie, *Antoine Lavoisier: The father of modern chemistry.* (London, 1935); Antoine Lavoisier, (1743–1794) French chemist.

[5] Frank Sherwood Taylor had recently published *The attitude of St. Thomas to natural science*, Aquinas papers no. 3 (Oxford, 1944). Thomas Aquinas, (*c.*1225–1274) medieval theologian in Italy; see William A Wallace, 'Aquinas, Saint Thomas', *Complete dictionary of scientific biography*, vol. 1. (Detroit: Charles Scribner's Sons, 2008), 196–200.

[6] Herbert H. Dingle (1890–1978), British physicist and historian of science. He was appointed to the chair in 1946, see letter 324.

[7] E. A. Underwood.

[8] see Letter 178.

312

Sigerist to Singer, Baltimore?, 28 May 1945

My dear Singer:

The proofs have come back and the article will appear soon.[1] Thanks for your letters of April 23 and 28. I will be glad to follow all your instructions.

I noticed that you plan to do some work on the oriental terms in the Tabulae Sex.[2] I have a manuscript here entitled, "The Hebrew-Aramaic Element in Vesalius' Tabulae Anatomicae Sex, a critical analysis" by Mordecai Etziony. It was submitted to the American Association of the History of Medicine for the Osler Medal Contest.[3] It is a solid piece of work that you should see. The author is a student of W. W. Francis in Montreal,[4] and I should advise you to ask them for a copy. I have accepted the essay for publication in the Bulletin.[5]

With kind regards, I am

Yours very cordially

Henry E. Sigerist

[1] Singer (1945b).
[2] Singer and Rabin (1946).
[3] A prize awarded by the American Association of the History of Medicine.
[4] William W. Francis, head of the Osler Library in Montreal; see John F. Fulton, 'William Willoughby Francis, M. D. 1878–1959', *Journal of the History of Medicine and Allied Sciences*, 1960, **15**: 1–6.
[5] Mordecai Etzioni, 'The Hebrew-Aramaic element in Vesalius' Tabulae anatomicae sex', *Bulletin of the History of Medicine*, 1945, **18**: 413–424.

313

Singer to Sigerist, Kilmarth, Cornwall, 18 July 1945[1]

My dear Sigerist,

Many thanks for your letter of June 30th.[2] I have at once communicated with the Provost of University College. My feeling is that, if we could arrange for you to come over, the difficulties on the Physical and Mathematical side could be over-come. There are, in fact, two Assistants in the Department of the History of Science who survived from pre-war conditions. One of them is a mathematician and the other a chemist. Should it fall out that it would be possible to get you, it might also be possible to get the mathematical side further strengthened.

I wish that I had known your feelings a little earlier. The post on the Wellcome Institution might have suited you better, but I really never thought that you would have accepted it. The Library there is magnificent, and the finances, even on the American scale, are ample.[3] The objection to that position is that nothing can be done unless or until the new Director has been able to get rid of every one of the old staff. It really never occurred to me that you would have accepted that position. I wish I had heard from you earlier.

I have always realised that the non-medical departments of the Johns Hopkins are unsatisfactory, but your own department is undoubtedly the most active of its kind in the world.

What you write about the Argentine greatly surprises me. The general picture that has been put about is that the United States was against admitting the Argentine, but that Britain pressed for its admission because of the immense British industrial interests there. I am also astonished at what you say about the enforced silence concerning India. It really is a most distressing world.

I have had a most painful letter from Von Fritz,[4] who writes that his sister in Germany is diabetic and cannot get Insulin. I have made several efforts to send her some through the Red Cross, but they cannot do anything for civilians. I have, however, got hold of an American officer who has taken her some, and I will endeavour to keep her supplied. By the last post Von Fritz, himself, sent me some Insulin which I will also endeavour to get to her. If you do not know Von Fritz you ought to make a point of doing so. He is a fine man and I have a real admiration for his character.

We were so very sorry to hear that you have been unwell, and hope you may improve with your stay at Ithaca. I know what a lovely place it is. Unfortunately I was there in winter and had a frightful attack of influenza, followed by bronchitis. It is certainly more a place for summer!

Yesterday I sent off the Introduction of my Vesalius. I enclose a copy of the final Table of Contents. I have re-arranged it about twenty times. The text and translation is actually in print.[5]

I wonder if we shall ever meet? It would be wonderful if we could get you over to London. It would be a source of immense personal gratification to me, and I think it would take some years off my age.

With best regards to all the family from us both.

Yours ever,

Charles Singer

[1] This letter was addressed to Ithaca, NY, where Sigerist spent the summer of 1945.

[2] Sigerist's letter is missing; in it he presumably told of his growing dissatisfaction with his situation at Johns Hopkins, of his interest in the Chair of the History of Science in London (see letter 311), and of his incompetence in the history of mathematics and physics.

[3] The Wellcome Library became the biggest library of the history of medicine.

[4] Kurt von Fritz (1900–1985), scholar in ancient philosophy and history of science in Germany and the U.S. See 'Karl Albert Kurt von Fritz', in Ward W. Briggs, Jr (ed.), *Biographical dictionary of North American classicists*, (Westport, Conn.; London: Greenwood Press, 1994), 203–205.

[5] Singer and Rabin (1946).

314

Singer to Sigerist, Kilmarth, Cornwall, 22 July 1945

My dear Sigerist,

The attached letter from Pye, Provost of University College, needs some explanation.[1] When I was in London earlier in the month he told me that the appointment must be made very shortly, and I discussed with him the various possibilities, names of which I sent you.[2] When I received your letter from Corson Place[3] I realised that there was no time to lose, and therefore sent it express to Pye. This seemed to me both quicker and clearer than any explanation that I could give, and I hope that you think I acted rightly. As it has fallen out it reached Pye just in time, and the enclosed letter from him to me reached me last night. In my reply to him I have advised that he should both cable to you and write by Air Mail. I also said that he was quite welcome to say that he had seen your letter to me.

I do hope that this will come off. Your diffidence on the mathematico-physical side can be over-come by strengthening the staff in that direction. The supply of such people in England is pretty ample. It is on the Biologico-medical side that they are so very weak.[4]

With kindest greetings,

Yours always,

Charles Singer

[1] Sir David Randall Pye (1886–1960), mechanical engineer and academic administrator, was provost of UCL between 1943 and 1951; see O. A. Saunders, 'Pye, Sir David Randall (1886–1960)', rev. John Bosnell, *Oxford dictionary of national biography* (Oxford: Oxford University Press, 2004), vol.45, 606.

[2] See letter 311.

[3] Sigerist's address in Ithaca, NY.

[4] Sigerist did not go to London in 1945, see following letter; instead he resigned his post at Johns Hopkins in 1947, moved to Switzerland in order to tackle his multi-volume History of Medicine.

315

Sigerist to Singer, Baltimore, 28 September 1945

My dear Singer:

I had meant to write you long ago to thank you for your letters and for all the trouble you had taken on my behalf, but in Ithaca I had no secretary and was very busy with my book so that my correspondence suffered quite considerably.[1] Now that I have just returned to Baltimore, I want to write you without further delay.

In the meantime you must have heard from Provost Pye that I had written him that I would not be able to consider the chair at University College. I thought the matter over a great deal. It would have been very tempting to work with men such as you, Saxl, Haldane,[2] and the splendid group that you have in London and as I wrote you before, ten years ago I would probably have accepted without hesitation. London does present unique opportunities and I think that the atmosphere for developing a Department for the History of Science is much better than in America.

There can be no doubt, however, that the Department at University College would require a great deal of organizational and administrative work, particularly in the beginning, and as you know, my chief interest at the moment is the writing of a History and Sociology of Medicine that I have been preparing for so many years. I am subordinating everything to this task and I find that I should not give up my present position unless it were for one that would give me more time and leisure for research and writing.

We had a pleasant time in Ithaca. The region is perfectly lovely in the summer and the climate infinitely better than in Baltimore. The University has a good library and I came home with the first 250 pages of Volume I. It was a pleasure to see Saxl who spent a short week-end with us. He has not changed a bit in all these years.

We met Harold Braham and his wife a few days ago. They are perfectly charming people and we hope to see them often. They live a block away from us so that we are practically neighbors.

Your book on Vesalius sounds admirable and I am looking forward to seeing it.[3] I do hope you have received the much-delayed May number of the <u>Bulletin</u> with your article.[4]

With kind regards to Mrs. Singer and yourself, I am

Yours very cordially,

Henry E. Sigerist

[1] Ithaca, NY, site of Cornell University. Henry E. Sigerist, *A history of medicine*, Vol. I (New York, 1951).
[2] John B. S. Haldane (1892–1964) British biologist; see V. M. Quirke, 'Haldane, John Burdon Sanderson (1892–1964)', *Oxford dictionary of national biography* (Oxford: Oxford University Press, 2004), vol. 24, 507–509.
[3] Singer and Rabin (1946).
[4] Singer (1945b).

316

Sigerist to Singer, Baltimore?, 26 November 1945

My dear Singer:

We just received a book for review, John P. Arcieri, <u>The Circulation of the Blood and Andrea Cesalpino of Arezzo</u>.[1]

The author is a New York Italian, a wild nationalist who once tried to sue me because I called him a fascist,[2] but he still is on the job and has written a book to prove once and for all that Cesalpino discovered the circulation of blood and that Harvey and you were wrong.

Since he quotes you repeatedly and since I am very anxious to have a thorough review of the book, I would very much like to have you do the job. You know the facts probably better than anyone else. Please let me know if I may send you the book.

Yours very sincerely,

Henry E. Sigerist

[1] John P. Arcieri, *The circulation of the blood; and Andrea Cesalpino of Arezzo* (New York, 1945). Andrea Cesalpino (1519–1603), Italian physician and botanist; see Karl Mägdefrau, 'Cesalpino, Andrea (or Andreas Caesalpinus)', *Complete dictionary of scientific biography*, vol. 15 (Detroit: Charles Scribner's Sons, 2008), 80–81.
[2] See letter 319.

317

Singer to Sigerist, Kilmarth, 4 December 1945

My dear Sigerist,

Thanks for your air-mail letter of Nov. 26 which reached me only yesterday. Unusually slow for the present service.

Arcieri. He's off his head all right. I have already reviewed his book for the British Medical Journal and have the book by me. I have written another review for you & enclose it.[1] If there is anything that you do not like in it, by all means cut out the offending bit.

One small point needs verification. It is the century in which Ibn al-Nafis made his suggestion of the circulation.[2] I have all the literature but cannot put my hand on it. I think it is the 14th century but perhaps one of your assistants would verify this. See page 2 of accompanying review, last paragraph, line 4.

If the review is too long do please shorten it. Arcieri has made a really shocking exhibition of bad manners.

Yours always,

Charles Singer

Vesalius now all in print & about half in page proofs.[3]

[1] Charles Singer, 'Review of the circulation of the blood and Andrea Cesalpino, by J. P. Arcieri.', *Bulletin of the History of Medicine*, 1946, **19**: 122.
[2] Ibn al-Nafis (1213–1288), Syrian physician and writer; see Albert Z. Iskandar, 'Ibn Al-Nafīs, 'Alā' Al-Dīn Abu 'L-Ḥasan 'Alī Ibn Abi 'L-Ḥazm Al-Qurashī (or Al-Qarashī)', *Complete dictionary of scientific biography*, vol. 9 (Detroit: Charles Scribner's Sons, 2008), 602–606.
[3] Singer and Rabin (1946).

318

Singer to Sigerist, Kilmarth?, 13 December 1945

My dear Sigerist,

During the last week I have had with me Rabin – of Christ Church, Oxford – who has been doing the Semitic terms in the Tabulae Sex with me.[1] We have been correcting the galleys. Underwood, the new Director of the Wellcome Historical Institute, is spending Christmas with us here, and he is very eager to get it out as soon as possible as one of their series.

Rabin tells me that there is at Oxford a young medical man named Hill, who has a permanent job in the Eye Hospital there and who has spent some years in Egypt and learned literary Arabic. He is anxious to do a piece of historical work, and Rabin and I are looking for something simple to suggest to him. Can you think of some fairly easy text, preferably in print, that needs translation? Alternatively could you suggest some manuscript text that he is likely to find in the Bodleian?[2] I should like to see him started on something that is not too discouraging. There are good hopes that he will become an Arabic scholar – a thing which we all need badly.

I have just come across the Al-Tasrif of Albucasis in the Vienna 1519 Latin version. There is something queer about it. The translator seems to be spurious if it is indeed the man Grimm (who claims it). It is obviously a medieval translation. Steinschneider, Wüstenfeld,[3] Meyerhof and Sarton know nothing about it. It is bursting with Semitic terms. Perhaps Rabin and I may tackle the anatomical section unless someone else will, but it is, of course, much too difficult for Hill.

A question that has arisen in the course of our work is the name Bukht-Isho – the well-known family of Syriac translators. The name is usually rendered "Jesus hath delivered" and I see that you and Sudhoff have rendered it "Servant of Jesus". Rabin is much exercised about this because he cannot get the first part of the name into Arabic, Syriac, Hebrew or any other Semitic language. He inclines to Persian – making it "Fortune of Jesus" which seems senseless. Are there any suggestions on your side of the water?[4]

The economic outlook is pretty bad is it not?[5]

With best wishes to you and the family from us all for 1946.

Yours ever,

Charles Singer

---

[1] Singer and Rabin (1946).

[2] Bodleian Library in Oxford, England

[3] Heinrich F. Wüstenfeld (1808–1899), German orientalist and professor at Göttingen. See J. Wellhausen. 'Wüstenfeld, Ferdinand', in *Allgemeine Deutsche Biographie (ADB)*, Band 55 (Leipzig: Duncker & Humblot 1910), 139–40.

[4] Sigerist had this letter answered by his associate Temkin.

[5] For years after World War II the economic situation in Britan was quite bad.

319

Sigerist to Singer, Baltimore, 14 December 1945

My dear Singer:

Thank you ever so much for the excellent review. It is just what I needed and it came in time to be published in the January number of the <u>Bulletin</u>.[1]

Arcieri is a viscious fascist and I am astonished that he still has the courage to open his mouth. In 1939 I wrote a note about his journal, Alcmeone, in which I strongly criticised his nationalist tendency whereupon he wrote to the President of the Johns Hopkins University that I was a damned Bolshevik and that he was going to sue me – which he obviously did not.

I just had a letter from Castiglioni in which he says that Arcieri never was professor of the history of medicine at the University of Rome, that he merely once had the title of libero docente and that he never gave a single lecture.

Nicola Pende who wrote the preface to Arcieri's present book is a notorious fascist and was one of the ten professors who endorsed Mussolini's anti-Jewish legislation.[2] He has now been kicked out of the Senate and retired from the University but he apparently still writes prefaces that are published in the United States.

Thanks for your good wishes. We had missed your card during the last few years and it is a sign of peace that you have resumed this delightful custom.

I am sending you under separate cover a copy of Dr. Temkin's book, THE FALLING SICKNESS. It is a good, solid piece of work which I am sure you will appreciate and enjoy.[3]

In a few weeks I will be able to send you a two-volume book of Edelstein on Asclepius. Volume I is ready and we just sent in the corrected page proofs of Volume II.[4] I will also send you a little book of mine that Schuman is publishing under the title, "The University at the Crossroads", a collection of 12 addresses and essays delivered and written during the war.[5] And at about the same time, we will send you a book that Genevieve Miller is preparing, the diaries of William Beaumont.[6]

With all good wishes from house to house, I am

Yours very cordially,

Henry E. Sigerist

[1] See letter 317.
[2] Nicola Pende (1880–1970), Italian endocrinologist.
[3] Temkin (1945).
[4] Edelstein and Edelstein (1945).
[5] Sigerist (1946).
[6] Genevieve Miller (ed.), *William Beaumont's formative years* (New York, 1946). William Beaumont (1785–1853) U.S. Army surgeon, physiologist; see George Rosen, 'Beaumont, William', *Complete dictionary of scientific biography*, vol. 1, (Detroit: Charles Scribner's Sons, 2008), 542–545.

320

Sigerist to Singer, Baltimore?, 21 February 1946

Dear Singer:

Thank you very much for your letter of February 4[1] and for the carbon of your letter to Professor Reynolds at Wisconsin.[2] I was also consulted and recommended primo loco

Owsei Temkin who, I am sure, is fully prepared to take over a chair and secundo loco I. E. Drabkin whom you probably do not know.

I am sending you enclosed a carbon of my letter. Temkin has really done very well in recent years and at the moment he has several books in preparation that promise to be first-rate. I am including a copy of his bibliography which I thought you might like to have.

Dr. J.M.D. Olmsted is with us this week giving an excellent course of Noguchi Lectures on Brown-Séquard.[3] We recollected the winter of 1931–1932 when we all met in California. It seems long ago. We are going to publish Olmsted's lectures which, I am sure, complete beautifully the picture of 19th century French physiology that he has traced in his two other books.

Edelstein's Asclepius has just come from the press and I am sending you a copy under separate cover.[4] Please do not feel that you have to review all these books. I am sending them because I want you to have what our Institute publishes. I am also adding a Supplement to the Bulletin that came out recently on public baths and health in England in the late 16th to the 18th century.[5]

With kind regards, I am

Yours very cordially,

Henry E. Sigerist

[1] Singer's letter is missing.

[2] Professor Reynolds at the Department of History at the University of Wisconsin; the chair of the history of medicine was eventually filled by Ackerknecht in 1947.

[3] James M. D. Olmsted (1886–1956), biographer of the French physiologists Charles Edward Brown-Séquard (1817–1894), François Magendie (1783–1855) and Claude Bernard (1813–1878). His Noguchi lectures were published as *Charles-Eduard Brown-Séquard, a nineteenth Century neurologist and endocrinologist* (Baltimore, 1946); his two other books refer to his works on Magendie and Bernard. For Olmsted see John F. Fulton, 'Prof. J. M. D. Olmsted', *Nature*, 1956, **178**: 15–16.

[4] Edelstein and Edelstein (1946).

[5] Charles F. Mullett, *Public baths and health in England, 16th–18th Century*, Supplement to the *Bulletin of the History of Medicine*, 1946, no. 5, 1–85.

321

Singer to Sigerist, Kilmarth, 27 February 1946

My dear Sigerist,

I have written a notice on the death of Madame Metzger which either has appeared or is about to appear in Nature. You might care to put it also in the Bulletin or else some abstract of it. Put it in either with my name or without it – just as you think best, or leave it out if you prefer. But she did most meritorious work and should, I think, be mentioned in the Bulletin.[1]

Yours always,

Charles Singer

[1] Hélène Metzger-Brühl (born 1889), French historian of science, was murdered by the Nazis during the war. Singer's announcement appeared in the *Bulletin of the History of Medicine*, 1946, **19**: 461–462 and in *Nature*, 1946, 157: 472.

322

Singer to Sigerist, Kilmarth?, 8 March 1946

My dear Sigerist,

Many thanks for your letter of Feb. 21 with enclosures concerning Temkin and the University of Wisconsin. I agree that Temkin's record is excellent and he is of the right age, and probably better than anyone I suggested.

If Cortesao whom I suggested does, by any chance, come to America mind you get in touch with him – he is such a very pleasant, amusing fellow and I am sure you would enjoy his company and have some good laughs with him. I like him immensely and we get on finely together. But I hope he will soon get back to his native Portugal.[1]

I have Saxl with me here for a few days, and he was telling me of his visit to you. I rather gather from him that you felt that if you had been offered the University College appointment for a relatively short period – say for three years – it would have better suited you. I wish I had had any inkling of this, for there would have been no difficulty in making that particular change, nor even in making terms that McKie should run the department. Nevertheless, quite frankly, I do not think it is as good a post as that which you have at Johns Hopkins. Had you come it would have been a great score for University College, but not much from your point of view.

Apart from all this I do hope we shall be able to see you in Europe. I have got to go to London at the end of this month, and I will try and see if something cannot be done in the way of invitations to lecture. I hope if you do come to Europe you would stay with us.

Dorothea asks me particularly to thank Mrs. Sigerist for her welcome to our friends the Brahams.

The printing situation in England is perfectly maddening. All my books are inaccessible. They are either out of print or out of binding. The Short History of Biology has gone clean out, and the Oxford University Press does not see its way to re-printing it for years.[2] I have written to Harpers suggesting a revised edition to them, printed on thinner paper and with nothing but line blocks in it. As for my Vesalius – I am simply sick of writing to the printers and being told that I shall get proofs in a fortnight.[3] There are twenty-six fortnights in a year and that is about the number of times I have been given this answer.

With all kind wishes,
Very cordially yours,
Charles Singer

[1] Armando Cortesao (1891–1977), Portuguese historian, see letter 326. Francisco de Solano y Perez-Lila, 'In Memoriam: Armando Cortesâo (1891–1977)', *Revista de Indias*, 1977, **37**: 695–699.
[2] Singer (1931).
[3] Singer and Rabin (1946).

323

Sigerist to Singer, Baltimore?, 26 March 1946

My dear Singer:

I am very grateful to you for sending me proofs of your article on Madame Metzger. I shall, of course, be very glad to publish it in the Bulletin.[1] I am terribly sorry for the poor little woman. What a tragic end. She was a fine scholar, a most enthusiastic historian of science. You know, of course, that she was the niece of L. Lévy-Bruhl.[2] I went to visit him once with her shortly before he died. What a terrible world we are living in.

I have just signed a contract with the Oxford University Press. The American branch is going to publish my History of Medicine in 8 volumes and I am delighted because I could not think of a better publisher for this kind of book.

I plan to go to Switzerland in July to see my Mother who is in her 81st year but I do not intend to stay long.[3] I am anxious to finish the first volume of my History[4] and know I can do best here.

With kind regards, I am
Yours very cordially,
Henry E. Sigerist

[1] See letter 321.
[2] Lucien Levy-Brühl (1857–1939) French scholar, see Jean Cazeneuve, *Lucien Lévy-Bruhl*, trans. Peter Rivie're. (Oxford: Blackwell, 1972).
[3] Sigerist's mother Emma Sigerist
[4] Sigerist (1951).

324

Singer to Sigerist, Kilmarth?, 27 March 1946

My dear Sigerist,

You may care to see the enclosed unsigned review of Arcieri which has appeared in the British Medical Journal.[1] I have sent another copy to Fulton.

The Board of Advisors on the chair of the History and Philosophy of Science of London University met yesterday, and we recommended Dingle for the position. I proposed that there should be two chairs – one of History and one of Philosophy. I did not press the point because it would have meant delay in the election, but I think the idea may be taken up. Dingle's appointment is not public yet. It has to be approved by the Senate.

I also spent an hour or two at the new Wellcome Institute. It has certainly become impressive, but until it is fully open to scholars it cannot be said to be functioning. I think it will become open within a very few weeks.

All kind wishes,
Yours always,
Charles Singer

[1] 'Cesalpino and the circulation', *British Medical Journal*, 1946, **i**: 436. See letter 317.

325

Singer to Sigerist, Kilmarth, 17 April 1946

My dear Sigerist,

Many thanks for your letter of March 26 received to-day. What good news about your History of Medicine. When do you anticipate the first part will be out? What good news too that you will be in Europe. Could we not meet in London? I have to be in London for some ten days in July and shall also be there the whole of May and June. If you would let me know by return when we could meet I would arrange my movements accordingly. Of course one has to book one's rooms months in advance.

Naturally we should be delighted if you could come down here. We always travel by night as that does not consume time. I would even come down with you if you could see your way to do that.

When is your mother's birthday? We would like to send her a line on that occasion. I think we have her address but perhaps you would attach it to your answer.

With all best wishes from us all to you and the family,
Yours always,
Charles Singer

326

Singer to Sigerist, London, 23 May 1946a[1]

My dear Sigerist,

There is in London an interesting fellow whom [sic] I think could give a very accep-table lecture tour in America. He does not want to settle in America and he would,

I believe, raise general interest by his personality if he were invited for a course of lectures. He is :Dr. Armando Cortesao

48 Stamford Court
London W.6.

Cortesao is a Portuguese and was in the Portuguese Colonial service. He is a distinguished scholar and may be regarded as the real article. He is about fifty years of age, tall and very good-looking and speaks and writes English fluently and perfectly. He has been exiled by Salazaar [sic][2] for his liberal views, but his children are not molested and his wife comes backwards and forward to Portugal quite freely. I like him greatly & have seen a good deal of him.

I think he would interest Americans because he has some novel views with new material on the origin, work and personality of Columbus. He has written several very fine books on the History of Cartography and has recently published two large volumes for the Hakluyt Society.[3] He has also published a volume issued by the British Museum.

While Schuman was in London I introduced him to Cortesao to write a book for him. Once we got him on your side of the Atlantic I feel sure that he would be a very great success, perhaps the more so in that he does not want to settle there. His one desire is to get back to his own country as soon as Salazaar [sic] falls ?].

If you could help in the matter I should be very greatly indebted to you
Yours always,
Charles Singer

[1] Address until end of June: Mount Royal Hotel, Marble Arch, London W.1
[2] Antonio de Oliveira Salazar (1889–1970), Portuguese fascist dictator from 1932 to 1968.
[3] Hakluyt Society, for advancement of knowledge by publications. Armando Cortesão (ed.), *The Suma oriental of Tomé Pires . . . and, The book of Francisco Rodrigues*, 2 vols (London: Printed for the Hakluyt Society, 1944); *The discovery of Abyssinia by the Portuguese in 1520. A facsimile of the relation entitled 'Carta das Novas . . .* (Lisbon, 1521), with an introduction and English translation by H. Thomas and a transcription into modern Portugese by A. Cortesão (London: British Museum, 1938).

327

Singer to Sigerist, London, 23 May 1946b

My dear Sigerist,

As soon as you get this letter do let us know at once when you will be in London, when in Switzerland and when in Cornwall. We shall be in Switzerland from August 15th to September 15th and we shall be passing through Zürich. I should of course come to London if you were to pass through there and not be able to get to Cornwall.

I have to-day had a letter from Herbert Reichner – the bookseller of New York – in which he says that Emil Starkenstein of Prague was exterminated at Auschwitz. I had a strong impression that he had a chair of Pharmacology in America, but Reichner writes on the authority of Erik Waller.[1] If it is true would you – or someone else – write an obituary notice to put in <u>Nature</u>.[2] The more of these things appear the better.

Do let us hear from you.

Yours ever,

Charles Singer

[1] Erik Waller (1875–1955), Swedish physician and book collector; see Dorothy M. Schullian, 'Axel Erik Waller, 1875–1955', *Journal of the History of Medicine and Allied Sciences*, 1955 **10**: 226–227.

[2] An obituary of Starkenstein did not appear in *Nature*.

328

Sigerist to Singer, Baltimore?, 30 May 1946

My dear Singer:

I just received your letter of May23 and I hasten to answer it. Mrs. Sigerist is in Switzerland already. She left here by boat on May 1. The girls and I have reservations on an airplane to Geneva on July 23 and plan to stay in Switzerland for about two months. I am delighted to know that you will be there also and we must arrange to meet by all means. My permanent address in Switzerland is that of my Mother (182 St. Albanring, Basel) and around the middle of August we plan to spend a few weeks in the Tessin where we shall have the use of a house that belongs to one of my wife's friends who is in California at the moment.[1] Perhaps you could arrange to come and see us there. In the early part of August, I plan to go to one of the Swiss health resorts and have a complete rest of a few weeks and a treatment. I feel infinitely better than last year but these water treatments always do me a lot of good.

I do not plan to go to England or any other country this year. Travelling, as you know, is still very complicated. The food situation is difficult in most countries and I do not want to interrupt my work here for too long a time because I am anxious to complete the first volume of my History this year.[2]

The chief purpose of my trip will be to see my Mother, my sister[3] and a few other relatives and friends and to resume contact with Europe. Next year, if conditions permit, I would like to stay abroad for at least six months and visit a number of countries including, of course, England.

Thanks for drawing my attention to Dr. Armando Cortesao. The time is not very opportune for arranging lectures now that universities are closing for the summer but it may be possible to arrange some for next autumn.

We just had a very successful and pleasant annual meeting of the American Association of the History of Medicine and we plan to meet next year in April in Cleveland together with the Medical Library Association. I wish you could be with us at that time. Unfortunately our Noguchi Lectureship Fund is completely exhausted at the moment because we had a course of Lectures last winter and two volumes still have to be published, otherwise I would have invited you under that foundation. We also have quite a considerable deficit in this year's operation of the Institute due primarily to the increased cost of printing. Edelstein's book alone cost us $ 2,000 more than had been estimated.[4] We have to cut down on personnel and our funds will be very limited next year.

With all good wishes, I am

Yours very cordially,

Henry E. Sigerist

[1] Tessin, the Italian-speaking part of Switzerland; the house was Hilda Brown's Il Roccolo in Montagnola, close to Pura.

[2] Sigerist (1951).

[3] Marguerite Bickel-Sigerist.

[4] Edelstein and Edelstein (1945).

329

Dorothea Singer to Sigerist, Kilmarth, 6 June 1946

My dear Dr. Sigerist,

We were most delighted to receive your letter to Charlie this morning and to know that Mrs. Sigerist and you will be in Switzerland. Our programme (which will certainly be modified if in its present form it does not enable us to see you) is as follows:-

Thursday, 15th August arrive by airplane at Geneva.

Friday, 16th August, Sleep at Ouchy in order to call on Professor Raymond [sic] at Lausanne.

Saturday, 17th August to Wednesday, 28th August – Les Plans de Frenières.

Wednesday 28th August to Saturday, September 7th Ringgenberg on Lake Brienz.

Saturday 7th September to Tuesday, 10th September St. Gall.

Tuesday, 10th September to Thursday 12th September – Schaffhausen.

Thursday 12th September, to Saturday, 14th September – Zürich.

Return home on Saturday, 14th September.

We had thought that probably you would be spending some time near Lake Brienz or at Zürich. If you will be at Basel from 11th or 12th to 14th or 15 September we can cancel our Zürich sojourn and go straight to Basel. Perhaps you would let me know which hotel there will be nearest to your mother's house.

We shall have Nancy with us and one reason that I chose Les Plans is in order that she shall see a glacier as there happens to be one within easy reach & Les Plans has a tempting looking little stream for swimming. We are planning to stop for an hour or two at Chur on our way to St. Gall as Charlie is tracing Alum trade routes through those regions.

With our most cordial greetings,

Yours very sincerely,

Dorothea Waley Singer

330

Sigerist to Dorothea Singer, Baltimore?, 13 June 1946

Dear Mrs. Singer:

Many thanks for your letter of June 6 with the program of your Swiss tour. I think the best for us would be to meet in Zurich because I am sure to be there from September 12 to 14. I will attend the annual meeting of the Société Helvétique des Sciences naturelles which takes place from September 6 to 9 and I will certainly stay in Zurich for some time thereafter.

It just occurs to me that the Swiss Society of the History of Science and Medicine is meeting in Zurich at the same time and that you may wish to attend some of the sessions. I will see to it that you will receive a program.

Looking forward with greatest pleasure to seeing you this summer, I am, with kind regards
Yours very cordially,
Henry E. Sigerist

331

Dorothea Singer to Sigerist, Kilmarth, 27 June 1946

Dear Dr. Sigerist,

Thank you for your letter of June 13th. We are delighted to hear that you will be in Zurich from September 12 to September 14, and we are writing to book rooms there for these dates.

If the Swiss Society for the History of Science and Medicine will be meeting then would you like a ten minute paper from me on Sir John Pringle?[1] I am preparing a study on him for the Annals of Science. I feel he is rather topical at the moment because of his interest in hospitals and goals [sic], & for Switzerland he has ideas on the neutrality of army hospitals in war.

Nancy will be with us. I think she was five years old when you last saw her in Switzerland.

Charlie joins me in cordial greetings.
Yours most sincerely,
Dorothea Singer

---

[1] John Pringle (1707–1782), British physician and author on military medicine; Dorothea Waley Singer, 'Sir John Pringle and his circle.—Part I. Life', *Annals of Science*, 1949, **6** (2): 127–180; 'Sir John Pringle and his circle. Part II.—Public health', *ibid.*, 1950, **6** (3): 229—247; 'Sir John Pringle and his circle.—Part III. Copley discourses', *ibid.*, 1950, **6** (3): 248—261.

332

Singer to Sigerist, Kilmarth, 1 January 1947

My dear Sigerist,

I have been intending to answer your delightful wire on my birthday by sending you the Vesalius volume.[1] Week by week has passed and the printer has always temporised. At last he has produced it and it has gone to you. You will probably have received it by now and I hope that it will give you some pleasure.

I very deeply appreciated the letter that was addressed to me by some 154 colleagues of whom you were one. I can but express my grateful and humble thanks.

I am sorry to say that all is not well with the Wellcome Historical Medical Museum.[2] Wellcome himself and the Wellcome Trustees have spent more than £ 500,000 (2,500,000 dollars) on it with scientific results that are almost nothing! The museum has a staff of 51 persons! This is far too large for usefulness. It has really almost no educational value and administration absorbs far too much energy and time. It is a shame to saddle Underwood with it.

The business now wants to absorb the space occupied by the museum. If it is to be re-established on another site, the whole of Underwood's life will go on it. My view is that it is best to recognise frankly the obvious fact that Wellcome's plan of a vast museum with no integration of parts is really unworkable and would be of little use even if, with much labour and treasure, it could be made to work. Most of the money should go on research. The lines of my suggestion are set out in the attached letter.[3] It says nothing that I have not said a hundred times.

I believe (though I have no authority to speak for them) that the Trustees have similar views to mine. I hope that they will be glad to have the matter raised in this way. My hope is too that they will invite you to come over to discuss the situation.

The simple fact is that the Wellcome Museum is a white elephant. Another precious year has been lost in getting it open and it really isn't worth opening. It has been wrongly conceived from the first and had best go into cold storage before more lives are sacrificed to an unattainable and rather vulgar ideal.

All good wishes for 1947 to the family,
Yours ever,
Charles Singer

My latest information is that the Foundation (not the Trustees) want to be quit of the whole Wellcome Historical outfit. I cannot blame them. They are just businessmen & the Wellcome results are merely pitiable. But I have good hope that the Trustees will stand out &, if they do, they have the whip-hand.

I will keep you posted but though my letter to the Provost is not confidential, you had best keep quiet for a bit. Of course if I can get you invited over to report I would be delighted.
CS

[1] Singer and Rabin (1946). Singer's 70th birthday was on 2 November 1946.
[2] Sigerist and Singer had met in September 1946 in Switzerland and discussed the Wellcome business.
[3] A letter to the Provost of University College London.

333

Sigerist to Singer, Baltimore?, 7 February 1947

My dear Singer:

Ever since I came back from Europe last autumn, I meant to write you. I wanted to tell you how much I had enjoyed seeing Mrs. Singer and you and your charming daughter after all these many years. It was like old times again and coming back to Switzerland, I sometimes had the feeling as if the war had been just a nightmare.

I had all kind of difficulties in getting home. Erica and I were fortunate in being able to fly but my poor wife and Nora who could not get airplane tickets sailed from Genoa on a filthy old cargo that was flying the Panama flag and it took them 28 days to reach New York. Nora was four weeks late for her courses at Columbia but they admitted her nevertheless and she has caught up by now.[1]

Then I meant to write you for your birthday[2] in order to tell you more than I could put in a telegram but I was so swamped with work that my correspondence was badly neglected. Well, you know that all of us remembered you when you completed your 70th year. We are grateful for all that you have done for us and for suffering humanity, and I only hope that you will have many more years, years of peace that you may devote to rounding up your historical work.

It was excellent news to hear that your Vesalius is out. It has not arrived yet but I expect it any day and I am looking forward with greatest pleasure to seeing it soon.[3]

Did I ever send you my book, CIVILIZATION AND DISEASE, the Messenger Lectures that I gave at Cornell University?[4] My last year's little volume, THE UNIVERSITY AT THE CROSSROADS, was sent to you by the publisher I hope.[5] The Institute just published a very delightful little book on Brown-Séquard, the Noguchi Lectures that Olmsted gave here last year. I am mailing you a copy under separate cover and I am sure you will like the little book.[6]

I am sorry to hear that there is some trouble with the Wellcome Historical Museum.[7] I also had a letter from Underwood on the subject. I have read your memorandum very carefully and I can only say that I agree with every word you wrote.[8] There can be no doubt that the Museum should develop into a department of the University and the best the Trustees could do would be to endow a chair. I am fully aware that this will take a great deal of time and I am sorry for Underwood who will probably spend the rest of his life preparing somebody else's nest.

One result of last year's summer in Switzerland was that I have just resigned my position at the Johns Hopkins University and that we plan to return to Switzerland permanently and to settle down somewhere in the Ticino.[9] I find it absolutely impossible to write my History of Medicine here where I am swamped day and night with visitors and requests and where I am wasting an enormous amount of time with petty routine or showing people around. I can write my book only if I can devote all my time and attention to the task and I very strongly feel that this book is the most important contribution that I can make under the circumstances. I am, of course, fully aware that I am giving up a great deal here and that I shall miss my students very much but the subject of medical history is well established in the States by now and the Institute will continue its work.

You may have heard that the University of Wisconsin appointed my old student, Erwin H. Ackerknecht as Professor of the History of Medicine in the Medical School. The chair of the History of Science was divided into two associate professorships, one for the history of biological sciences that was given to Stauffer, a young man, student of Sarton who has not published much because he spent three years in the armed forces but seems to be promising. The other chair for the history of the exact sciences was offered to I. Bernard Cohen who, however, preferred to remain at Harvard.[10] Wisconsin in addition has George Urdang and the American Institute of Pharmacy [sic] and they have just purchased the beautiful Thordarson Collection for $300,000.[11]

Henry Guerlac is now professor of the history of science at Cornell University in Ithaca where he is doing extremely well and is becoming very popular.[12] And so, I really feel that the field is well established and will continue to develop in a satisfactory way.

We plan to leave here in the last week of June and by October 1, I hope to be well settled in Switzerland. I am looking forward to being closer to you and my other old European friends and I hope that we shall meet often. It is not too easy to find a house these days but it is not too difficult in the Ticino where one sometimes finds very pleasant old houses that have stood the test of time. I have been promised a research fellowship and a grant-in-aid of research by one of the foundations and with this, my Retirement Annuity, and royalties from books I expect to be able to manage quite well.

There is one more matter that I would like to bring up, namely, that of the series of ancient classics of science that we once discussed with Underwood in Europe. I think Drabkin has written you in the matter concerning his edition and translation of Caelius Aurelianus.[13] He is anxious to get it out soon and so am I. It is the first translation into any modern language and the text is greatly improved although there is no manuscript available. Drabkin's manuscript is in perfect shape and could go to the press immediately. I have in addition two other manuscripts that are ready, namely, the fragments of Praxagoris [sic],[14] Greek text and translation and an English translation of Soranus. I think it would be a pity if these books were scattered. They should appear in the same series. I approached the Loeb Classical Library people at Harvard last year but they were not very encouraging. They are anxious to complete the series as soon as possible because at that time under the will of the donor all money will be turned over to the Classics Department of Harvard. If the Wellcome Museum could start such a series of classics soon it would be splendid, otherwise I would have to try to publish the books somewhere here in the States.

So much for today. With kind regards to Mrs. Singer and yourself, I am
Yours very cordially,
Henry E. Sigerist

[1] Sigerist's daughters Erica and Nora.
[2] See previous letter.
[3] Singer and Rabin (1946).
[4] Sigerist (1943a).
[5] Sigerist (1946).
[6] Olmsted (1946).
[7] Wellcome Medical Historical Museum.
[8] Memorandum to the Provost of University College
[9] Ticino = Tessin, the Italian-speaking part of Switzerland.

[10] Robert C. Stauffer (1913–1992), historian of science, pupil of Sarton. I. Bernard Cohen (1914–2003) historian of science, see J. W. Dauben, M. L. Gleason and G. E. Smith, 'Seven decades of history of science: I. Bernard Cohen (1914–2003), second editor of Isis', *Isis*, 2009, **100**: 4–35.

[11] George Urdang (1882–1960), German-American historian of pharmacy, director of the American Institute of the History of Pharmacy. See Andrea Ludwig, *Georg Urdang (1882–1960): ein Pharmaziehistoriker als Mittler zwischen alter und neuer Welt*, mit einem Geleitwort von Fritz Krafft, (Stuttgart: Wisenschaftliche Verlagsgesellschaft, 2009), and 'George Urdang (1882–1960)', *Pharmacy in History*, 1960, **5**: 17–19. The Thordarson Collection contained books on Iceland and the history of science.

[12] Henry Guerlac (1910–1985), historian of science; see Marie Boas Hall, 'Eloge: Henry Guerlac, 10 June 1910–29 May 1985', *Isis*, 1986, **77**: 504–506.

[13] Caelius Aurelianus (5th ct. AD) Roman physician and author; Israel Drabkin (ed.), *Aurelianus, Caelius: On acute diseases and on chronic diseases* (Chicago, 1950).

[14] Praxagoras (born 340 BC), Greek physician and author. The Praxagoras material was never published, but the Soranus was published: *Soranus' Gynecology*, translated with an introduction by Owsei Temkin; with the assistance of Nicholson J. Eastman, Ludwig Edelstein, and Alan F. Guttmacher (Baltimore, Johns Hopkins Press, 1956).

334

Singer to Sigerist's secretary, Kilmarth, 3 March 1947

Dear Miss Miller,[1]

Would you be so very kind as to let me have a complete list of the publications of the Johns Hopkins Institute of the History of Medicine? That is to say those during the time of Professor Sigerist.

I should also be very grateful if you would let me have the dates in Professor Sigerist's life and a list of his major works. I want to write something about him in one of the English journals. You can give me all the information required and save my searching on this side.[2]

With kind regards,

Believe me to be,

Yours sincerely,

Charles Singer

[1] Genevieve Miller, Sigerist's research secretary, see letter 304.
[2] Singer did not publish on Sigerist before 1951.

335

Singer to Sigerist, Kilmarth, 14 March 1947

My dear Sigerist,

Many thanks for your letter of February 7 which I should have answered weeks ago.

I think you have to be congratulated on resigning your chair. I am sure you will get far more work done and it is the right thing to do while you are young enough to work. How delightful if you can really settle at Lugano. Upon my word if I could get such property as I have out of this country – which I certainly cannot – I would join you so that we could combine our libraries. It was such a great pleasure meeting in Switzerland and rediscovering each other. Would it not be delightful if you could stay with us on your way to Switzerland? Do try. What an awful time Mrs. Sigerist and Nora must have had.[1] I know those boats flying the Panama flag. For some reason or other they escape some sort of toll in going through the Canal.

Yes I got your Civilization and Disease and wrote to you about it, and also your University at the Crossroads.[2] You will be able to fire off a good many atomic bombs of that kind from Switzerland. I think you are fortunate in planning to leave America just now. It looks to me as though there can't be much good coming with the mood that is crystallising there.[3]

Of course we agree about the Wellcome. I have no doubt that the advice that I ventured to tender to them will be accepted in due course for the simple reason that there is no other way to run their Institute. For the moment, however, I seem to have blotted my copy book. They are rather annoyed with me for telling them the truth. I am particularly sorry for Underwood. His handicap is that he is a late starter and the refusal of his Board to face the fact that their scheme for a Museum is no good will waste his best years. In the old days I used to worry that I had not an Institute and a staff. Looking back on it all I am quite sure that I have had the best of it, and have been much happier and have done more for not having had those[?] things. I don't despair that the Wellcome Trustees may see that I am right and ask you and me to report on the matter.

I was very glad to hear about Ackerknecht at Wisconsin, and have written to congratulate him. I am also writing to Guerlac.

I heard that Drabkin had edited Caelius Aurelianus, but I don't think that I have heard from him. Philologically it is an extraordinarily interesting book. I can't remember that it has been edited since the 18th century.[4]

Of course the Wellcome people should endow your Classical series, and I will do what I can. It is a most complicated situation there because really there are two separate Boards and Underwood has to deal with the difficult one. I fortunately have the easy one though they are a little angry with me at the moment. However they treated me pretty well over Vesalius and I can't complain.

I am putting up to them a project for a translation of Galen's De anatomicis administrationibus.[5] I am asking for the full time services of a Greek scholar for a year, and at the same time for the publication of a translation which I have completed of Book VII of the Fabrica.[6] I don't think that requests of this kind in the least interfere with suggestions such as yours about Drabkin and your Fragments of Praxagoras and the translation of Soranus. They have plenty of money (even on the American scale) and they don't really know what to do with it. I think, therefore that a large scheme really appeals to them more than a small one, and if I can put to them a whole series of translations they are more likely to help than for one or two. The difficulty is not money but getting them to see the point of the thing.

Do try to see if Nora could get me Vol. 1 of the 4th series of the Surgeon General's Catalogue. I have all four series except for this one volume. It really would be a kind act if you can get it for me.

I have finished the text of my Alum volume.[7] I am touching it up and attending to pictures, maps etc. By the way if you ever want anything of the sort you would find that Alinari of Florence does extraordinarily good colour work at an extremely low rate.[8] I am having four or five coloured collotypes made by him for this Alum volume.

You know, do you not, that McKie and I have undertaken to do an Anthology of Science for the Encylopaedia Britannica? As soon as I can get this Alum book away I must look through his material. It will be a volume of readings for my Short History of Science.[9]

We have just had Farrington and his wife here for a couple of weeks. They asked a good deal after you. I fear that his health is not good and that his strength is not equal to doing Galen's De anatomicis administrationibus. That is one of the reasons why I am doing it, but in fact it is a book I always wanted to tackle.

With all good wishes from us both to you both and looking forward to seeing you in England.

Yours most cordially,

Charles Singer

You will come to stay with us – both of you – on your way to Switzerland. I shall build on that.

---

[1] See letter 333.

[2] Sigerist (1943a) and (1946).

[3] McCarthyism.

[4] Drabkin (1950).

[5] Charles Singer, 'A MS. translation of the Arabic version of Galen's "De anatomicis administrationibus"', *Journal of the History of Medicine and Allied Sciences*, 1952, **7**: 85–86; Charles Singer (ed.), *Galen on anatomical procedures: de anatomicis administrationibus / translation of the surviving books* (London, 1956).

[6] Andreas Vesalius, *De humani corporis fabrica* (Leyden, 1552). Charles Singer, *Vesalius on the human brain.* (London 1952).

[7] Charles Singer, *The earliest chemical industry. An essay in the historical relations of economics and technology illustrated from the alum trade* (London[?], 1948).

[8] Alinari, a publisher in Florence.

[9] Singer (1941).

336

Sigerist's secretary to Singer, Baltimore?, 15 March 1947[1]

Dear Dr. Singer:

Thank you for your letter of March 3. I hope that the enclosed material will give you the information which you need. If you are interested in a detailed account of the activities of the Institute, may I refer you to the <u>Bulletin</u> 1941, Vol. 10, pp. 364–416 and other annual reports of the Institute from 1940 on which appear each year in the July issue.

You can doubtless imagine how desolated we all feel at the idea of Dr. Sigerist's leaving us. But as far as his own creative activities are concerned, it is certain that he has made the correct decision.

With kindest regards,
Yours sincerely,
Genevieve Miller

[1] This letter answers Singer's request of 3 March 1947, see letter 334.

337

Sigerist to Singer, Baltimore?, 18 June 1947[1]

Dear Singer:

I just discovered that I have not answered your last letter yet and I am using the last few days at the Institute for paying off old debts.

It was very kind of you to ask us to stay at your home on our way to Europe but we expect to fly from Washington to Geneva on a TWA[2] plane on the 24th of this month. It is very difficult to get passage on ships and besides I am restless and am anxious to get settled in Switzerland soon so that I can resume my work. My mother bought a little house for us in Pura, a village between Lugano and Ponte Theresa [sic][3] about two miles from the Italian border. The house is in the midst of vineyards, has an ideal location and I only hope that it is large enough for my books. We have not seen it yet but I hope to be there in less than two weeks. Until the time we get settled, you can always reach us through the address of my Mother (182 St.Albanring, Basel, Switzerland) where I am sure to spend some time while we are waiting for the books and furniture to arrive.

We saw a good deal of Underwood and enjoyed very much having him with us. He gave an excellent address at the Cleveland meeting and made many friends.[4] He is a most likeable fellow and he certainly has not an easy job at the Wellcome Museum.

The question of my successor has not been settled yet and I do not expect any decision to be made before the autumn.[5] The Committee that has been appointed to make recommendations is a very good one with Sidney Painter, head of the History Department as chairman, the deans of the School of Medicine and School of Hygiene, George Corner and Larkey.[6] The University seems determined not only to maintain the Institute but to expand it and to continue to cultivate both history and sociology of medicine. I do not envy my successor beccause he will have to spend his entire first year running around in search of funds.

I was delighted to hear about your project of a translation of Galen's De anatomicis administrationibus.[7] This is an extremely important book and a translation is badly needed.

Well, so much for today. I'll write again from Switzerland soon. I do not know yet when we shall be able to move into the house but we should be there by the end of July latest and if you should come to Switzerland again this summer, do by all means look us up. We have a guest room and in addition a small pension near by, for the overflow.

With all good wishes to Mrs. Singer and yourself, I am

Yours very cordially,

Henry E. Sigerist

[1] This is probably Sigerist's last letter to Singer from the U.S..

[2] Trans World Airlines.

[3] Ponte Tresa, the border town.

[4] Cleveland meeting of the American Association of the History of Medicine.

[5] Sigerist's successor, Richard Harrison Shryock (1893–1972), was not appointed until 1949; see Whitfield Bell, Jr., 'Richard Harrison Shryock, 1893–1972', *Bulletin of the History of Medicine*, 1972, **46**: 499–503.

[6] Sidney Painter (1902–1960) Johns Hopkins medievalist; see William H. Dunham, Gaines Post and Joseph R. Strayer, 'Sidney Painter', *Speculum*, 1960, **35**: 521–522. George W. Corner (1889–1981) anatomist and medical historian; see Lord Zuckerman, 'George Washington Corner. 12 December 1889–28 September 1981', *Biographical Memoirs of Fellows of the Royal Society*, 1983, **29**: 93–112.

[7] Singer (1956a).

338

Singer to Sigerist, Par, Cornwall, 5 September 1947 (telegram)[1]

WILL YOU JOIN PROTEST AGAINST PARTICIPATION IN LAUSANNE CONFERENCE OF DIPGEN [sic] AND FELDHAUS AND STICKER WHO ALL THREE HAVE SHOCKING RECORDS STOP[2] MRS SINGER AND I ALSO BELIEVE OTHER ENGLISH SCIENTISTS WILL ONLY ATTEND IF THOSE THREE ARE EXCLUDED FROM CONGRESS

   CHARLES SINGER KILMARTH PAR CORNWALL ENGLAND

[1] Addressed to Sigerist in Casa Serena, Pura, Switzerland.

[2] International Congress of the History of Science to be held in Lausanne in 1948. Diepgen, Feldhaus and Georg Sticker (1860–1960), German medical historian, had "shocking records" as active Nazis. For Sticker see Michael Quick, 'Zur Erinnerung an Georg Sticker (1860–1960)', *Medizinhistorisches Journal*, 1987, **22**: 382–386.

339

Sigerist to Singer, Pura, Switzerland, 7 September 1947

My dear Singer,

Thank you for your telegram. I had solved my problem by deciding not to attend the Lausanne conference. I feel exactly as you do, and do not want to meet the Germans, particularly those you mention. Sticker is a vicious old fool; Feldhauser [sic] criminal, and Diepgen is the worst of all because he is thoroughly dishonest, a clerico-fascist opportunist, who went along with Hitler as long as things went well, but always kept a door open for retreat. Now he can boast that he never joined the Nazi party, and I hear that he has a very influential position in Germany, being chairman of the National medical examination board, – a most despicable individual.

Now, I am not sure that protesting will help much, and I can imagine that Raymond [sic][1] is in a difficult situation. The conference is one of the Academy of which these Germans are members, and it may be difficult not to invite them, since they have not been expelled from the Academy. On the other hand it would be difficult to expel them, since they have been cleared by de-Nazification courts.[2]

The problem is really very hard to solve because if we simply abstain from attending the meetings, the Germans in their traditional aggressiveness will soon take over the organizations. It would have been much better to hold the first conference of the Academy in London or Paris, where it would have been much easier to leave out the Germans. I for one will not attend the Lausanne conference.

I sometimes wonder if it would not be better to disband the old organizations, the International Academy of the History of Science, and the International Society of the History of Medicine, and to create new ones. There was so much failure and unpleasantness in the short history of both these groups that it might be better to bury them and to make a fresh start. You did not attend the Congress in Yugoslavia in 1938,[3] or you would remember how it developed into a regular battlefield on which Gomoiu[4] and other Balkan celebrities fought out their personal feuds, and the large German and Italian delegations practically took over the Society. At that time I decided that I would never again attend any meeting of this Society.

We are beginning to be settled here and like the place very much.[5] It is about ten miles from Lugano on the way to Ponte Tresa, entirely off the tourist lane. The house is a little small for the many books[6] but very comfortable, and we have a nice garden. I hope you will visit us some day soon.

I was much upset to hear that the collections of the Wellcome Museum are going to be stored for a number of years. I had counted on them for the illustrations of my book. Underwood, I am sure, must be very disappointed.

With kind regards to Mrs. Singer and to yourself I am
Yours as ever,
Henry E. Sigerist

[1] Reymond was president of the Lausanne Conference

[2] De-Nazification courts, operated after the War by the occupation forces in Germany.

[3] Henry E. Sigerist, 'Yugoslavia and the XIth International Congress of the History of Medicine', *Bulletin of the History of Medicine*, 1939, **7**: 93–147.

[4] Victor Gomoiu (1882–1960), Romanian medical historian. See Benone Dutescu, *Victor Gomoiu: 1882–1960* (Bucureşti: Editura medicală, 1970).

[5] In Casa Serena at Pura, since July 1947

[6] About 10,000 books

340

Singer to Sigerist, Kilmarth, Cornwall, 15 September 1947

My dear Sigerist,

Many thanks for your letter of September 7. Dorothea gets into a flutter about the invitation to the Germans to Lausanne. Personally I feel that the meeting at Lausanne must be such a poor sort of show because of the European situation, that it matters very little. Anyhow the invitation to the three Germans – who are all thoroughly undesirable even as Germans, – has been withdrawn & they will not be given visas. So we have thus got in one on them. Your solution, busting the whole thing & starting again is, I am sure, the right one.[1]

I have said that I am going to Lausanne. This is very much against my will. I dislike these meetings but Dorothea is so very keen on them. But I more than half hope that it will be impossible to go. The financial and food crisis is such in this country that travelling may well be impossible. Also we get weekly poorer or prices weekly rise, which is the same thing[.]

I should love to come or to see you but I had better not. It is really no time to be out of one[']s own country. Nobody knows when frontiers will close or currencies be closed. It is missing an opportunity that may not come again but the times are just not propitious.

As for the Wellcome Museum, I grieve less than you. The trouble was that the exhibition was too large. They have an excellent house for it in an excellent position. My hope is that they will have a series of exhibitions illustrating special points & I feel confident that they will be able to give you all the illustrations that you want.[2]

My book on Chemical Industry is now going into page proof. It has been through 2 sets of galleys.[3]

What a world.

All good wishes from us both to you both: it is good to think that you are comfortably settled[4] – I wish I was settled in mind!

Yours ever,

Charles Singer

[1] See previous letter.

[2] For Sigerist's *History of medicine*.

[3] Singer (1948).

[4] At Pura.

341

Sigerist to Singer, Pura, 22 September 1947

My dear Singer,

Just a line to thank you for your letter of September 15 and to tell you how delighted I am to hear that the Germans will not be invited to the Lausanne Conference.[1] Those three certainly are a particularly bad lot, and it would have been a disgrace to have them come to the meeting.

If you do go to Lausanne, I wish Dorothea and you would come and visit with us. We have no maid at the moment, and the house is not quite furnished yet, but there is a little pension a few minutes from our house, and we would be delighted to put you up there as our guests. I need not tell you what a very great pleasure it would be to all of us to have you here.[2]

It was good news to hear that your book on Chemical Industry will be out soon.[3] I shall be very glad to review it for the Bulletin. I have been writing a lot of reviews these days and find it the best way to keep up-to-date.

A new edition of my book on Soviet medicine should be out soon, completely rewritten, rearranged, and with the statistics brought up-to-date.[4] There will be about a dozen translations of it because there is much demand for such a book in many European countries.

Hoping very much to see you, I am with warm regards to both of you
Yours very cordially,
Henry E. Sigerist

---

[1] See letter 339.
[2] Sigerist, Mrs Sigerist and their daughter Erica, who was Sigerist's secretary in 1947 and 1948.
[3] Singer (1948).
[4] Henry E. Sigerist, *Medicine and health in the Soviet Union* (New York, 1947).

342

Singer to Sigerist, Kilmarth, Cornwall, 12 December 1948

My dear Sigerist,

Although I passed my seventieth birthday more than two years ago, it is only within the last few weeks that I have been allowed even to see the articles for the volume to have been presented to me on that occasion.[1] I have just read your contribution & it is on that account, in the first instance, that I am writing to you, to thank you from the bottom of my heart for the great honour that you have done me.[2] It is an honour that comes to few who are far worthier of it than I. That is always in my mind. And I understand that at long last there really is some hope of getting the volume into print. But you know, as well as I, of the massive difficulties now in every step in publication.

I have read your essay on Hartlieb with the utmost interest & profit.[3] It throws much light on many publications of the sort & you have greatly enlightened me on the part of Albertus & pseudo-Albertus in 'curiosa' literature.[4]

I came across one point on which I can throw a little light[.] It is on the curious word[?] GUMMERAS. In a difficulty of that sort I always fly to Goetz & Loewe Thesaurus Glossarum Emendatarum which always seems to me by far the most useful dictionary of medieval Latin in our line of country. It gives GUNNARII = ARTEPELLONES & then ARTEPELLONES = ARTEPELLIONES and then again PELLIO = δερματ??ργ?? [5] & again PELLIONES = SEDUCTORES. So that it seems that Gunnarii i.e. gummares are cosmeticists which is just what one would expect them to be!

I hope that you have benefitted by your quiet life & that your great book advances.[6] We had good news of you from the Sartons who spent a week or two with us. We had hoped to have visited you this autumn but the political situation looked too threatening.[7] Not only did it seem possible that there would be war but the repeated strikes in France would have made travel very difficult if we had not been able to get seats in a plane, which in any case was not easy. Perhaps we may come in 1949.

My History of Chemical Industry is printed & I am told that a very few copies are now available, though I have not yet seen one.[8] I go to London this week to sign the special copies. The book (in which I have no financial interest) must be extremely dear for the illustrations have been immensely costly & nothing has been spared in printing & design. I am now preparing for press that Anglo-Saxon magical text on which I have been working for ages with J.H.G. Grattan. I am hoping to get off the MS by the end of this year. Grattan's health is failing rapidly & I want him to see it before he dies.[9]

We go on pretty well here. Dorothea is somewhat of an invalid and has to rest a good deal. She cannot walk far but she could, I think, safely fly to Switzerland. I am well & in full work & have become a grandfather. Andrew's wife had a son a few days ago.

I am toying with the idea of taking a trip to the West Indies in Februar –March–April with an old medical friend who has just retired. But I daresay nothing will come of it.

Do let us hear how you are & how the work goes. And our affectionate greetings to Emmy, Erica and yourself.

Yours ever & again many thanks

Charles Singer

Let me know if I can do anything for you in England

[1] Articles for Singer's 70 birthday in 1947 were published in the monumental Festschrift that was delayed until 1953; E. Ashworth Underwood (ed.), *Science, medicine and history. Essays on the evolution of scientific thought and medical practice, written in honour of Charles Singer*, 2 vols (London,1953).

[2] Henry E. Sigerist, 'Johannes Hartlieb's gynaecological collection and the Johns Hopkins manuscript', in Underwood (1953) vol. 1, 231–246.

[3] Johannes Hartlieb (15th century) German physician, see F. Fürbeth, *Johannes Hartlieb, Untersuchungen zu Leben und Werk* (Niemeyer: Tübingen,1992).

[4] Albertus Magnus (*c.*1193–1280), German natural philosopher and scholar; see Henryk Anzulewicz, 'Albertus Magnus, Saint', *Complete dictionary of scientific biography*, vol. 19 (Detroit: Charles Scribner's Sons, 2008), 36–40.

[5] Literally a 'skin worker'.

[6] Sigerist (1951).

[7] The beginning of the Cold War, the Berlin blockade, and the Communist takeover of Czechoslavakia etc..

[8] Singer (1948).

[9] Charles Singer and John H. G. Grattan, *Anglo-Saxon magic and medicine* (London, 1952). Grattan died in 1951.

343

Sigerist to Singer, Pura, 12 January 1949

My dear Singer,

Many thanks for your letter of December 12. I was very glad to hear that you have been told that we have written a volume for your 70th birthday. It is such a long time that I sent the manuscript to Underwood that I hardly remember what I wrote. All I know is that the Hopkins manuscript is very interesting and raises a lot of problems many of which I have not solved.[1] I am very interested in your interpretation of the term gummeras and I have no doubt that it is correct.

I had a letter from Underwood a few days ago and I was very glad to hear that he was going ahead with your volume.[2] He is an extremely nice fellow and means very well indeed – he is sending me illustrations of my book in a most charming way – but we all know that he has a very difficult Board to deal with.

We like it here very much and I do not think that I could ever live in a city again. Last week I sent the first 525 type-written pages of my first volume to the Oxford Press in New York and the rest will follow soon.[3] The first volume took somewhat more time than I had expected partly because the Babylonian literature is so frightfully scattered but chiefly because in this first volume I developed my method of approach and presentation. After having spent months with the evil spirits and devils of Babylonia I am looking forward to writing volume 2 that deals with Greece and Rome.

The West Indies are delightful particularly at this time of the year. I once spent some time on the Bahamas and I do not think that I have ever seen such happy looking Negroes anywhere in the world. I also remember two visits to Trinidad with much pleasure. But I hope first of all to see you and Mrs. Singer in Pura in the course of the year. You can fly to Zurich and from there it is only four hours to Lugano by train.

I was very sorry to hear that Mrs. Singer does not feel well but I am sure that a few weeks in Switzerland would be very good for her. Leading a quiet life here I feel better than ever and I can work twelve hours a day without effort as long as I stay in my retreat.

Well I very much hope to see you both in the course of the year and in the meantime I am with warm regards in which Emmy joins

Yours as ever,

Henry E. Sigerist

[1] Sigerist (1953a).

[2] His volume for the 70th birthday of Sigerist, see letter 342.

[3] Sigerist (1951).

344

Sigerist to Singer, Pura, 22 March 1950

My dear Singer,

I have not written for ages but there was actually very little to report, as I am leading a very quiet and contemplative life in my village. The first volume of my History is in the press.[1] I am writing the second that deals with Graeco-Roman and Hindu medicine, and if all goes well, I hope to complete the manuscript by the end of the year. At the same time I have been doing some preparatory work for Volume III, which will be devoted to the Middle Ages, and in which the Arabs will take a central place. It is a gigantic piece of work, as you well realize, for which I have to re-read all the basic texts and this means that I had to brush up on my Oriental languages. It is an immense satisfaction, however, to have the time and leisure to do this kind of work.

Emmy and I are perfectly delighted to know that you will be in Switzerland this summer, and I wish you would plan to stay as long as possible in Pura. I am including a prospectus of our local inn, which can be recommended very highly. It has been completely reconditioned and is under new management.

I think it is an excellent idea to hold an informal medico-historical conference here, where the environment is most pleasant and where we shall have ample time for discussion. Many American colleagues will be here, and I am sure you will enjoy meeting them. I also count on Underwood, Guthrie and probably some others from England.[2]

This coming weekend I expect ten Swiss medical historians and historians of science for a similar conference, and I am sending you the program enclosed.[3] It is quite inofficial and will be very informal, but it is the type of meeting that I like best. The annual convention of the Swiss Society of the History of Medicine and Science is usually so rushed that there is not sufficient time for discussion and personal intercourse.

I may see you before August, because Janet Vaughan persuaded me to give the Bryce Lecture at Somerville College in Oxford June 1st. I will speak on the Latin medical literature of the early Middle Ages, and it will be my swan song on this subject.[4] I also promised Underwood to address the Historical Section of the Royal Society of Medicine. I would like to take advantage of my visit to London to secure illustrations for my second volume. No city in the world has such a wealth of museums and libraries.

It is hard to realize that four years have passed since we last met,[5] but it is good to know that we shall be together again this summer.

With warm wishes to Dorothea and yourself, in which Emmy joins
Yours very cordially,
Henry E. Sigerist

---

[1] Sigerist (1951).
[2] Anglo-American Symposium in Pura of August 9–11, 1950 with G. Urdang (Madison, WI), W. R. Bett (London), Genevieve Miller (Baltimore), P. William (New York), E. A. Underwood (London), E. R. Weinerman (California), J. N. Morris (London), P. Kibre (New York), I. Perry (California). Douglas J. Guthrie (Edinburgh).

[3] The first Pura Conference of Swiss medical historians in spring 1950; the participants were Heinrich Buess, Eduard Fueter, Edgar Goldschmid, Erich Hintzsche, Johannes Karcher, Nikolaus Mani, Bernhard Milt, Karl Reucker, and Charles Salzmann.

[4] Sigerist's Bryce Lecture was published: Henry E. Sigerist, 'The Latin medical literature in the Early Middle Ages', *Journal of the History of Medicine and Allied Sciences*, 1958, **13**: 127–146.

[5] The encounter four years previously took place in Zurich.

345

Singer to Sigerist, Kilmarth, Cornwall, 27 March 1950

CONFIDENTIAL

My dear Sigerist,

I was indeed glad of your long and friendly letter of March 22nd, and to learn that you are so well and happy. I was especially glad at the news that Vol. I of your History is in the press.[1] I look forward to it eagerly. It shows wonderful courage to have attacked such an enormous task. I congratulate you.

I would like nothing so much as to join the party at Pura,[2] and I hope to do so; but there are difficulties. I have been thinking them over and have decided that I must tell you frankly about them.

The first is Dorothea's health. She is now extremely deaf and can hear only with an apparatus. Unfortunately she is bad with anything mechanical, and it is constantly out of order. Further, her sight has deteriorated, her blood-pressure is high, and she has much atheroma. She is medically 10–15 years older than her age (66), but remains irrepressibly and dangerously active. Of course what I fear is a cerebral haemorrhage. The prospect of that, far from home, unnerves me. She is very anxious to travel but is medically quite unfit for it. Nor do I like to leave her for any length of time.

There is another matter which is even harder to explain on paper, but I must try. I have been receiving a subvention from the Wellcome Trustees for the last seven years. They most generously published my Tabulae sex and have now in the press my Anglo-Saxon Medicine and translation of Vesalius on the Brain.[3] They have stood by me really nobly. I am finishing the revision of a translation of Galen's De anatomicis administrationibus for them.[4]

Five years ago the Wellcome Foundation (not quite the same as the Wellcome Trustees) asked my advice on a Director to their Historical Medical Museum. I named Underwood, who I then knew but little but whose work I had followed. He was quite the best available. But a year ago he became my son-in-law, which was an event of which I had not even thought. This raises a fear in me of the appearance of nepotism, which I would avoid at all costs. This relation is further complicated by the fact that Underwood has now naturally become the literary adviser of the Wellcome Trust in place of the inefficient Dawkes [sic] who in the meantime has died.[5]

The complications do not end here. Underwood undertook the editing of my Festschrift four years ago.[6] This has got into printing difficulties, of the nature of which I am only too glad to be ignorant.

Nor does the complication end at this. Imperial Chemical Industries – I.C.I., the largest industrial undertaking in the Empire – approached me ten months ago, asking for suggestions for some 'cultural' undertaking. The firm is, after Nuffield, the largest benefactor of British universities.[7] Some of the directors are anxious at the low cultural level of technicians. I was asked to plan a major work that might be used for higher, that is postgraduate, educational purposes. After some discussion, I suggested a five-volume history of technology with Holmyard as my co-editor.[8] I felt a younger collaborator necessary, because of my age. I think that the scheme will go through, and that I shall get the 'all clear' about June next. I therefore want to finish Galen by then and so fulfill my undertakings for the Wellcome Trust, and then hitch on to I.C.I. Should this mature, I should spend the summer vacation getting this scheme going. (I have of course told the Wellcome Trustees of this).

I enclose a rough draft of the plan of the work. Neither the scheme nor any announcement of it may be published, but it is not secret – just confidential. It may be discussed with any reasonably discreet person. (I have express permission for this.) Criticisms at this stage are more than welcome. I am assured that any further funds needed are likely to be forthcoming, but that it is inadvisable to enlarge the plan until it has been formally passed. To do so might prejudice or delay its passage. But any modification within the plan will certainly be most gratefully and carefully considered.

Now you know the outline of my position. If you come to Oxford in June, as I hope you will, I will make a point of seeing you. I shall be in London all or most of May and can stay on. Or alternatively you would be most welcome here. Do let me know early what you decide.

With warmest wishes to Emmy and to yourself,

Yours always,

Charles Singer

---

[1] Sigerist (1951).

[2] The Anglo-American Symposium in Pura.

[3] Singer aned Rabin (1946); Singer and Grattan (1952). Charles Singer, *Vesalius on the human brain* (London, 1952).

[4] Singer (1952b) and Singer (1956a).

[5] Sidney Herbert Daukes (1879–1947), Director of the Wellcome Historical Medical Museum from 1941 to 1945; see *British Medical Journal*, 1947, **ii**: 435–436 and John Symons, *Wellcome Institute for the History of Medicine: a short history* (London: The Wellcome Trust, [1993]).

[6] Underwood (1953).

[7] Nuffields Export Ltd., (Morris Motors).

[8] Charles Singer, Eric Holmyard and A. R. Hall (eds), 5 vols, *A history of technology* (Oxford, 1954–1958).

346

Sigerist to Singer, Pura, 19 April 1950

My dear Singer,

Thanks ever so much for your very informative letter. You certainly had plenty of complications, and I fully appreciate the situation. I am very delighted, however, to see that you are so active and full of plans. I need not tell you that I am looking forward to every one of your publications.

Your translation of Galen's De anatomicis administrationibus will be a most important contribution.[1] Do you know, by the way, that Dr. Sidney Licht in Boston has commissioned a retired Harvard classicist, Professor Green, to translate some Galenic writings, and I understand that De sanitate tuenda is in the press. Charles C. Thomas in Springfield, Illinois, is publishing the book, and I have been asked to write a preface for it.[2]

Your project for a history of technology is admirable.[3] Strange enough there is no such book, and it is needed today more than ever. It is the kind of book that all historians, no matter what their specialty may be, will have to use, because it is impossible to write any history today without considering the influence of science and technology.

I plan to fly to London Monday, May 29, and hope that you will still be there at that time. I expect to be at Oxford from May 31 to June 5; then again in London until June 12, when I will be flying back to Zurich.

With warm wishes and hoping to see you soon, I am
Yours very sincerely,
Henry E. Sigerist

[1] Singer (1956a).

[2] Sidney Licht (1907–1979) American physician, see H. D. Bouman and W. J. Erdman WJ 2nd, 'In memoriam. Sidney Licht, M.D., 1908—1979. Member editorial board, American Journal of Physical Medicine, 1952—1979', *American Journal of Physical Medicine*, 1979, **58**(6): 269–272. Robert Montraville Green (1880–1955), Professor of Anatomy, Harvard Medical School, published, *A translation of Galen's Hygiene: (De sanitate tuenda)* with an introduction by Henry E. Sigerist (Springfield, Ill.: Charles C. Thomas, [1951]); see letter 367.

[3] Singer et al. (eds), (1954–1958).

347

Singer to Sigerist, Kilmarth, Cornwall, 25 April 1950

My dear Sigerist,

Very many thanks for your letter of April 19th.

I expect to be in London when you arrive on Monday, May 29th. I shall probably have to leave on Tuesday, June 6th, and after then I shall be in the North. I may be in Oxford on June 4th or 5th, but at any rate we shall have May 29th–31st in London at the same time.

I was glad you told me about Green's translation of the Galenic writings. I have written to Charles Thomas of Springfield, (who you say is publishing it,) to tell him of my project, so that we do not overlap. As it happens, I know Thomas well by correspondence, because he is printing a translation by me of Benivieni which I am bringing out with Esmond Long.[1]

About the summer. We really don't know. It is all a question of Dorothea's health. She is very anxious to go to Amsterdam, and I do not see how she can possibly do Pura as well, within a few days. There is moreover the question of expense which, now that the £. has fallen, is a very serious matter. Even if she goes to Amsterdam, I do not think she will hear very much, because her hearing-aid is more often out of order than in, and she needs now the very highest magnification. My experience with her is, that she is the better for short visits, but quite unable to sustain long ones; so perhaps, if it can be at all managed, she will be the better for a visit to Amsterdam.

I have just received from Schuman copies of the new edition of my History of Biology.[2] I have altered the text quite a bit, but the reproduction of the figures is poor.

You will be sorry to have heard of the death of Clifford Dobell. He was a first class scholar and a very nice fellow, though almost pathologically retiring.

I wish I could go to Florence to greet Corsini, but I cannot get away.[3] Indeed, all my movements are uncertain, for reasons which I have told you.

With kindest greetings, and best wishes to the family.

Yours always,

Charles Singer

P.S. Peyer has been staying with us for two or three days and has just left.[4] He is a good fellow, and what an excellent book that is by him on the vertebral theory of the skull.

I leave tomorrow for London where I shall be for the whole of May. My address there is, as usual, The Athenaeum, Pall Mall, SW. You will, of course, be a guest there.

---

[1] Charles Singer and Esmond R. Long, *De abditis nonnullis ac mirandis morborum et sanationum Causis* (Springfield, IL,1954). Antonio Benivieni (*c*.1443–1502) Italian anatomist; see Pietro Franceschini, 'Benivieni, Antonio', *Complete dictionary of scientific biography*, vol. 1. (Detroit: Charles Scribner's Sons, 2008), 611–612. Esmond Long (1890–1979), pathologist and medical historian; see R. E. Stowell, 'Esmond R. Long, MD, 1890—1979', *American Journal of Pathology*, 1980, **100**(2): 321–325, and 'Correspondence and reports', *Bulletin of the History of Medicine*, 1980, **54**: 273–274.

[2] Henry Schuman, a Publisher in New York. Charles Singer, *A history of biology*, revised edition (New York, 1950).

[3] Andrea Corsini (1875–1963), Italian historian of science.

[4] Bernhard Peyer (1885–1963) Swiss palaeontologist; see Rudolf Schlatter, 'Peyer, Bernhard', *Complete dictionary of scientific biography*, vol. 18, (Detroit: Charles Scribner's Sons, 2008), 711–712.

348

Sigerist to Singer, Pura, 2 May 1950

My dear Singer,

Underwood just wrote me that Nancy had a baby, which makes you a grandfather; I wish to congratulate you most cordially and can tell you that the same is going to happen to me toward the end of the year. Nora is expecting a child.[1] You probably saw her in Zurich in 1946. She and her husband are still in Rome at the moment, but are returning to the States in September.

I had not heard of the death of Clifford Dobell. He was a first-rate scholar, indeed, and his death is a great loss,

How nice that Peyer was with you. He is a perfectly delightful man, of whom I am very fond, and his latest book is very remarkable.[2] He has a summer house not very far from us, in a region that is rich in fossils and where he does some digging.

I did not go to Florence either, much as I would have liked to pay my tribute to Corsini and to see Florence again, where I have not been since the war. However, I cannot interrupt my work too often, and now during the Holy Year Italy is frightfully crow[ded].

I am so glad that you will be in London at the end of May when I arrive, and I am looking forward with greatest pleasure to seeing you soon.

With all good wishes, I am

Yours as ever

Henry E. Sigerist

[1] Nora Sigerist (born 1922), Sigerist's younger daughter, married to the composer Jack Beeson
[2] Peyer's latest book, probably Bernhard Peyer, *Goethes Wirbeltheorie des Schädels* (Zurich, 1950).

349

Singer to Sigerist, Truro, Cornwall, 16 April 1951[1]

My dear Sigerist,

I hope all is well with you, and that Vol. II of the great work is making good progress.[2]

There is a point concerning the Hippocratic Works that has just come under my notice. I write this because you will have that matter in hand for the next volume. I am at the moment examining a thesis for the Ph.D. of the University of London presented by one W.C. Wake, the title of which is "The Corpus Hippocraticum".[3] It deals with the question of assignation to different (of course unknown and un-named) authors of the various members of the Collection. The method it adopts is statistical analysis of sentences length as a criterion of style. I believe that it is a valuable method which in future will have to be considered in connection with all classical literary products. It is very recent in origin, the pioneer being G. Udney [sic] Yule,[4] and it practically dates from 1945 and is practically confined to English writers. The actual results are interesting and in general they agree with the literary results, They have been applied not only to the Hippocratic Corpus but also the biological works of Aristotle. Wake has abstracted them for an article in the <u>Classical Quarterly</u>, which I hope will accept it. If I can get a typewritten copy of the thesis itself or a typewritten copy of the article for the <u>Classical Quarterly</u> I will let you have it as soon as I can. You ought at least to refer to the method.

Now something about myself. You know we have had an influenza epidemic in England. Just as it was disappearing I managed to catch it and it was followed by pneumonia. I was sent into hospital eighteen days ago feeling very ill, but was put at once on penicillin and responded immediately. I cannot say that after the first day I was other than perfectly comfortable. I am still in hospital though now getting up and walking a little way each day. I feel now perfectly well and as well as I ever have in my life.

As you know, I had intended to come to Lugano to consult with you about the History of Technology,[5] and Imperial Chemical Industries are willing to pay for the trip. Under the circumstances I think I had better come as early as possible, if you think that this season of the year is propitious for Lugano. Is it sunny and warm at the end of April or the beginning of May? I should, of course, come by air to the nearest point. I think I should probably put up in one of those comfortable hotels at Paradiso[6] and spend a day or two with you at Pura, if this is agreeable to you. Of course I don't want to come if the weather is likely to be the wrong sort for me. If this is so I'd rather come later in the year when I can equally well manage.

I just don't know whether Dorothea will come with me or not. It depends upon her general state of health and her other engagements. I think myself she is better in Cornwall. Whether she comes or not, I thought of travelling with a very old friend of mine, R. A. Greeves, who is at present convalescing from an operation on the prostate. He is much in the same state as I am, needing a little sun and quiet change. He is a distinguished ophthalmic surgeon, extremely musical and a very good linguist. I am sure you'd enjoy his company. He and I have been very close friends since we were young men.[7]

A little later in the year I intend to go to Amsterdam to spend a time with R. J. Forbes.[8] Originally I had intended to go to Amsterdam first, but owing to this pneumonia I think I'd better get south before I go to Holland.

My secretary, to whom this is dictated, tells me that the galleys of the translation of the Seventh Book of Vesalius have arrived, but I have not seen them yet.[9] I am hoping to get hold of them during the day. I wish the Galen had got as far, but the work really is finished and can go to the printer as soon as he will accept it.[10]

This letter is dictated in hospital to my secretary, who calls for that purpose daily, but by the time it reaches you I shall, I hope, be at home.

With all kind wishes to the family and yourself,

Yours ever,

Charles Singer

---

[1] This letter was dictated from the Royal Cornwall Infirmary at Truro.
[2] Henry E. Sigerist, *A history of medicine*, vol. II (New York, 1961).

[3] William Charles Wake (1916–1989), his unpublished thesis was summarised in W. C. Wake, 'Who was Hippocrates?' *The Listener*, 19 Dec. 1966, 966–968.

[4] George Udny Yule (1871–1951), British statistician; see Frank Yates, 'Yule, George Udny (1871–1951)', rev. Alan Yoshioka, *Oxford dictionary of national biography* (Oxford: Oxford University Press, 2004), vol. 60, 975–976.

[5] Singer et al. (eds), (1954–1958).

[6] Paradiso, the hotel section of Lugano.

[7] Reginald Affleck Greeves (1878–1966), ophthalmic surgeon; see 'Reginald Affleck Greeves, 1878–1966', *British Journal of Ophthalmology*, 1966, **50**: 744.

[8] Robert James Forbes (1900–1973) Dutch historian of science; see D.A. Wittopkoning, 'Robert James Forbes', *Janus*, 1975, **62**: 217–233.

[9] The Seventh Book of the *Fabrica* (translated by Singer, 1952a) deals with the brain.

[10] Singer (1952b).

350

Singer to Sigerist, Par, Cornwall, 23 April 1951 (telegram)

IS LUGANO WEATHER USUALLY FAVOURABLE END APRIL STOP THINKING
OF COMING NEXT WEEK
SINGER

351

Sigerist to Singer, Pura, late April 1951 (telegram)

JUST BACK FROM ITALY. WEATHER BEAUTIFUL. HOPE TO SEE YOU SOON.
SIGERIST

352

Singer to Sigerist, London, 30 April 1951 (telegram)

ARRIVING EDEN HOTEL PARADISO LUGANO WEDNESDAY AFTERNOON
MAY SECOND STAYING ABOUT FORTNIGHT MUCH LOOKING FORWARD
TO MEETING
SINGER

353

Singer to Sigerist, London, 19 June 1951

My dear Sigerist,

I sent by post yesterday to you a copy of my "Earliest Chemical Industry".[1] Drop me a line that it reaches you safely. For some mysterious reason it was impossible to register it, and for an equally mysterious reason it could not be insured unless it was cut in two! This is the new economics! It was also necessary to fill up a form in quadruplicate. If these things go on in a free world, what must it be like in Spain![2]

It was lovely seeing you amidst all your books and labours.[3]

With affectionate greetings from us both to Emmy and yourself,

Yours ever,

Charles Singer

P.S. I have reviewed the first volume of your History for the B.M.J. I used a good deal of the material I had used for the Bulletin, but added a few new points and took out a note of criticism.[4]

[1] Singer (1948).
[2] Spain was still under the Franco dictatorship.
[3] Singer's first visit to Sigerist at Pura.
[4] Charles Singer, 'Review of *A history of medicine*, vol. I, by H. E. Sigerist', *British Medical Journal*, 1951, **ii**: 587–588; Charles Singer, 'Review of *A history of medicine*, vol. I, by H. E. Sigerist', *Bulletin of the History of Medicine*, 1951, **15**: 91–93.

354

Singer to Sigerist, Kilmarth, Cornwall, 2 August 1951

My dear Sigerist,

You'd like to see the present stage of the plan for Vol. I of A History of Technology, of which I enclose a copy.[1]

It really is going on very well, and it looks as though we shall be in a position to send something to the press by the end of this year.

With all good wishes to you both from us all,

Yours ever,

Charles Singer

[1] Singer et al. (eds), (1954).

355

Singer to Sigerist, Kilmarth, Cornwall, 8 September 1951

My dear Sigerist,

I am so very sorry to hear about Erica.[1] Do let us hear how she goes on. One would have thought that Switzerland of all countries would be free from typhoid. What an anxiety for you both.

I am glad you liked my note on the Hippocratic Oath.[2] Fischer did really collect a fine lot of essays for that number of Gesnerus.[3]

I am enclosing a copy of my review of your book in this week's British Medical Journal.[4] It is largely the same though not identical with the review in the Johns Hopkins Bulletin.

Yours ever,

Charles Singer

---

[1] Sigerist's daughter.

[2] Charles Singer, 'An early parallel to the Hippocratic Oath', *Gesnerus*, 1951, **8**: 177–180.

[3] Hans Fischer (1892–1976) Swiss pharmacologist and medical historian, editor of *Gesnerus*, the Swiss Journal of the History of Medicine and Science, see Erwin H. Ackerknecht, 'Hans Fischer 15.12.1892–21.5.1976', *Gesnerus*, 1976, **33**: 162–182.

[4] Singer (1951a).

356

Singer to Sigerist, Kilmarth, Cornwall, 7 November 1951

My dear Sigerist,

How is Erica? Is her temperature and condition normal yet?

This letter finds both Dorothea and myself in bed with some mild infection of the usual respiratory type. My temperature has quite gone down and has now been normal for two days but hers is still hovering. I suppose we shall be living a half-cock sort of life for another week. We both had or are having injections of penicillin, which certainly take immediate effect.

I have just had a letter from the London School of Hygiene and Tropical Medicine asking my advice on a point. They tell me that one of their staff has prepared an English translation of :

PETTENKOFER (Max) Uber den Luftwechsel in Wohngebäuden. München 1858.[1]

I wrote to them saying that I thought it was of value but that I required to ask your opinion. They say there is no copy of the German edition in any library of this country. This is an enquiry as to your view on the subject. There is no difficulty about getting it printed at an early date if you think it advisable.

The History of Technology is really going better than I could possibly have hoped. It looks as though we can get a substantial part of it into the press in January.[2] I wish I could see any chance of getting my various other works out of the press!

With all kind wishes to Emmie and yourself from us both,

Yours ever,

Charles Singer

P.S. My friend Greeves, whom I often see, alwasy asks to be remembered to you both.

[1] Max Pettenkofer (1818–1901) German hygienist, see Claude E. Dolman, 'Pettenkofer, Max Josef von', *Complete dictionary of scientific biography*, vol. 10 (Detroit: Charles Scribner's Sons, 2008), 556–563.
[2] See letter 354.

357

Sigerist to Singer, Pura, 20 November 1951

My dear Singer,

Thanks for your letter of 7th November. I was very sorry to hear that Dorothea and yourself had been ill, but I hope that you have recovered entirely by now. Erica is fine and back at work. She was very sick in spite of chloromycetine, and her recovery was very slow.[1] She was with us in Pura for seven weeks, but has completely recovered by now.

I also had a letter from Cyril C. Barnard concerning Pettenkofer.[2] I am sorry to say that I have never read his treatise "Uber den Luftwechsel in Wohngebäuden". I am trying to get a copy from Zurich or Basle, and will let you know what I think of it.

It was good news to hear that the History of Technology is progressing so well and so rapidly. I shall of course be most anxious to see the first volume.[3]

Warm wishes to Dorothea and yourself in which Emmy joins,

Yours as ever,

Henry E. Sigerist

[1] Chloromycetine, an early antibiotic, no longer in use.
[2] Cyril C. Barnard (1894–1959) British medical historian.
[3] See previous letter.

358

Sigerist to Singer, Pura, 25 January 1952

My dear Singer,

What a charming little book.[1] Thank you ever so much for it. Of course I knew most of your essays, but those from the Times Literary Supplement were new to me, and I see that you have made a good many changes in the others. Those on Graeco-Roman subjects are particularly useful to me at the moment, and I am very glad to have them collected in one volume.

I am also delighted that you included chapters from The Christian Failure.[2] I think I wrote you at the time that I liked this little book very much and devoted two hours of a seminar to its discussion.

I think one should publish collected essays more often, because it is so much more convenient to the reader to have them together in one volume instead of scattered in journals. Besides it gives the author a chance to revise some of his earlier writings. We never stop learning and after many years it is good to be able to take a subject up again.

We are having a beautiful winter, rather cold for this section of the country, although night temperatures of 28–32°F are not formidable. For many weeks we have had glorious sunshine almost every day and it will be spring very soon. I am sure that in Cornwall the spring flowers are beginning to bloom also. We very much hope that you will come to Lugano again, even without the excuse of a pneumonia. This certainly would be a very great pleasure.

Warm wishes to Dorothea and yourself in which Emmy joins.

Yours as ever,

Henry E. Sigerist

[1] Charles Singer, *New worlds and old* (London, 1951).
[2] Charles Singer, *The Christian failure* (London, 1943).

359

Sigerist to Singer, Pura, 12 February 1952

My dear Singer,

I am sending you enclosed a carbon[1] of my letter to Mr. Barnard, which I think is self-explanatory. Pettenkofer's book makes rather dull reading,[2] but it undoubtedly is a landmark in the history of the subject, and if funds are available for the publication of an English translation, I would recommend to go ahead with it.

With kind regards, I am,

Yours as ever,

Henry E. Sigerist

[1] Carbon copy.
[2] Pettenkofer (1858).

360

Singer to Sigerist, Kilmarth, Cornwall, 19 February 1952

My dear Sigerist,

Many thanks for having written about that book of Pettenkofer.[1] I am sure they will be very glad to have your opinion.

I enclose a copy of the lecture which is the formal announcement of A History of Technology. It has only just become accessible. We are having a conference here on the subject this coming weekend and I am presenting copies at that time.

I enclose a letter from the Secretary of our History of Science Society.[2] It would be delightful if you could accept this invitation. The Royal Academy has organised a series of lectures on Leonardo da Vinci on his quincentenary, and I am closing the course on May 29th with a talk on his knowledge of the structure and action of the body.[3] It is thus certain that I shall be in London on the 26th May. If you and Emmy would consider coming down here just after 29th we should be delighted. Alternatively I am sure Nancy would be very pleased to put you up at Esher.[4]

With fraternal greetings,

Yours as ever,

Charles Singer

[1] Pettenkofer (1858).
[2] Singer was the President of the newly founded British Society for the History of Science.
[3] Leonardo da Vinci (1452–1519) Italian scholar and artist; Charles Singer, 'Leonardo da Vinci', *British Medical Journal*, 1952, **ii**: 804–805.
[4] Esher, a town south of London.

361

Sigerist to Singer, Pura, 26 February 1952

My dear Singer,

Very many thanks for your letter of 19 February, and for your very interesting lecture.[1] Now the cat is out of the bag and everybody is waiting for the first volume of your History of Technology.[2]

I deeply appreciate the very kind invitation to address the British Society for the History of Science on Monday, 26 May, and deeply regret that I cannot possibly accept it. I plan to be in Florence at that time where I want to get pictures from Alinari and other dealers for the second volume of my History. Moreover, I cannot get away too often, as I must finish the volume as soon as possible. If all goes well, I should like to attend the International Congress in France in September,[3] and I think I wrote you before that I will be in England in November for the Heath Clark Lectures at the London School of Hygiene and Tropical Medicine. This is about all I can do this year.

Is there a chance of seeing you in the Ticino this year? I remember with so much pleasure your last year's visit. We had a perfectly delightful winter and spring has come by now, as I suppose it has in Cornwall. In about ten days our camellia bushes should be in bloom.

I am returning Mr. Butler's letter as it is addressed to you.[4]

With warm greetings to Dorothy and yourself, I am,

Yours as ever,

Henry E. Sigerist

[1] See previous letter.
[2] Singer et al. (eds), vol I (1954).
[3] The International Congress of the History of Medicine, held in Nice, France.
[4] Mr. Butler, Secretary of the British Society for the History of Science, see previous letter.

362

Singer to Sigerist, Kilmarth, Cornwall, 21 April 1952

My dear Sigerist,

It occurred to me that you would find it convenient to have my translation of Galen's De anatomicis administrationibus.[1] Underwood has sent you a copy of the proof. Of course this is uncorrected and is, in fact, the first proof. I am not getting any galleys. There are fairly extensive notes and a number of figures, but you would hardly need these.

I am just going off to London, where the Athenaeum, Pall Mall, S.W.1 will reach me for the next month or two.

With all kind wishes to you both from us both,

Yours ever,

Charles Singer

---

[1] Singer (1956a).

363

Sigerist to Singer, Pura, 27 January 1953

My dear Singer,

I was much distressed to hear from Underwood that you had another touch of pneumonia, and I only hope that you have recovered by now. You should not specialise on viruses, as other pneumonias can be killed so much more easily. I really wish that this attack of pneumonia will give you a chance to recover in Lugano as it did last time, and that we shall meet again in Pura.

I am just reading Sarton's History of Science and I thank heaven that I do not have to review it.[1] It is a strange book, highly personalised, capricious and pedantic in parts, but of course written by a man who has a profound erudition. When is your first volume coming out? Then we shall all be on the stage in the limelight and open to criticism.[2]

Warm wishes for a prompt recovery, and hoping to see you in this region, I am,

Yours as ever,

Henry E. Sigerist

---

[1] George Sarton, *A history of science* (Cambridge, MA, 1952-).
[2] "We shall all be on the stage" refers to Sigerist, Sarton, and Singer. with their opera magna.

364

Singer to Sigerist, Kilmarth, Cornwall, 30 January 1953

My dear Sigerist,

Many thanks for your letter of January 27 received this morning. I got back from hospital yesterday. Neither influenza nor the subsequent (virus) pneumonia were really much to worry about. The troublesome feature is convalescence, as I have heard you remark yourself. It cheered me up, however, to receive your letter. I have begun to be at work, though, of course, shall be taking things slowly for another week or so still.

Upon my word, I have forgotten whether or not I have sent you Anglo-Saxon Magic and Medicine by Grattan and myself and my own Vesalius on the Human Brain.[1] Both have been published and if you have not received any, I would gladly send you copies.

Sarton is a queer psychological case. I expect the gods think that we are all queer psychological cases! Of course his History of Science is a tour de force,[2] but it is so badly printed and in such small type that I cannot think anyone will ever read it. Personally I found it most trying to study, though he expresses himself remarkably well at times. It is a very individual project. I suppose I shall have to review it, chiefly because he will be so frightfully offended if I do not.[3]

Is there any chance of your coming to the International Congress of the History of Science in Jerusalem in August next? We are making up a party on a boat which goes all the way by sea and calls at Naples. There are twelve cabins and we are trying to fill them all with our group. It would be marvellous if you could join it. Sarton thinks of joining it at Naples. I am sure you and he would not be incompatibles!

You might like to see one or two of my recent reviews in the British Medical Journal which I enclose.[4]

With most cordial greetings to Emmie and yourself from us both,

Yours ever,

Charles Singer

How goes your Vol. II? You do not say a word about it.[5]

[1] Singer and Grattan (1952); Singer (1952a).
[2] Sarton (1952);
[3] A review of this book by Singer does not show up in his bibliography.
[4] In 1952 fourteen book reviews by Singer appeared in the *British Medical Journal*; a further thirteen in 1951.
[5] Sigerist (1961), which appeared after Sigerist's death

365

Sigerist to Singer, Pura, 3 February 1953

My dear Singer,

Underwood just sent me your last two books and I wish to tell you how delighted I am with them.[1] Anglo-Saxon Magic and Medicine will be most useful to me when I write the 3rd volume of my history, which I hope will be soon, and I need not tell you that I am vitally interested in all that concerns Vesalius. I think that detailed studies like yours, are most revealing, and give us a better idea of Vesalius' actual knowledge, than general studies possibly could. Congratulations on these new contributions. A few years ago you told me that you had had a vintage year, but it seems to me that you have had one ever since.

I sincerely hope that you have overcome your pneumonia, and that you are at home again.

With warm wishes, I am yours as ever,

Henry E. Sigerist

[1] Singer (1952a), Singer and Grattan (1952).

366

Sigerist to Singer, Pura, 4 February 1953

My dear Singer,

My letter of yesterday's date had just been posted when I received your letter of the 30th January, and I want to tell you how delighted I am to know that you are back from the hospital. I have a perfect horror of hospitals, and this reminds me that I probably never sent you an article in which I touch this subject. It was written for a book that was published in America last year under the title When Doctors are patients. My essay had an advance publication in the Atlantic Monthly.[1]

I do not plan to join the Congress in Jerusalem.[2] August is the best month here when all our American friends come. The trip besides is expensive, and if I went to Israel I would like to spend more than 10 days there; I would like to study their social organisation, and spend some time in the neighbouring countries like Lebanon, Syria, Egypt etc. August, however, is hardly the season for it. If I go East again it will be India, where they plan to establish an Institute of the History of Medicine, and where I was very happy in 1944.[3]

You enquire about my second volume. It is coming, and I hope to complete the manuscript very soon. What delayed me particularly was not Greece, but India. You know yourself how confused the chronology is. Sarton says that he is not discussing Indian Science, since it did not influence our Science. This Europa [sic]-centre point of view is just what I am trying to avoid, and I am giving Indian Medicine almost as much space as to that of Greece. I think that to the time of the renaissance Western, Arabic, Indian and Chinese medicine were probably equally efficient, or rather inefficient. It is only in the renaissance that our medicine became scientific and that the centre of development from then on, was in the West. Ackerknecht[4] once remarked, that the English naval surgeons who came to America were hardly more successful in their treatments than the Indian Medicine Man: they knew about the circulation of the blood, they had more anatomical knowledge, but in the treatment of patients and particularly of the wounded the Indian often had much better results.

Of course I was most interested in your book reviews, and am very glad to have them. I just read Chauncey Leak's [sic] little book, and I do not think that it advances our knowledge very much. It gives and [sic] excellent survey, as you very correctly say, but I did not find much that was not in my book also, except his chapter on weights and measures, which is by far the best.[5] Weights and measures were important in the case of a few expensive drugs, but otherwise had little significance as most of the <u>materia medica</u> was inefficient anyway.

I very much hope that Chauncey Leak [sic] will soon give us a new edition of the Hearst Papyrus. This, undoubtedly, would be the best contribution he could make to Egyptian Medicine.

With all best wishes for your further recovery, I am,

Yours as ever,

Henry E. Sigerist

[1] Henry E. Sigerist, 'Living under the shadow', *Atlantic Monthly*, 1952, **189**: 25–30.

[2] International Congress of the History of Science.

[3] Sigerist's study tour in India.

[4] Erwin H. Ackerknecht (1906–1988) medical historian in the U.S. and Europe.

[5] Chauncey D. Leake (1896–1978) pharmacologist and medical historian, friend of Sigerist; see Gert Brieger, 'Chauncey D. Leake', *Bulletin of the History of Medicine*, 1978, **52**: 121–123. Chauncey D Leake, *The old Egyptian medical papyri* (Lawrence, KS, 1952), reviewed by Charles Singer, *British Medical Journal*, 1952, **ii**: 1201.

367

Sigerist to Singer, Pura, 6 March 1953

My dear Singer,

What an excellent idea to translate Galen's little work on bones,[1] I am particularly pleased to have it at this moment, when I am nearing the end of my second volume. You certainly have done more than anybody else to make Galen's anatomy known. His anatomical works require translations because they are not easy to understand. It would be foolish to wait for the <u>Corpus Medicorum Graecorum</u>. The new critical editions improve the text in very minor points and I am sure that for most of our purposes the early editions are quite adequate. You probably saw the English translation of Galen's <u>Hygiene</u> which Charles C. Thomas brought out some time ago.[2] The translation is not very good, but I and other reviewers felt that we should not discourage Sydney [sic] Licht who gave the money for such translations. Of course I need not tell you that I was not responsible for his foolish idea of publishing Le Clerk's [sic] biography of Galen,[3] nor am I responsible for the Claudius.[4]

I hope that you have recovered entirely by now, I had my wife and the maid in bed with the flu. It is strange that this year's epidemic although extraordinarily widespread has a totally different character from that of 1918–19.

With warm wishes I am,

Yours as ever,

Henry Sigerist

¹ Charles Singer, 'Galen's elementary course on bones', *Proceedings of the Royal Society of Medicine*, 1952, **xlv**: 25–34.
² Robert Montraville Green, *A translation of Galen's Hygiene : (De sanitate tuenda)* with an introduction by Henry E. Sigerist (Springfield, Ill.: Charles C. Thomas, [1951]); see letter 346.
³ The volume included a translation by Sidney Licht of Daniel Le Clerc's 'The life of Galen', taken from his textbook, *Histoire de la medecine* (Amsterdam, 1723).
⁴ Claudius, Galen's questionable first name

368

Singer to Sigerist, Kilmarth, Cornwall, 10 March 1953,

My dear Sigerist,

Many thanks for your letter of March 6. I am sorry to hear that you also had flu. My experience of this epidemic is that the convalescene is worse than the acute stage. We found that with quite a number of people. We are all right here now but everyone in the house had it in turn.

Of course I knew at once that you were not responsible for letting Licht publish that old biography of Galen or for the use of the name Claudius! The translator of the Hygiene should either have put no notes at all or made them more adequate. I feel as you do that the thing was to encourage Licht and I gave it a very favourable review in the B.M.J.[1]

I am glad you can find some use for my Galen's work on bones.[2] The larger work is now quite complete, but there are about half a dozen passages as to the rendering of which I am still doubtful.[3] I am having a conference on them next week when I hope to be rid of it at last. It is in page proof. Going over it again, I feel that the manuscript text has probably been confused in places by the binder. There are also quite a number of obvious scribal errors which are easy to correct, such as writing "above" for "below" and "three" for "four", but I have made no attempt to do any drastic re-arrangement, though I have put in their right places several obviously displaced passages. So far as I can make out, the only two MSS that are worth having are that in the Medician Library and one in Paris.[4] Both must have been available to the Renaissance editors. There is thus little hope of any substantial improvement in the text. Considering that the MS was copied for hundreds of years without anyone having the slightest idea of its meaning, the real marvel is that so much has survived. I suppose, to have done my duty, I should really have got someone to translate the first 8 ½ books from the Arabic, but life is too short for that.

I have just seen the page proofs of the first volume of the presentation to me on my 70th birthday – now 6 ½ years ago![5] I see your contribution, and I will read it during the next few days.[6] It is very good of you to have contributed and I am deeply grateful. Why I have not been allowed to see this volume earlier is a mystery to me, but so it is.

With cordial greetings to you both from us both,

Yours as ever,

Charles Singer

[1] Charles Singer, 'Personal hygiene in Ancient Rome. Review of *A translation of Galen's Hygiene* by Robert Montraville Green', *British Medical Journal*, 1952, **i**: 1404.
[2] Singer (1952e).
[3] Singer (1956a).
[4] The Two MSS are Florence, Biblioteca Medicea-Laurenziana 74,10, and Paris, Bibliothèque Nationale gr. 1849.
[5] First volume of the Singer Festschrift, Underwood (1953).
[6] Sigerist (1953a).

369

Singer to Sigerist, Kilmarth, Cornwall, 25 March 1953

My dear Sigerist,

We have now got Vol. I safely in the press and are trying to run Vols. II and III simultaneously. I enclose a table of contents of Vol. I and rough drafts of Vols. II and III.[1] We should so much like something from you.

Would you consider Chapter 11 of Vol. II, on 'Mechanics of Urban Life', by which we mean the sanitation of cities, their paving and the general conduct of human life within them? We thought of an article of about 7,000 words. It would describe the mechanics of urban life in classical antiquity and its remains and/or revival in medieval times. There will, of course, be an article on 'Building Construction' and we should have to be careful that yours did not overlap that too much. The story would begin, we hope, by being concentrated on the Mediterranean, gradually diffusing toward the North-West.

We make a special point of illustration and you could have as many as you are likely to ask for. They would be specially prepared for you.

Will you consider taking this on? You must have gone over the area very thoroughly in working on your second volume.[2]

With all kind wishes,
Yours as ever,
Charles Singer

[1] Singer et al. (eds), vol I (1954); vol. II (1956); vol III (1957).
[2] Sigerist (1961).

370

Sigerist to Singer, Pura, 7 April 1953

My dear Singer,

I was delighted to hear that the first Volume of your History of Technology is in the press, and I[,] like many others[,] am of course most anxious to see it.[1]

The outline of vols. 2 and 3 looks very promising. These two volumes will certainly cover an enormous field. I wish I could contribute an article, but at the moment I do not see any possibility of doing it. As you know I must bring out three books this year and have promised an infinity of articles for Festschrifts so that I cannot commit myself to anything new. However, why don't you ask Leon Homo to write the article on Mechanics of Urban Life. He recently published an excellent book, Rome Impériale et l'Urbanism [sic] dans l'Antiquité in Henri Berr's series L'évolution de l'humanité.[2] It is an excellent book of 700 pages and Homo is at the moment professeur honoraire de la faculté de lettres de Lyons [sic], has all the materials available so that he could write you an excellent article in next to no time. I am making extensive use of his findings.

With warm wishes, I am,

Yours as ever,

Henry E. Sigerist

[1] Singer et al. (eds), vol I (1954).

[2] Léon Homo, *Rome Impériale et l'urbanisme dans l'antiquité* (Paris, 1951); Henri Berr (1863–1954) French historian. See Agnès Biard, Dominique Bourel, Eric Brian (eds), *Henri Berr et la culture du XXe siècle: histoire, science et philosophie actes du colloque international, 24–26 octobre 1994, Paris* (Paris: Albin Michel/Centre International de Synthèse, 1997); and Suzanne Delorme, 'Henri Berr', *Osiris*, 1952, **10**: 4–9.

371

Sigerist to Singer, Pura, 21 April 1953

My dear Singer,

I very much appreciate that you would like to have me represented in the next volume of your History of Technology[1] and I myself would very much like to contribute an article to it, but at the moment it is just impossible. I cannot undertake anything until I have the manuscripts of three books in the hands of the publishers. I am sorry, but I just cannot write more than a certain number of pages a day.

We are expecting the Edelsteins in a few days, you probably heard that he is teaching at Oxford for a year and he and his wife just spent their spring vacation in Greece. They are both very fine scholars. He is always full of ideas and I am sure that you will see them sooner or later. He behaved splendidly at the University of California, refusing to sign the outrageous oath that the university authorities required all faculty members to sign.[2] He declared that this was just the kind of oath that Hitler and Mussolini had forced on their professors. He has a chair at the Johns Hopkins now and I know that he is very happy to be in Oxford for the time being. England is the only liberal country in the world, and I only hope she will be able to remain so.

With all good wishes,

Yours as ever,

Henry E. Sigerist

---

[1] Singer et al. (eds), vol II (1956).
[2] A measure of McCarthyism.

372

Singer to Sigerist, Kilmarth, Cornwall, 31 August 1953

My dear Sigerist,

A line to introduce my friend and Co-editor of A History of Technology, Dr. E. J. Holmyard. You will already know him as editor of Endeavour.[1] You will, I am sure, have much to discuss with him and he is looking forward to seeing your beautiful home.

In the October number of Endeavour I have written a short essay-review on Sarton.[2]

I do hope we shall meet again. I had intended to go abroad this year and would have gone to the Jerusalem Congress but I just could not afford it.[3] Had I done so I might have called on you on the way. Maybe an opportunity may arise next year.

With kindest wishes to Emmy and yourself in which Dorothea joins,

Yours as ever,

Charles Singer

---

[1] A British scientific journal established in 1942 as "a quarterly review designed to record the progress of the sciences in the sevice of mankind".

[2] Singer reviewed Sarton's *A history of science* (1953) and *A guide to the history of science* (1952) in *Endeavour*, 1953, **12**: 217–218.

[3] The Jerusalem Congress of the International Society of the History of Science; Sigerist did not attend the congress either.

373

Singer to Sigerist, Kilmarth, Cornwall, 1 April 1954

My dear Sigerist,

It is a long time since I have heard of you. I hope all goes well.

The first volume of our History of Technology is advertised by the Clarendon Press for May of this year.[1] I enclose the account of it. So far as I can see, there is not the slightest chance of getting it out within at least six months and, I think, probably a year of that date. The Clarendon Press, like other printers, is the slave of the unions. My Galen has made no appreciable progress for at least a year.[2] Everything seems to be stuck with the printer.

There is a technical point I wanted to get right with you. One of the troubles of the History of Technology is its frontiers. I have always said we do not want to do what other people are obviously likely to do better. Thus we have kept off medicine, except so far as sanitation involves certain constructional factors, which are naturally included in our book. A point has been raised in connection with drugs. We have several excellent articles on industrial chemistry. I have, however, erased all that is concerned with drugs except by indirect reference. I have always said that since your History of Medicine[3] is on a larger scale than our History of Technology it is obvious that drugs come in your province and not ours. I hope you will agree with this.

Have you made any arrangements for attending the Congress in Rome this year?[4] If so, I wonder if we could meet and perhaps spend a day or two together. I would like to go all the way by sea to Naples. If you have any work to do in that region, I wonder if we could not meet in Naples and then go together by train to Rome. I should like to return again by sea. I enjoy the sea and it makes a holiday for me. I am not quite sure yet whether Dorothea will come with me or not.

When is your Volume II coming out? I have not seen any notices of it.[5]

With best regards to Emmy and yourself from us both,

Yours as ever,

Charles Singer

[1] Singer et al. (eds), vol I (1954).
[2] Singer (1956a).
[3] Sigerist (1951).
[4] Congress of the International Society of the History of Medicine in Rome.
[5] Volume II, Sigerist (1961), appeared posthumously.

374

Sigerist to Singer, Pura, 6 April 1954

My dear Singer,

Many thanks for your letter of the 1st April. All goes well here. My health obviously does not improve with the years, but as long as I can carry on I have nothing to complain about and like you, I love living in the country. Sometimes one misses a large library just to look up a few references, but then I must go to Zürich and Basle from time to time just as you go to London.

Congratulations on the completion of your first volume of the History of Technology.[1] The description of it in the Oxford catalogue sounds very promising indeed. You were very wise to make it a co-operative undertaking so you will be sure that the work will be completed, while Sarton and I will probably not have enough years left to finish our histories.[2] I am anxious to have the first four volumes written by myself, that is up to and including the Renaissance because these are the volumes that require knowledge of ancient and oriental languages that the young people usually no longer have. The last four volumes could always be written by my former students and co-workers, who would be well prepared to handle the period from the 17th century to the present. I think you should include the drug industry as I will not be able to go very much into detail on this subject.[3] You should do it particularly when you come to the modern period when the pharmaceutical industry developed so tremendously. It is besides, so closely tied up with the dyes industry that it can hardly be separated from it.

Yes, I have made arrangements to attend the International Congress in Rome. The [sic] asked me to give one of the main addresses on The Influence of Medicine upon Civilisation. I am not a friend of these international gatherings but the lure of Rome and Salerno is hard to resist and I know that our Italian colleagues are working very hard to make the Congress a success. Now that Laignel-Lavastine is dead there may be a chance to re-organise the International Society and to divorce it from Aesculap, which I think is a very unholy alliance.[4] It would be very nice to meet in Naples and let us try to have a few nice days there.

I think I never mentioned how much I loved the two volumes presented to you.[5] They took a long time to come out, but the final result is good. Your picture in Volume II reminded me of the time when we first met soon after world war I. What an excellent idea of yours to send out those facsimile letters. I wish I had done the same at the time of my 60th birthday because it took me months to acknowledge all the messages I received at that time.

Warm wishes to you and Dorothey [sic] in which Emmy joins,

Yours as ever,

Henry E. Sigerist

---

[1] Singer et al. (eds), vol I (1954).
[2] Sarton (1952).
[3] See previous letter.

[4] International Society of the History of Medicine; *Aesculape*, its journal, founded in 1923 in Paris, continued in 1995 as *Vesalius*.
[5] The Festschrift, Underwood (ed.), (1953).

375

Singer to Sigerist, Kilmarth, Cornwall, 15 April 1954

My dear Sigerist,

Many thanks for your letter of April 6.

On the subject of drugs in connection with your History of Medicine and our History of Technology.[1] I do not think we ought to treat drugs until we get to the nineteenth century when, of course, we must deal with fine chemicals. This will not be until Volume V. The volume we are particularly concerned with at the moment is Volume II which involves the classical civilisation and its outcome in the north-west up till renaissance times. There was in that period, of course, nothing in the way of fine chemicals. We are naturally dealing with industrial chemical processes and drugs come in there now and again incidentally. For the most part, since they are of vegetable origin, they represent an economic factor with which I do not think we ought to deal. In fact, economics is exactly the subject that we want to keep away from because there is the Cambridge Economic History appearing neck and neck with ours and yours.[2] When it comes to the sixteenth and seventeenth centuries of Volume III we shall have something to say, of course, about true chemical processes, and some of them, e.g. Glauber salts, are of medical application. This, however, will not involve a chapter or section on drugs. I think you will agree with this decision.

Quite apart from all this, your own studies on the early receipts and antidotaries make you far more efficient in dealing with this subject than anyone we could find for it. I need hardly say that if you were to consider doing a short section yourself on early processes of drug preparation for our Vol. II we should be delighted, but I really think that it would go better in your book.

I was very sorry not to have a more cheerful letter about your health. Maybe the advance of summer will bring a different outlook. I do hope that Emmy will be able to come to Naples. I shall come all the way by sea, possibly with my friend Greeves. I am really not sure about Dorothea and do not quite know what to say about her. She suffers a good deal with high blood pressure, and three weeks ago had some rather bad nosebleeding which frightened us a good deal. She was in hospital for a fortnight under sedation and slept almost the whole time. She is back home now distinctly better, but still has a strong tendency to turn night into day. We have a nice nurse in the house – an old friend – who manages her very well and does everything also to make me comfortable. We are rather hoping to keep her with us, but really do not quite know yet. My general impression is that Dorothea will not come to Naples. She does not like the sea and the heat does not suit her as it does me.

I am very glad that you liked my volumes.[3] They certainly were a surprise. I knew, of course, that they were coming but I really did not know what impressive productions they would be. Their production and especially their indexing really does Underwood great credit. I am still very worried about the whole Wellcome layout.[4] It is so obvious that the whole thing should be made a University department, and that it will not go properly until it is. It appears that there are technical difficulties arising out of the terms of the Wellcome Trust in turning the thing over to the University, but I cannot for the life of me see why they should not establish a department next door to University College so as to make it a University department in everything but name. I do not think that we shall persuade Dale to this but I am, in fact, seeing him in the near future and will just drop a hint.[5] The trouble is that he gets angry at the very suggestion.

I had a nice card from Fischer in Zürich from Greece this morning.

Have you seen Ffrangcon Robert's pamphlet Medical Terms: Their Origin and Construction, William Heinemann Medical Books, London 1954?[6] What an excellent bit of work. Like all good ideas, one thinks when one sees it, "Why on earth didn't I do that years ago?"! You ought to look at it. It should be in the hands of every medical student and, more especially, of every American medical student, that is of everyone who knows no Latin or Greek. I commend it heartily.

Again, my dear friend, I am most eagerly looking forward to our meeting. I do not think we could meet more comfortably from the point of view of both of us than at Naples. Where do you propose to put up there? Is it worth being vaccinated and inoculated for typhoid at my age?

In the current number of Endeavour you will find an article by me with a coloured picture which I believe to be a historic one.[7] It is of the inner coffin of Tutankhamen, and it is the first one that I have seen which represents contoured gold properly. An immense amount of technical skill has gone into its production. Let me know if you do not see it and I will ensure that a copy is sent to you.

With all good wishes to you and yours,

Yours as always,

Charles Singer

---

[1] Sigerist (1951); Singer et al. (eds), (1954–1958).

[2] J. H. Clapham and E. E. Power (eds), *Cambridge economic history*, 9 vols (Cambridge, 1951–89).

[3] Underwood (ed.), (1953).

[4] Wellcome Library and Museum of the History of Medicine

[5] Henry H. Dale (1875–1968) English pharmacologist, Nobel Prize winner; chairman of the trustees of the Wellcome Trust between 1938 and 1960.

[6] Ffrangcon Robert, *Medical terms: their origin and construction* (London, 1954).

[7] Charles Singer, 'Some early goldwork', *Endeavour*, 1954, **13**: 86–93.

376

Sigerist to Singer, Pura, 7 May 1954

My dear Singer,

Many thanks for your letter of the 15th April. You probably have also received the enclosed sheet about the Greek Tour. Since I apparently suggested it I shall have to join the group. I had thought that the tour would take place after the Rome meeting, but our American colleagues apparently must be back home by the end of September. If a sufficient number joins the group, which I very much doubt, I would not be able to meet you in Naples and I would regret it very much. $ 400 is a lot of money for two weeks even for Americans, and seems rather unlikely to me that a group of twenty will come together.

A very nice hotel in Naples is Santa Lucia. It is on the waterfront and my daughter Nora and her husband[1] liked it very much. In Rome I asked for reservations at the Hotel Continental, it is not a particularly pleasant hotel but has a good central location.

I quite agree with you about the subject of drugs. I of course shall have to discuss them and their preparation in my book,[2] but I cannot possibly devote too much space to them either. The policy you outline for your book is absolutely correct and as a matter of fact the only possible one.[3]

My health is better than when I wrote you last time, I am on a strict reducing diet and have to take off twenty lbs. I am also taking Serpasil with good results. It is a drug that Ciba[4] is producing, and which actually is a very old drug[,] a glucoside extract from Rauwolfia, a plant used in India for 2000 years. Maybe Dorothy [sic] should take it also, it lowers the blood pressure and is at the same time a sedative.

You need not be vaccinated for smallpox, but inoculation for typhoid may be advisable as there is a good deal of typhoid in Naples and the whole of Southern Italy. I keep my immunisation up by having a shot every year when I go to WHO in Geneva.[5] On the other hand if you are a little careful, drink wine instead of water and avoid salads etc. you should be perfectly safe. I do not know if I ever wrote you that my daughter Erica got typhoid in Geneva a few years ago.[6] There are sporadic cases even in Switzerland. A few years ago there were about 12 cases in Basle and it was quite impossible to find the source of infection. One obviously can never quite avoid having typhoid carriers in the country.

I have not seen <u>Endeavour</u> for some time. Holmyard promised to send me a few numbers and I am particularly anxious to see your article.[7]

I have subscribed to the <u>Times Literary Supplement</u> and read it every week with great delight. It is so infinitely superior to the book section of the New York Times. Some of their leading and front articles are simply superb.

You may have heard that last week I was elected a Fellow of the Royal College of Physicians, and this was perhaps the greatest satisfaction I ever experienced. England has been very good to me in recent years, an hon. D.Sc. of the University of London last November and now the R.C.P. As a matter of fact and between ourselves I feel infinitely closer to England than I ever did to America.[8]

Emmy is in Zurich to get an American visa as she would like to spend two months with our daughter Nora and her family. Getting an American visa even for a short visit is a matter of six months and Americans are certainly trying to erect an iron curtain in front of their country.

With all good wishes and hoping that we shall meet in Naples, I am,

Yours as ever,

Henry E. Sigerist

[1] Nora and Jack Beeson-Sigerist (1921–2010), composer.
[2] Sigerist (1951, 1961).
[3] See previous letter
[4] Swiss pharmaceutical firm, now part of Novartis
[5] World Health Organization
[6] See letter 355.
[7] Singer (1954a).
[8] This may be an exaggeration of the moment.

377

Singer to Sigerist, Kilmarth, Cornwall, 1 June 1954

My dear Henry,

Many thanks for your letter of May 7. I am very sorry to hear that you may be going to the eastern Mediterranean. I hope it won't come off and that we shall duly meet at Naples. I went to have a general medical examination the other day and the report was that there is no reason at all why I should not go by sea provided I could have a companion to travel with me. Next week I am going to the University to see if they will run to the expense of a companion. My general idea would be to go by sea and come back by air. I have to be in London on September 30 to give the Lloyd Roberts Lecture,[1] which is a combined lecture of the R.C.P.,[2] the Royal Society of Medicine and the Medical Society of London. The Subject I thought of doing was "How Medicine became anatomical". Of course, I can do that without any work at all. It is just a question of collecting lantern slides!

I was very glad to hear of your "promotion" to be a D.Sc. of the University of London and an F.R.C.P.[3] I should have written to congratulate you, but I knew well that these things were for you just a routine matter.

Do let me know as soon as you can what are, in fact, your arrangements about Naples. I met J. Z. Young the other day and told him of the situation of you and me, and he promised to look after us and to entertain us at the Aquarium.[4]

We have just received here the dummy of Vol. I of A History of Technology. It certainly is a formidable-looking volume.[5]

With all kind wishes,

Yours as always,

Charles Singer

[1] David Lloyd Roberts (1835–1920), British physician who endowed the Lloyd-Roberts Lectures, given annually on a subject of medical or scientific interest; see 'David Lloyd Roberts, M.D., F.R.C.P', *British Medical Journal*, 1920, **ii**: 569.
[2] Royal College of Physicians
[3] Fellow of the Royal College of Physicians
[4] John Z. Young (1907–1997), English zoologist and Professor of Anatomy at UCL, at the Zoological Station at Naples; see B. B. Boycott, 'Young, John Zachary (1907–1997)', *Oxford dictionary of national biography* (Oxford: Oxford University Press, 2004), vol. 60, 921–924.
[5] Singer et al. (eds), vol I (1954).

378

Sigerist to Singer, Pura, 4 June 1954

My dear Singer,

It decidedly looks as if the Greek Tour were off. It was announced too late and

$ 400 is a lot of money even for Americans. So I am looking forward to seeing you in Naples, I have not made any definite arrangements yet, but there should be no difficulty in getting hotel rooms. I plan to go to a health resort for a couple of weeks and after that I hope to be well again.

Of course I am looking forward to seeing the first volume of your History of Technology[1] and in the last few weeks I have been devoting a great deal of thought to[?] my own History[2] and I came to the conclusion that the thing to do now is to make the book from volume four on if not sooner a co-operative venture like yours. I am too old and not well enough to write the eight volumes myself and it is better to make plans now than postpone them indefinitely. If I mobilise my colleagues we may get the eight volumes out in four or five years and I even think of the possibility of doing the Sociology of Medicine which I had planned in four volumes along similar lines.[3] I am working on a plan which I will submit to John Fulton when I see him in September and I would like to do the two books completely under the auspices of his department so that there will be a certain guarantee that the work will be completed.

With warm regards to Dorothy and yourself, I am,

Yours as ever,

Henry E. Sigerist

[1] Singer et al. (eds), vol I (1954).
[2] Sigerist (1951).
[3] Volume III-VIII of *History of medicine* and the *Sociology of medicine* did not materialize

379

Sigerist to Singer, Pura, 3 August 1954

My dear Singer,

I am just making plans for September and I am very much afraid that I shall not be able to meet you in Naples before the Congress. Genevieve Miller, Ilsa [sic] Veith, Anna Tjomsland,[1] Henry Schuman, John Fulton probably and a few other old friends will be in Pura at that time and I am afraid that I could not get away before the 10th or 11th of the month.

Why not spend a few quiet days in Naples after the meeting. Naples is close to Salerno and we may need a rest after the many official functions the congress is offering.

With all good wishes, I am,
Yours as ever,
Henry E. Sigerist

[1] Ilza Veith (born 1915), German-born American medical historian, Sigerist's pupil. Anna Tjomsland (1880–1968) anesthetist and medical historian; see 'Anne Tjomsland, 1880–1968', *Journal of the History of Medicine and Allied Sciences*, 1969, 24: 482.

380

Sigerist to Singer, Pura, 28 September 1954

My dear Singer,

Congratulations upon the Benivieni. Your translation is excellent and the book is beautifully presented. It is a great classic of medicine and it is good to have the book in such a handy edition. I have to review it, but at the moment I am not quite sure whether it is for Centaurus or Isis.[1]

I missed you very much in Rome. The Congress was the usual Vanity Fair, but went off quite well, and Rome and Salerno at this time of the year are most pleasant.

You may have heard that the International Society of the History of Medicine would very much like to hold its next Congress in 1956 in London. It is over thirty years that we had that brilliant gathering in London, and we all felt that England has so much to offer that we could not think of a better place.[2] Of course an invitation would have to be sent to the Society. The best would be to address it to its President: Wickersheimer. At any rate the Council decided that should an invitation come forth from England it would be accepted enthusiastically. Guthrie suggested that the last two days should be held at Edinburgh, which I think should be feasible.[3]

I hope you are keeping well. With warm regards, I am,

Yours very sincerely,

Henry E. Sigerist

---

[1] Singer and Long (1954); *Centaurus* and *Isis*, Journals of the history of medicine and of science, respectively, the review appeared as Henry E. Sigerist, 'Review of Antonio Benivieni *De abditis nunnullis ac mirandis morborum et sanationum causis*', in *Centaurus*, 1955, **4**: 175–176.

[2] The last London Congress was held in 1922 under Singer's presidency. The Congress did take place eventually but not until 1972.

[3] Douglas J. Guthrie (1885–1975) British medical historian; see H. P. Tait, 'Douglas James Guthrie', *Bulletin of the History of Medicine*, 1975, **49**:575–576.

381

Singer to Sigerist, Kilmarth, Cornwall, 7 October 1954

Confidential

My dear Sigerist,

Many thanks for your letter of September 28 and the kind things that you say in it. I am rather glad that I did not go to Rome. It would have taken up time and would have been very tiring, and, of course, I should not have learned anything. Moreover, it would have interrupted work and it would probably have left me in every way the worse. Had I been able to meet you at Naples, it would have been a very different matter.

Underwood has told me about the question of the International Congress 1956. I think London would be admirable, and I am quite sure that we could arrange to have a very good show indeed and that a special effort would be made to repeat the success of the previous meeting there.[1]

The matter is of some delicacy because it is really not practical politics to have a meeting both in London and Edinburgh. Rome and Salerno are no more than four hours apart, and four hours through very interesting country. But London and Edinburgh are eight hours apart and it is a very tiring and dull and expensive journey. Furthermore – as between fellow augurs – Guthrie really is not quite up to it. He is a very good fellow but also a very late beginner, and he really has not got the root of the matter in him. Yet further, there is really very little of medical interest to see in Edinburgh. After all, the Medical School in Edinburgh is one of the younger children of Boerhaave.[2] Of course, if St. Andrews, Glasgow and Aberdeen were added, there would be more to show and to do, but all this would mean much more travelling.

Against such possibilities, we have in London an endless wealth of historical medical material, with the Royal Society of Medicine, the Wellcome Foundation, the College of Surgeons and the College of Physicians all willing and anxious to give entertainment. And Oxford and Cambridge are only 1 $\frac{1}{4}$ hours away.

The basic awkwardness is, of course, about Guthrie. If there were anybody obvious to put in his place, it would not matter so much, but it is difficult for <u>me</u> to suggest Underwood.[3] The alternative is to get some really big noise outside. If I am alive in 1956 I shall be 80 myself, as will H. H. Dale. Lord Webb-Johnson is in rather poor health. Lord Moran is out of the question on many grounds. Lord Horder will be 87 or more. MacNalty is the same age as I am and in very poor health indeed.[4] If we do not have either Guthrie or Underwood, my best suggestion is Zachary Cope, who is a sensible and amiable man, though also getting on in years.[5] As I turn the matter over, I think, in fact, it really boils down to have Guthrie and Underwood as Joint Presidents with as many Presidents of Honour as the Committee jolly well like!

I should be glad to have the results of your contemplation on this matter, which I would treat in confidence.

Yours as ever,

Charles Singer

[1] See previous letter.

[2] Hermann Boerhaave (1668–1738), Dutch professor of medicine at Leyden. See G. A. Lindeboom, 'Boerhaave, Hermann', in *Complete dictionary of scientific biography*, Vol. 2 (Detroit: Charles Scribner's Sons, 2008), 224–228.

[3] As Underwood's father-in-law.

[4] Alfred Webb-Johnson (1880–1958), British surgeon; see Eric Riches, 'Johnson, Alfred Edward Webb-, Baron Webb-Johnson (1880–1958)', rev. Michael Hobsley, *Oxford dictionary of national biography* (Oxford: Oxford University Press, 2004), vol. 30, 231–232. Charles McMoran Wilson, first Baron Moran (1882–1977), physician and writer; see R. R. H. Lovell, 'Wilson, Charles McMoran, first Baron Moran (1882–1977)', *ibid*, vol. 59, 502–504. Thomas Jeeves Horder, first Baron Horder (1871–1955), British physician; see L. J. Witts, 'Horder, Thomas Jeeves, first Baron Horder (1871–1955)', *ibid*, vol. 28, 106–108. Sir Arthur MacNalty (1880–1969), English physician and public health administrator; see George E. Godber, 'MacNalty, Sir Arthur Salusbury (1880–1969)', rev. Michael Bevan, *ibid*, vol. 35, 934–935.

[5] Zachary Cope (1881–1974), English surgeon; see David Hamilton, 'Cope, Sir (Vincent) Zachary (1881–1974)', *ibid*, vol. 13, 317–318.

382

Sigerist to Singer, Pura, 11 October 1954

My dear Singer,

I just received your letter of 7th October and I hasten to answer it. I quite agree with you that Edinburgh is too far and has too little to offer. I think, moreover, that it never is good to have an International Congress to meet in two places. You lose track of the people and many members of the Congress do not travel to the second place. This was the case with Salerno. John Fulton and quite a few others did not make the trip but went home instead, and it is a nuisance to have to change hotels, etc. Thus I would suggest to drop the idea of Edinburgh altogether.

As to the Presidency of the Congress you are the obvious man for the job. You are the outstanding medical historian of Britain and you played your part so well twice in the past as President of that memorable Congress of 1922, and later of the Congress of the History of Science, that if your health permitted you simply must assume the Presidency. Why not have Underwood and Guthrie as Vice-presidents? They could do all the rough work for you, but you must be in charge of the Congress. A man like Lefann [sic][1] could be Secretary General, I hear that he did a very good job organising the International Congress of Medical Librarians last year.

London is the ideal place in every respect, and this is why I suggested it at the meeting of permanent committee at Rome. With the Royal Colleges, the Royal Society, the Wellcome Foundation, the British Museum, Apothecary Hall, etc., it has so much to offer, and I know of no country where there is a more delightful hospitality.

I fully agree with your judgement of Guthrie. His History is the work of a beginner and amateur, and it is full of obvious mistakes, but if he could be made Vice-president he would probably be satisfied.[2]

All in all I can only urge you to go ahead in the matter and I am quite sure that the Congress in London 1956 will be a huge success.

With warm regards, I am,

Yours Sincerely,

Henry

---

[1] William R. LeFanu (1904–1995), librarian at the Royal College of Surgeons, London; see Ian Lyle 'William LeFanu', *Medical History*, 1995, **39**: 501.

[2] Douglas Guthrie, *A history of medicine* (London, 1945).

383

Singer to Sigerist, Kilmarth, Cornwall, 22 October 1954

My dear Sigerist,

Many thanks for your letter on the next History of Medicine Congress. I suppose that it should be in London and, I suppose, that I should be president. I can always gracefully retire. I quite agree too that it should be in one place, but I think we could easily have a side-show at Oxford which is only one and a quarter hours by rail. For some reason which I don't understand Underwood would prefer Oxford. I think him wrong.

I am sorry to hear, though I am not surprised, that you do not feel equal to completing your enormous task unaided.[1] It is a superhuman undertaking. If I might venture on a word of advice, it is that you associate a much younger colleague with yourself as editor. Quite apart from securing continuity, it has the great advantage, as I have repeatedly found, that if a contribution is rejected or treated critically or his work be modified, in accordance with the plan, the offended author can always be assured that the difficulty lies with the other editor!

We are now expecting advance copies of our History of Technology, Volume I, daily, but official publication is on November 18 and Volume II will be with the printer before then.[2]

That you may have some idea of what is in the air with reference to the history of medicine in England, I enclose copy of correspondence. You have doubtless received a copy of the agendum on the fate of the R.C.P. library. The Royal College of Physicians is an ultra-conservative body, and is getting so obviously out of date and functionless that something must happen to it soon. I can say these things to you as we are both Fellows! It should have united with the Royal College of Surgeons, which has funds, enterprise, a better library, and a working scheme for teaching. This was prevented by purely personal antagonisms.

You know too that Dingle retires from the chair of Philosophy of Science and as head of the department of the History and Philosophy of Science next June. I hope that McKie will be elected as Professor and in charge of the department, partly because he has earned it and is the best man available, but also partly because it is, in fact, much easier to get a philosopher than an historian of science.[3] The success of the department, measured by the number of post-graduate students, has been immense. Last session there were something like 60 of them. The weakest point is their standard – they are mostly schoolmasters – but this is certainly steadily rising. The biological sciences are another weak point, but in this the department shares in the general trend of scientific education which treats biology lightly. On the whole my judgement is that the department has been a great success and has well justified itself. Personally I think it would be healthier to have a department of the history of medicine in close association with the department of the history of science. Yours as ever,
Charles Singer

[1] Sigerist's *History of medicine*.
[2] Singer et al. (eds), vol I (1954); vol II (1956).
[3] For Dingle and McKie see letter 311.

384

Sigerist's secretary to Singer, Pura, 6 November 1954

Dear Dr. Singer,

This is to let you know that Dr. Sigerist has been ill since October 18th and is at the clinic St. Anna in Lugano. He has an embolism, which paralysed his right side and prevented him from speaking. He is consequently unable to deal with any correspondence and is not even allowed visitors. Mrs. Sigerist stays with him night and day, although recently his condition has improved and it is hoped he will continue to make steady progress. He will in any case have to remain in hospital several more weeks.

I would be most grateful if you could let Sir Russel [sic] Brain know about Dr. Sigerist's illness, in case he is expecting him to communicate on any business.[1]

Yours sincerely,

Phyllis H. Arnold

(Secretary)

[1] Walter Russell Brain (1895–1966) British neurologist; see George Pickering, 'Brain, Walter Russell, first Baron Brain (1895–1966)', rev. *Oxford dictionary of national biography* (Oxford: Oxford University Press, 2004), vol. 7, 291–292.

385

Singer to Sigerist's secretary, Kilmarth, Cornwall, 10 November 1954

Dear Miss Arnold,

Thank you very much for your letter of November 6, which grieved me greatly. Do let me know if there is, by any chance, anything that I can do.

I have written to Mrs. Sigerist at the St. Anna Clinic, and I have also informed Sir Russell Brain of the situation.

Yours sincerely,

Charles Singer

386

Singer to Sigerist, Kilmarth, Cornwall, 19 November 1954

My dear Henry,

I am so very sorry to hear that you are laid by for a while. But I have a piece of historical intelligence that may perhaps encourage you. You will remember that Pasteur was afflicted with precisely the same condition as that from which you are now suffering, and that much of his best work was done after it.[1] May it be so with you.

Were you not in bed, I should burden you with a copy of the first volume of our History of Technology, but it is such an enormously weighty volume – far too big and far too heavy – that I hesitate to let you see it until you are home again.[2] I hope that may be a reason for hastening your recovery.

I have had several enquiries about you, among others from Sir Russell Brain.

With kindest wishes,

Yours as ever,

Charles Singer

[1] Louis Pasteur (1822–1895) French microbiologist. See Gerald L. Geison, 'Pasteur, Louis', in *Complete dictionary of scientific biography*, Vol. 10 (Detroit: Charles Scribner's Sons, 2008), 350–416; and Nils Roll-Hansen, 'Pasteur, Louis', *ibid*, Vol. 24, 21–30.

[2] Singer et al. (eds), vol I (1954); the first volume has 827 pages.

387

Singer to Sigerist, Kilmarth, Cornwall, 16 January 1955

My dear Henry,

I was so very glad to hear from Emmy that you are making good progress. You will take comfort from the history of Pasteur, some of whose best work was done after just such an attack as yours. All your friends here are hoping that 1955 will bring you just such a restoration. Your circumstances & surroundings must be about the best in the world for recovery.

You would perhaps like to have news of our subject from this country. During the last few weeks I have been having distressing letters from poor old W.H.S. Jones (Malaria Jones) complaining that he has to eke out his pension with elementary teaching. He is just bringing out the second of his endless volumes of the Loeb Pliny and wants to write a book on Roman popular medicine.[1] I have spoken to H. H. Dale about it and have written to the Wellcome Trustees making an appeal on his behalf. I have good hope that they will respond. I chose the opportunity to put forward also the suggestion of Stapleton & Plessner of a reasoned catalogue of the Arabic scientific and medical MSS in Great Britain and Ireland.[2] I think that Dale is sympathetic to that too.

At the last International Congress of the History of Medicine – at Rome – Guthrie was rather unfortunately, the British representative[.] He is proposing Edinburgh as the centre, with secondary centre in London! As it happens the railway fare from London to Edinburgh is about 18 pounds sterling return without sleeper so that no visitor from the Continent would be likely to make the journey – especially as in doing so he would pass York and Durham, both more beautiful than Edinburgh – when in fact the medical remains are exiguous. So the problem is to detach it from Edinburgh & get it to London, Cambridge or Oxford. However[,] we have 2 years in which to operate!

My own news is that we have at last got out the first volume of our history of technology, & the second volume is mostly in galleys. All this has meant further delay with my unfortunate Galen which is in page proof.[3] The trouble with that is that the anatomical nomenclature has had to be largely changed, which has made a dreadful mess with the proofs. There are still one or two passages resistant of translation. I don't mind about them for they can be either left blank or I can just do the best I can with them, frankly saying so. But the nomenclature is a real headache.

I am now well on in my 79th year. Naturally I cannot quite make such long hours as I did formerly, but I have so much [....] help that I think that 1954 has probably been my most productive year. We had half thought of going to California this winter, but it seemed a pity to leave the History of Technology at this early stage. By next winter

Vol. II should be published, Vol. III in galleys & Vols IV & V mostly in MS.[4] We might perhaps if our health still holds go then by all sea route. Who knows?

I often turn to the masterly first Volume of your great history.[5] I do hope that you may have similar good fortune to mine & be able to continue it.

With affectionate & fraternal greetings,

Yours ever,

Charles Singer

[1] William H. S. Jones (1876–1963), British author, wrote on malaria and Pliny; see Vivian Nutton, 'Jones, William Henry Samuel', in Robert B. Todd (ed.), *The dictionary of British classicists*, 3 vols (Bristol: Thoemmes Continuum, 2004), vol. 2, 525–527. Jones translated volumes VI-VIII of Pliny the Elder's *Natural history*, published in the Loeb Classical Library series.

[2] Stapleton and Plessner probably unpublished.

[3] Singer (1956a).

[4] Volumes II to V of *A History of Technology* appeared in 1956, 1957, 1958, 1958.

[5] Sigerist (1951).

388

Sigerist to Singer, Pura, 26 January 1955

My dear Charlie,

It's too bad about poor Jones. I don't remember whether I told you what my experience has been with the Loeb Classical Library, which is now at Harvard.[1] They make a charge for every quotation used, and while there is an agreement between American university presses that they won't make a charge for each other, the Oxford and Cambridge University Press are not included in this agreement. This means that the excellent translation of Hippocrates of Jones' cannot be used, and in quoting I am using the old translation of Francis Adams, which isn't copyright.[2] Of course I alter it to suit my purpose.

Congratulations upon the completion of volume I of your <u>History of Technology</u>.[3] You were wise not to plan to do it alone, as I have done and as Sarton is doing.[4] At our age you cannot tell whether you will be stricken by illness. I understand that Sarton did have some trouble too. Of course we would have started writing long ago if the war had not interfered. Now I am at home I would appreciate it if you sent me the <u>History of Technology</u>.

Guthrie's antics are most unfortunate, in that he will invite the Congress to be held in Edinburgh. You must dissuade him from carrying out his plan. It was I who suggested London, because I have good memories of the Congress of 1923 [sic].[5] As you say, there are many institutions that are eager to entertain in London.

I am progressing and I am hoping for a complete recovery. My leg carries me without a stick, and my arm, although not quite good as yet, I hope to improve through gymnastics. As you see I can dictate letters, so that my speech is also coming back.

With affectionate greetings,

Yours ever,

Henry E. Sigerist

[1] Loeb Classical Library, a series of Greek and Latin literature with text and English translation.
[2] Francis Adams, *Genuine works of Hippocrates; translated from the Greek* (London, 1849).
[3] Singer et al. (eds), vol I (1954).
[4] Sarton (1952).
[5] Sigerist means 1922.

389

Singer to Sigerist, Kilmarth, Cornwall, 2 February 1955

My dear Henry,

I cannot tell you with what relief I got your letter of January 26 which assures me that you are better and back at work.

I am arranging for you to receive a copy of the first volume of A History of Technology.[1] It may be a week or two before it reaches you; if it doesn't reach you within the next month do drop me a line.

I am trying to get hold of Guthrie when he comes to London in a couple of months' time. I have asked him and his wife to stay with us here. I can perhaps then talk matters over with him about this congress.

You may care to see an article that I wrote for the Christmas number of the British Medical Journal.[2]

I shall be in Cornwall until the beginning of May, when I shall be going to Town for two or three months.[3]

With kindest wishes for your further progress and affectionate greetings,

Yours ever,

Charles Singer

[1] Singer et al. (eds), vol I (1954).
[2] Charles Singer, 'How medicine became anatomical', *British Medical Journal*, 1954, **ii**: 1499–1503
[3] i.e. to London.

390

Singer to Sigerist, London, 26 April 1955

My dear Henry,

I am at last able to send you a copy of Volume I of 'A History of Technology', of which I assure you it has been quite difficult to secure copies, and I am sending one which we have been using in the office. I am hoping to hear your feelings about it.

Have you any help now with your second volume? That must of course come out at all costs.

With kindest regards,
Yours as always,
Charles Singer

391

Singer to Sigerist, London?, 4 May 1955

My dear Henry,

I am longing to have news of how you are. If you aren't up to writing, do please ask Emmy to answer this letter.

I hope that you have by now received a copy of Volume I of our History of Technology and that you have approved of it.[1]

I want your advice on the following matter. I have had a letter from Professor Boenheim, who holds the Chair of Internal Medicine at the "Karl Marx University" of Leipzig.[2] He writes on paper headed "Karl Sudhoff Institut" and I simply don't know whether there is a Professor of the History of Medicine there any longer. It seems that on 14 February 1906 Sudhoff gave his introductory lecture and they want to bring out a memorial volume to celebrate the occasion in 1956. He writes asking if I will contribute to it.

Boenheim has a son, a British subject, who has called on me and with whom I have discussed the matter. He is, it seems, in touch with Pagel.[3] The elder Boenheim himself was a refugee from the Hitler regime and became an American subject. He has now, however, returned and, according to the son, is really very happy under the present regime.[4] Of course, he admits, so his son tells me, that he belongs to the favoured class of highly trained scientific people of whom Eastern Germany is naturally very short. The chief trouble seems to be that they get hardly any Western literature so that Professor Boenheim could not even find my address! Of course, it is to be found both in the Medical Directory and in Who's Who.

I would very much like to hear your general reactions on the subject. I have no particular reason to commemorate Sudhoff personally but he was certainly a very great worker in his time, though he was also a very foolish and violent man. I suppose we must accustom ourselves to forget such things. I should not like myself to visit Germany but I am not really quite sure whether I could bring myself to write in a German journal.

Yours as ever,

Charles Singer

[1] Singer et al. (eds), vol I (1954).

[2] Felix Boenheim (1890–1960) head of the Sudhoff Institut (Leipzig Department of the History of Medicine) from 1950 to 1958; see Thomas Michael Ruprecht, *Felix Boenheim: Arzt, Politiker, Historiker, eine Biographie* (Hildesheim; New York: Olms, 1992).

[3] Walter Pagel (1898–1983) German/English medical historian, son of the Berlin medical historian Julius L. Pagel.

[4] German Democratic Republic, succeeding the Soviet occupation zone.

392

Sigerist to Singer, Pura, 6 May 1955

My dear Charly,

I am perfectly overwhelmed by your generous gift of the History of Technology and I realise that it wasn't easy to secure a copy. Both in quality, size and presentation the book is superb. How wise you were not to plan to write it singlehanded.[1] From Volume III of my History of Medicine I am going to imitate you. The second volume I shall finish alone, but from the third on I shall mobilise my old students who are now professors in various universities.[2]

Your History of Technology has been enthusiastically reviewed, which must be a great satisfaction to you. I saw the review in the Times Literary Supplement, and Sarton's excellent review in Isis.[3]

My health is making progress daily but my recovery is slower than I had hoped for. Well, I have written one paper, two book reviews, delivered the manuscript of the Heath Clark Lectures,[4] and now this week I have resumed work on the History after such a long interruption.

With kindest regards, and once more many thanks, I am,

yours ever,

Henry E. Sigerist

[1] Singer et al. (eds), vol I (1954); Sigerist (1951,1961), the latter volume appeared posthumously.

[2] Presumably Ackerknecht, Falk, Miller, Roemer, Temkin, Veith, and others.

[3] Sarton had reviewed Singer's *History of technology* in the history of science journal *Isis*, 1955, **46**: 294–296

[4] Henry E. Sigerist, *Landmarks in the history of hygiene* (London, 1956).

393

Sigerist to Singer, Pura, 10 May 1955

My dear Charly,

I hope my letter in which I thanked you for your magnificent <u>History of Technology</u> reached you.[1] It was addressed to Par.[2] I trust that mail is forwarded to you.

Now to your problem. Professor Boenheim asked me to contribute an article to their <u>Wissenschaftliche Zeitschrift</u> which is brought out by the university with a deadline of August 31st 1955. They plan to commemorate the 50th anniversary of the founding of the Institute of Medical History and they asked me to reminisce and to say what I had intended to do and what I achieved in the seven years in which I held the Chair of Karl Sudhoff.[3] Now I don't know whether we were asked to contribute to the same volume although I suppose that they didn't mean to have two publications for the occasion. Boenheim is Professor of clinical medicine, head of the polyclinic [sic], and Director ad interim of the Karl Sudhoff Institute of the History of Medicine. They could not find a successor to replace von Brunn,[4] they approached me several times to see whether I should consider resuming my old Chair, but I was not tempted to accept the offer as I felt too old. Now they appointed Boenheim as he was interested in medical history and contributed several papers.

Don't be shocked that they didn't find your address, probably there is no copy to be found in the entire University of either the Medical Directory or Whos Who [sic]. My advice is if you can bring yourself to write in a German journal at all, to drop prejudices and pay tribute to Karl Sudhoff, because he was a great man, although as you say he was violent and unbalanced in his judgement at times. I accepted to contribute a paper to that Festschrift,[5] although I have not set foot in Germany since 1932. I am sending you under separate cover the reprint of an article I wrote on the occasion of the centenary of Sudhoffs birth.[6]

With kind regards, I am,

Yours as ever,

Henry E. Sigerist

[1] Singer et al. (eds), vol I (1954).

[2] Par, the town next to Singer's Kilmarth.

[3] 1925–1932.

[4] Von Brunn held the Leipzig chair from 1934 to 1950.

[5] Henry E. Sigerist, 'Erinnerungen an meine Leipziger Tätigkeit', *Wissenschaftliche Zeitschrift der Karl-Marx-Universität Leipzig*. Mathematisch-Naturwissenschaftliche Reihe.1956, **5**: 17–21.

[6] Henry E. Sigerist, 'Erinnerungen an Karl Sudhoff', *Archiv für Geschichte der Medizin*, 1953, **37**: 97–103.

394

Singer to Sigerist, London, 13 May 1955

My dear Henry,

Many thanks for your prompt reply to my question about Sudhoff and for your Sudhoff article.[1]

I must just think it over. Sudhoff is certainly a queer choice for a Karl Marx University to celebrate!
Yours ever
Charles Singer

[1] Sigerist (1953b).

395

Singer to Sigerist, Kilmarth, Cornwall, 10 March 1956

My dear Henry,

I had the pleasure this morning of receiving a batch of your offprints & am particularly glad of this evidence of your great & continued activity. All this makes me hope that we shall soon see Vol. II of your magistral work.[1] Looking through your offprints I read first, of course, your memory of Sudhoff & feel I must congratulate you on the tact & good feeling that emanate from it.[2] And, by this token, did anything come of the volume to celebrate Sudhoff at the Leipzig Institute? One of my assistant [sic] christened it the Hitler-Stalin Institute of the History of Medicine! I have heard no more of it.

When is your volume II to be out?

You will by now have perhaps received my translation of Galen's De anatomicis admin.[3] It has been around my neck for 15 years, one accident after another has prevented it from appearing. I always received the various stages of proofs at a time when I could not possibly attend to them & correspondingly the printer always received them back when he could not attend to them!

Vol. II of the History of Technology has left my hands.[4] It is in page proof & I shall not see it again except in covers[?], I hope about May. Vol. III is in MS. Vol. IV is allocated & we are now at work on Vol. V.

I hope that you have not fared too badly in this very cold winter. We have been lucky in having been in almost the warmest part of Europe & have come out pretty well. Though cold, we had a quite exceptional amount of sunshine & enjoyed it.

Let us please have news of your family & yourself. Our children are doing well. Andrew, who is doing hospital administration, has had some promotion & is now secretary to a hospital for rehabilitation of Industrial Neurotics at Horsham in Sussex – a good position.

Fraternal greetings from house to house, Yours as always

Charles Singer

[1] Sigerist (1961).
[2] Sigerist (1953b).
[3] Charles Singer (ed.), *Galen on anatomical procedures: de anatomicis administrationibus / translation of the surviving books* (London, 1956).
[4] Singer et al. (eds), vol II (1956).

396

Sigerist to Singer, Pura, 20 March 1956

My dear Charlie,

Yesterday morning I received your Galen, On Anatomical Procedures for which I want to thank you most cordially and to congratulate you on a superb achievement.[1] One sees that it is the result of fifteen years of work. By the way, Underwood sent me a set of page proofs years ago so that I am familiar with the content of the book. Yesterday night I read your introduction and I was glad to see my guess confirmed that Galen describes human anatomy occasionally. What a good idea to have some Kopel illustrations added.[2] The book is beautifully presented as far as printing and paper go. I am sure you regret with me that you could not write Greek words in Greek letters and I am very much afraid that the Oxford Press will refuse me to use Greek type also. I have of course many Greek quotations in my second volume.

You asked what happened to the volume which is intended to commemorate the foundation of the Leipzig Institute. Well Boenheim has been appointed professor of medical history after he reached the age limit as a professor of medicine. He is not a historian but they could not get a real historian of medicine. Katner, his assistant, is a musicologist.[3] Under such leadership it is obvious that the Leipzig Institute is going to the dogs. This is a pity as it is the only institute the library of which was not bombed out. A celebration in memory of Sudhoff is to be held sometime in June, when the volume will be out. I wrote a short article in which a [sic] gave a summary of my activities while I was in charge of the Leipzig Institute.[4]

You are fifteen years older than I and I envy you your health and your productivity. My Heath Clark Lectures will be published this spring under the title Landmarks in the History of Hygiene.[5] I also wrote my Bryce Lecture that I gave some years ago at Somerville college on the Latin Medical Literature of the Early Middle Ages.[6] I only have to add the footnotes. And now at last I resumed the work on volume two of my History.[7] I hope to get through with the manuscript at the end of this year, so that the volume should come out next year. But I am progressing very slowly.

Congratulations on the completion of volume two of your History of Technology.[8] As I wrote you in a previous letter I was wrong in the assumption that I could write eight volumes alone. From volume three on I shall have to get some help.

We had a beastly cold winter and I am sure Cornwall was about the warmest spot in the whole of Europe. Even in the Ticino the thermometer dropped to about 15° F which is most unusual and it did last for about six weeks and played havoc with our garden. The mimosa, the olive tree, the oleander, the agave all are dead. The camelias [sic] have suffered a great deal. And the dahlias which we are accustomed to leave in the soil are frozen dead also.

As a result of this protracted cold I had a slight set back that kept me a few weeks in bed. My blood pressure dropped suddenly from 170 to 120 and I almost collapsed. This was at the end of last month and I feel better and my doctor allows me to get up a few hours in the morning and a few hours in the afternoon.

My wife is well and my oldest daughter Erica is still unmarried and works as a librarian at the World Health Organization. My youngest daughter is happily married in New York and has two children. She took a Ph.D. degree in Slavic languages and literature at Columbia. Her husband is a young composer, Jack Beeson, who is professor of composition at Columbia University. He has written three operas one of which has been performed in New York, St. Louis, Baltimore and Louisville. And one will be performed next winter. You met my girls in 1946, when you were in Zurich. You have not written in your letter anything about the health of Dorothea, and I sincerely hope that she is feeling comfortable.

Well, that is the news. With best wishes from house to house I am
Yours as always
[Henry E. Sigerist]

PS. I am just reviewing Ackerknecht's Short History of Medicine and I would like to refer to your Short History.[9] Could you tell me what was the latest edition. The first edition is of 1928, if I remember correctly.

---

[1] Singer (1956a).

[2] The majority of the figures at the end of the book were by Benjamin Kopel and taken from Carl G. Hartman and William L. Straus (eds), *The anatomy of the rhesus monkey (Macaca mulatta),* (London: Bailliere, Tindall & Cox, 1933)

[3] Wilhelm Katner (1903–1985), German medical historian, see Hans Schadewaldt, 'Laudatio in honorem sexagenarii quinti Guilelmi Katner', in *Medicinae et artibus: Festschrift für Professor Dr. phil. Dr. med. Wilhelm Katner zu seinem 65. Geburtstag* (Düsseldorf: Michael Triltsch, c1968), ix-xii.

[4] Sigerist (1956b).

[5] Sigerist (1956a).

[6] Sigerist (1958).

[7] Sigerist (1961).

[8] Singer et al. (eds), vol II (1956).

[9] Sigerist reviewed Erwin H. Ackerknecht, *A short history of medicine* (New York, 1955) in *Bulletin of the History of Medicine*, 1956, 30: 278–279; Singer, *Short history* (1928b).

397

Singer to Sigerist, Kilmarth, Cornwall, 5 April 1956

My dear Henry,

Many thanks for your letter of the 20th March.

You will have received my account of Sarton. I am writing a fuller one for Nature.[1] If there is any particular point you would like me to make, perhaps you will drop me a line.

I cannot tell you what a pleasure it is to me that you appreciate my Galen.[2] It was badly wanted but stuck in the press for years. I always got proofs just at the time that I could not attend to them and then by the time that I could attend to them I really had forgotten all about what was needed, and so it went on time and time again.

The Clarendon Press has become really intolerably slow and seems to me not to consider human relationships at all. I thought that Volume II of our History of Technology would have been out long before now but I don't see much hope of it until June, though there is really nothing whatever to add to it.[3]

I am much looking forward to seeing your Heath Clark Lectures.[4]

I don't think I quite agree with you about the need for Greek script. Since there are so very few people now who read it and since it can be reproduced perfectly well in Latin script, it seems to me to be doing a service to use the Latin script and so show the reader at least how the words that he uses are derived. After all, our books are written to be read and not as museum pieces.

You are asking about the last edition of my Short History of Medicine. The Clarendon Press attaches a special meaning to the word 'edition' which is not that of most publishers. By 'edition' they mean a revision in which either substantial additions have been made or the general character of the text has been substantially modified. In this sense there has never been but one edition, though I have, if my memory serves, revised it several times. However, the new edition will be the work of Underwood and it should be substantially ready by now. He knows about it more than I do for he has it under his immediate supervision and I am only too glad not to correct the proofs.[5]

I have actually on my desk a History of Anatomy which I hope to get to press before the autumn.[6] I am also pledged to produce in book form a revision of The Herbal in Antiquity,[7] and Dingle and I are to appear as joint authors of A Short History of Science.[8] For all these reasons I am only too glad to be let off the work on medicine which Underwood is taking on.

I thought Ackerknecht's little book was good of its kind and especially good in the modern section. I thought he was foolish to put in the illustrations, which are neither well produced nor well chosen. It would have been a better and cheaper book if he had left them out altogether. I said this in a very favourable review of the book which I wrote for Nature.[9]

With all good wishes from us both to you both,

Yours as always,

Charles Singer

[1] Sarton had died on 22 March 1956; Charles Singer, 'Obituary George Sarton', *Nature*, 1956, **178**: 67.

[2] Singer (1956a).

[3] Singer et al. (eds), vol II (1956).

[4] Sigerist (1956a).

[5] The second edition of Singer's *Short history of medicine* appeared in 1962 with Underwood as first author.

[6] Singer's second edition of *The evolution of anatomy*, published as *A short history of anatomy from the Greeks to Harvey* (New York: Dover Publications, 1957).

[7] No revised edition of Singer, *The herbal in antiquity* (1927), appeared.

[8] Charles Singer, *A short history of scientific ideas* (Oxford, 1959). Dingle was not co-author but in the introduction Singer wrote that "Professor H. Dingle has written the section from p. 418 to p.460 and has saved the text from some errors elsewhere".

[9] Ackerknecht (1955); Singer reviewed this is in *Nature*, 1956, **177**: 909.

398

Singer to Sigerist, Kilmarth, Cornwall, 18 April 1956

My dear Henry,

There is a matter in which you might be able to help us. We are seeking an article on the history of water-driven engines between 1850 and 1900. This, as you doubtless know, is a Swiss specialty and has been for a great many years. The firm of Escher Wyss[1] is regarded as the main producer of these engines and they produce a sort of journal 'The Escher Wyss News', now in its 28th volume or so, a version of which is printed in English. It is obviously a very highly scientific venture. Of course, the Swiss have a greater experience of this work than any other people in this world.

First of all, is the firm any relation of Emmie's?[2] Are you in any sort of communication with any of them? Secondly, the Escher Wyss firm produced a large quarto, beautifully illustrated brochure some years ago, from which I learn that the founder of the firm was Caspar Escher in 1805.[3] Two of the articles in this brochure (which, by the way, was published some time after 1939), one by J. Moser 'A Century of Water Turbines' and the other by J. Haefele 'Statistics concerning the Development of Water Turbines', contain the material that we are seeking, though we should want it a bit simplified. Can you tell me anything of these people? I have written to the firm itself asking their address but they had already written that there was no-one directly connected with the management of the firm who could undertake our task. Can you help us in the matter or alternatively could you suggest someone else who might do it? The article need not necessarily be written in English for we could arrange to have it adequately translated.

I expect you have heard of the discovery in the catacombs of Rome of an alleged dissection scene, said to be of the fourth century A.D. I have only before me a picture which appeared in the New York Times of April 11th. It is a very poor reproduction with a very imperfect screen. On the whole I am inclined to think that it is not a dissection scene, though I admit I am prejudiced because, if it is, I shall have to rewrite a section of a history of anatomy which is now approaching completion![4] Of course, even if it is a dissection scene, that does not prove that there was any dissecting at the time. In the picture before me there is no Christian symbol or suggestion of Christianity. I should want a lot of persuading that there was any dissection by early Christians. However, it is impossible to give an opinion until one gets a proper photograph of the original, for which I have written.[5]

I have been asked to go to California for the winter of this year and I am playing with the idea. It seems a ridiculous thing to do at 80 and I don't suppose anything will come of it, but I thought I would let you know. Should we go, we should go all the way by sea in order to get warm.

I feel sure that you should not be going to the meeting at Florence this year.[6] Should I not go to California, we might possibly consider going to Florence. In that case I think I should try and visit you on the way. Quite frankly, I don't believe either of these schemes will come off and also I think that it is my duty to finish the innumerable literary jobs that I have in hand.[7]

With all kind wishes from us both to you both,

Yours as ever,

Charles Singer

P.S. I have just read an interesting and affecting little book by Richard Goldschmidt, 'Portraits from Memory'. It is really a most interesting little volume and in places quite touching.[8]

---

[1] Escher-Wyss, an engineering firm in Zurich.

[2] Emmy Sigerist-Escher.

[3] Hans Caspar Escher (1775–1859), Swiss industrialist and architect.

[4] See previous letter

[5] The picture was finally published by A. Ferrua, *Le pitture della nuova catacomba di Via Latina* (Vatican City, 1960). For a reproduction and an English discussion, see J. Stevenson, *The catacombs. Rediscovered monuments of early Christianity* (London: Thames and Hudson, 1978) 84, 128–9, with pl. 103. Singer's scepticism has been borne out by recent discussions.

[6] To the International Congress of the History of Science and Technology.

[7] See previous letter.

[8] Richard B. Goldschmidt (1878–1958), German-American zoologist; see C. Stern, 'Richard Benedict Goldschmidt, April 12, 1878-April 24, 1958', *Perspectives in Biology and Medicine*, 1969, **12**: 179–203. Richard B. Goldschmidt, *Portraits from memory. Recollections of a zoologist* (Seattle, 1956).

399

Sigerist to Singer, Pura, 25 April 1956

My dear Singer,

Many thanks for two letters and for your obituary on Sarton. I wish you would write such an obituary for me when the time comes, for I have no doubt that you will outlive me.

Caspar Escher was no relative of Emmy's or at any rate a very distant relative of Emmy's great-grandfather. We have no connection with the firm and I cannot help you in the matter except that I am sending you a clipping from the "Neue Zürcher Zeitung" listing all the machines they have exhibited at the Sample Fair at Basle.[1]

As to the so-called dissection scene I agree with you, that from the picture reproduced in the "New York Times" one cannot say whether it is actually a dissection scene or an operation scene. Friends sent me the clipping. And although Proskauer and Fulton seem to agree that it is a dissection scene, I have my doubts.[2] To the Early Christians who believed in resurrection in the flesh it must have been abhorrent to dissect human bodies, particularly of children. Or it may be that the scene represents a rite unknown to us. I hesitate to give an opinion before I have seen a decent picture and if I were you I would not rewrite a section of your history of anatomy.

Congratulations upon the invitation to California. A winter in California is a very pleasant thing. Should you go to Florence, by all means visit me on the way.[3]

With kind regards from both of us to you both I am

Yours ever

[Henry E. Sigerist]

---

[1] See previous letter.

[2] Curt Proskauer (1887–1972) wrote on medical iconography; see Malvin E. Ring, In memoriam Curt Proskauer, 1887–1972', *Bulletin of the history of dentistry*, 1972, **20**: 34–36.

[3] The International Congress of the History of Science and Technology at Florence.

400

Sigerist to Singer, Pura, 29 August 1956

My dear Charlie,

I was very much disturbed to learn through Dorothea that you had suffered a slight heart attack. Take good care of yourself and don't get up too soon.

We have been looking forward to Dorothea's visit, and are very disappointed that we shall not have the pleasure of welcoming her, but we understand that she is anxious to be at your bedside.

Good luck to you my dear friend, and we hope that we shall hear soon that you recovered fully.

With warm greetings to you both from us both, I am,

Yours affectionately,

Henry E. Sigerist

401

Singer to Sigerist, Kilmarth, 3 September 1956[1]

My dear Henry,

Many thanks for your letter of the 29th August. The fact is that I have been afflicted with a very acute rheumatoid arthritis, the acuteness of which gives good hope of an early recovery. I am now quite free from pain and able to walk comfortably, though still almost confined to the house.

About ten days ago I had an attack of cardiac asthma which was very clearly related to a small personal anxiety. I recovered in a matter of minutes with a quarter of a grain of morphia and, though drowsy next day, I was up and the day after was practically normal. I am told that there is no reason why these things should recur.

The rheumatoid arthritis has subsided except in my hands and though I can write I am advised not to for several more weeks. The swelling of the hands is going down rapidly. It happens that I have a sister, now aged 88, who has been through precisely the same history. She is now perfectly normal except that she has a few bony outgrowths on the fingers. She writes perfectly well, has full use of her senses, does her own house-work and goes out daily, which is not bad for her age.

All this will clearly prevent me and, indeed, Dorothea from visiting you this month, so that you must forgive us. I am really not ill and, except for the stage of acute onset, have never felt ill, which is rather a comfort.

With warmest greetings to you both,

Yours affectionately,

Charles Singer

---

[1] This seems to be the last letter of the correspondence, half a year prior to Sigerist.'s death in March 1957. Singer died in 1960, aged 84.

3. Bibliography

Ackerknecht, Erwin H. (1942a) 'Problems of primitive medicine', *Bulletin of the History of Medicine*, **11**: 503–521.

Ackerknecht, Erwin H. (1942b) 'Primitive medicine and culture pattern', *Bulletin of the History of Medicine*, **12**: 545–574.

Ackerknecht, Erwin H. (1955) *A short history of medicine* (New York).

Adams, Francis (1849) *Genuine works of Hippocrates; translated from the Greek*, (London).

Allbutt, T. Clifford (1924) 'Letter of congratulation [to Sudhoff]', in Charles Singer and Henry E. Sigerist (eds) (1924) *Essays in the history of medicine presented to Karl Sudhoff on the occasion of his seventieth birthday November 25th 1923* (London and Zurich).

Arcieri, John P. (1945) *The circulation of the blood; and Andrea Cesalpino of Arezzo* (New York).

Arundel, Thomas H. (1841) *Catalogue of manuscripts in the British Museum* (London).

Aselli, Gaspare (1627) *De lactibus ....* (Milan).

Bayon, H. P. (1941) 'Paracelsus: personality, doctrines and his alleged influence in the reform of medicine', *Proceedings of the Royal Society of Medicine*, **35**: 69–76.

Berengario da Carpi, Jacopo (1522) *Isagoge breves prelucide ac uberime in anatomiam humani corporis* (Bologna).

Bevan, Edwyn R. and Singer, Charles, (eds) (1927) *The legacy of Israel* (Oxford).

Bickel, Marcel H. (ed.) (2008) *Henry E. Sigerist: Vier ausgewählte Briefwechsel mit Medizinhistorikern der Schweiz* (Bern).

Browne, Edward G. (1921) *Arabian medicine* (Cambridge).

Brunschwig, Hieronymus (1512) *Liber de arte distillandi de compositis* (Strassburg).

Capparoni, Pietro (1923) *Magistri salernitani nondum cogniti* (London).

Castiglioni, Arturo (1927) *Storia della medicina* (Milan).

Clapham, J. H. and Power, E. E. (eds) (1941–1989), *Cambridge economic history*, 9 vols (Cambridge).

Clarke, Edwin (1961) 'Charles Joseph Singer', *Journal of the History of Medicine and Allied Sciences*, **16**: 411–419.

Constantinus Africanus (1560) *Medicinae tam simplices ....* (Basel).

Cope, Zachary (1960) 'Charles Joseph Singer (1876–1960)', *Bulletin of the History of Medicine*, **24**: 471–473.

Cushing, Harvey and Streeter, Edward C. (eds) (1925) *Giovanni Battista Canano, Girolamo da Carpi: Musculorum humani corporis picturata dissectio* (Florence).

Dannemann, Friedrich (1898), *Grundriss einer Geschichte der Naturwissenschaften*, 2 vols (Leipzig).

Dannemann, Friedrich (1924), *Ueber den Parallelismus in der Entwicklung der Naturwissenschaften und der Heilkunde*, in Charles Singer and Henry E. Sigerist (eds) (1924), *Essays in the history of medicine presented to Karl Sudhoff on the occasion of his seventieth birthday November 25th 1923* (London and Zurich) 349–368.

Diels, Hermann (1912) *Die handschriftliche Ueberlieferung des Galenschen Commentars zum Prorrheticum des Hippokrates* (Berlin).

Dobell, Cecil Clifford (1932) *Antonie van Leeuwenhoek and his "little animals"*, (London).

Drabkin, Israel (ed.) (1950), *Aurelianus, Caelius: on acute diseases and on chronic diseases* (Chicago).

Dryander, Johannes (1536), *Anatomia capitis humani ....* (Marburg).

Edelstein, Emma J. and Edelstein, Ludwig (1945) *Asclepius; a collection and interpretation of the testimonies* (Baltimore).

Emmart, Emily W. (1940) *The Badianus Manuscript. An Aztec herbal of 1552* (Baltimore).

Etzioni, Mordecai (1945) 'The Hebrew-Aramaic Element in Vesalius' *Tabulae anatomicae sex*', *Bulletin of the History of Medicine*, **18**: 413–424.

Flexner, Simon and Flexner, James T. (1941) *William Henry Welch and the heroic age of American medicine*, (New York).

Garrison, Fielding H. (1913) *An Introduction to the History of Medicine* (Philadelphia and London).

Garrison, Fielding H. (1924) 'The newer epidemiology', in Charles Singer and Henry E. Sigerist (eds) (1924) *Essays in the history of medicine presented to Karl Sudhoff on the occasion of his seventieth birthday November 25th 1923* (London and Zurich) 255–268.

Giacosa, Piero (1898) *Magistri salernitani nondum editi ....* (Turin).

Green, Robert Montraville ([1951]), *A translation of Galen's Hygiene: (De sanitate tuenda)* with an introduction by Henry E. Sigerist (Springfield, Ill., Charles C. Thomas).

Green, Robert, and Licht, Sidney (1953) *Selected Works of Galen, Translated by R. M. Green for S. Licht* (New Haven).

Goldschmidt, Richard B. (1956) *Portraits from memory. Recollections of a zoologist* (Seattle).

Guthrie, Douglas (1945) *A history of medicine* (London).

Haeser, Heinrich (1881) *Lehrbuch der Geschichte der Medizin*, 2 vols, 3rd ed. (Jena).

Haggis, A. W. (1941) 'Fundamental errors in the early history of cinchona', *Bulletin of the History of Medicine*, **10**: 417–459.

Hall, A. Rupert (1960) 'Charles Joseph Singer (1876–1960)', *Isis*, **51**: 558–560.

Homo, Léon (1951) *Rome Impériale et l'urbanisme dans l'antiquité* (Paris).

Howald, Ernst and Sigerist, Henry E. (1927) *Pseudo-Apulei herbarius* (Leipzig and Berlin).

Hübotter, Franz, *3000 Jahre Medizin*, Berlin, 1920.

Hume, Edgar E. (1942) *Ornithologists of the United States Army Medical Corps* (Baltimore).

Ivins, W. M. (1943) 'A propos of the Fabrica of Vesalius', *Bulletin of the History of Medicine*, **14**: 576–593.

Jilla, Cyrus (1991) 'Charles Singer: his life, aims and achievements in the history of medicine', BSc Dissertation (London -Wellcome Institute for the History of Medicine).

Klebs, Arnold C., 'The Practica of Gianmatteo Ferrari da Gradi', in Charles Singer and Henry E. Sigerist (eds), *Essays in the history of medicine presented to Karl Sudh-*

off on the occasion of his seventieth birthday November 25th 1923, London and Zurich, 1924, 211–236.

Koebert, Hermann (1888) *De Pseudo-Apulei Herbarum Medicaminibus* (Bayreuth).

Kristeller, Paul Oskar (1945) 'The School of Salerno', *Bulletin of the History of Medicine*, **17**: 138–194.

Kühn, Herbert (1922) *Die Malerei der Eiszeit* (München).

Laignel-Lavastine, P. M. Maxime (ed) (1936–1949) *Histoire générale de la médecine, de la pharmacie, de l'art dentaire et de l'art vétérinaire.* 3 vols (Paris).

Leake, Chauncey D. (1952) *The Old Egyptian medical papyri* (Lawrence, KS).

Liechtenhan, Eduard (1917) *Sprachliche Bemerkungen zu Marcellus Empiricus* (Basel).

Lind, L. R. and Asling, C. W. (eds) (1949) *The Epitome of Andreas Vesalius* (New York).

Livingston, R.W. (ed) (1921) *The legacy of Greece* (Oxford).

Lockwood, Dean P. (1951) *Ugo Benzi; Medieval philosopher and physician* (Chicago).

Lowe, Elias A. (1914) *The Beneventan Script. A history of the South Italian minuscule* (Oxford).

Malpighi, Marcello (1661) *De pulmonibus observationes anatomicae* (Bologna).

Manget, Jean-Jacques (1685) *Bibliotheca anatomica* (Geneva).

McKie, Douglas (1935) *Antoine Lavoisier: the father of modern chemistry* (London).

Meyer-Steinegg, Theodor and Sudhoff, Karl (1921) *Geschichte der Medizin im Ueberblick mit Abbildungen* (Jena).

Miller, Genevieve (ed.) (1946) *William Beaumont's formative years* (New York).

Miller, Genevieve (ed.) (1983) *Letters of Edward Jenner and other documents concerning the early history of vaccination* (Baltimore).

Mullett, Charles F. (1946) *Public Baths and Health in England, 16th–18th Century.* Supplement No. 5 *Bulletin of the History of Medicine*, 1–85.

Neuburger, Max (1906/1911) *Geschichte der Medizin.* 2 vols (Stuttgart).

Neuburger, Max and Pagel, Julius L. (eds) (1902–1905) *Handbuch der Geschichte der Medizin*, 3 vols (Jena).

Norden, F. (1921) *Vom Altertum zur Gegenwart* (Leipzig and Berlin).

Olmsted, James M.D. (1946) *Charles-Eduard Brown-Séquard, a nineteenth century neurologist and endocrinologist* (Baltimore).

Pagel, Walter (1935) 'Religious motives in the medical biology of the XVIIth century', *Bulletin of the History of Medicine*, **3**: 97–128, 213–231, 265–314.

Pliny, the Elder, *Natural history*, with an English translation by W. H. S. Jones, vol 6 (1951), vol 7 (1956), vol 8 (1963), Loeb Classical Library Series (London: Heinemann).

Pettenkofer, Max (1858) *Ueber den Luftwechsel in Wohngebäuden* (Munich).

Peyer, Bernhard (1950) *Goethes Wirbeltheorie des Schädels* (Zurich).

Robert, Ffrangcon (1954) *Medical Terms: Their Origin and Construction* (London).

Rolleston, Humphry (1924) 'The reception of Harvey's doctrine of the circulation of blood in England', in Charles Singer and Henry E. Sigerist (eds) (1924) *Essays in the history of medicine presented to Karl Sudhoff on the occasion of his seventieth birthday November 25th 1923* (London and Zurich), 247–254.

Sanchez de Rivera y Moset, Daniel (1921) *Siluetas de médicos y libros de antaño ....* (Madrid).

Sarton, George (1952-) *A history of science* (Cambridge, MA).

Scott, Walter (1885) *Hermetica: the ancient Greek and Latin writings* .... (Boston).

Sigerist, Henry E. (1920) Die "Cirurgia Eliodori", *Archiv für Geschichte der Medizin*, **12**: 1–9.

Sigerist, Henry E. (1921) 'Die "Lecciones Heliodori'", *Archiv für Geschichte der Medizin*, **13**: 145–156.

Sigerist, Henry E. (1923a) *Studien und Texte zur frühmittelalterlichen Rezeptliteratur* (Leipzig).

Sigerist, Henry E. (ed.) (1923b) *Ambroise Paré, die Behandlung der Schusswunden* (Leipzig).

Sigerist, Henry E. (1923c) 'Eine deutsche Uebersetzung der Kethamschen Gynäkologie', *Archiv für Geschichte der Medizin*, **14**: 169–178.

Sigerist, Henry E. (ed.) (1923d) *The Book of Cirurgia by Hieronimus Brunschwig* (Milan).

Sigerist, Henry E. (1923e) *Albrecht von Hallers Briefe an Johannes Gesner 1728–1777* (Berlin).

Sigerist, Henry E. (1924) 'Die Geburt der abendländischen Medizin', in Charles Singer and Henry E. Sigerist (eds) (1924) *Essays in the history of medicine presented to Karl Sudhoff on the occasion of his seventieth birthday November 25th 1923* (London and Zurich), 185–205.

Sigerist, Henry E. (1933) *Great doctors* English translation (New York).

Sigerist, Henry E. (1934a) *American medicine* English Translation (New York).

Sigerist, Henry E. (1934b) 'The medical literature of the Early Middle Ages. A program and a report of a summer of research in Italy', *Bulletin of the History of Medicine*, **2**: 26–50.

Sigerist, Henry E. (1934c) 'On Hippocrates', *Bulletin of the History of Medicine*, **2**: 190–214.

Sigerist, Henry E. (1934d) 'A summer of research in European libraries', *Bulletin of the History of Medicine*, **2**: 559–610.

Sigerist, Henry E. (1936) 'The history of medicine and the history of science. An open letter to George Sarton', *Bulletin of the History of Medicine*, **4**: 1–13.

Sigerist, Henry E. (1937a) Fielding H. Garrison Memorial Number. *Bulletin of the History of Medicine*, **5**: 299–403.

Sigerist, Henry E. (1937b) *Socialized medicine in the Soviet Union* (New York).

Sigerist, Henry E. (1938) 'Report of the activities of the Institute of the History of Medicine of the Johns Hopkins University (1937–1938)', *Bulletin of the History of Medicine*, **6**: 858–881.

Sigerist, Henry E. (1939) 'Yugoslavia and the XIth International Congress of the History of Medicine', *Bulletin of the History of Medicine*, **7**: 93–147.

Sigerist, Henry E. (1940a) 'A physician's impression of South Africa', *Bulletin of the History of Medicine*, **8**: 22–27.

Sigerist, Henry E. et al. (1940b)' Congratulatory epistle to Arnold C. Klebs', *Bulletin of the History of Medicine* (Arnold C. Klebs Number), **8**: 319–328.

Sigerist, Henry E. (1940c) 18 articles in the New York Newspaper *PM*.

Sigerist, Henry E. (1941a) *Medicine and human welfare* (New Haven).

Sigerist, Henry E. (1941b) 'Paracelsus in the light of four hundred years', in New York Academy of Medicine (ed.) *The march of medicine* (New York), 28–51.

Sigerist, Henry E. (ed.) (1941c) *Four treatises of Theophrastus von Hohenheim called Paracelsus* (Baltimore).

Sigerist, Henry E. (ed.) (1941d) *The value of health to a city. Two lectures delivered in 1873 by Max von Pettenkofer*, translated by H. E. Sigerist (Baltimore).

Sigerist, Henry E. (1942) 'The Sphere of Life and Death in Early Medieval Manuscripts', *Bulletin of the History of Medicine*, **11**: 292–303.

Sigerist, Henry E. (1943a) *Civilization and disease*. (Ithaca, NY).

Sigerist, Henry E. (ed.) (1943b) *Maurice Arthus' philosophy of scientific investigation* (Baltimore).

Sigerist, Henry E. (1946) *The university at the crossroads. Addresses and essays* (New York).

Sigerist, Henry E. (1947) *Medicine and health in the Soviet Union* (New York).

Sigerist, Henry E. (1951) *A history of medicine*, vol. I (New York).

Sigerist, Henry E. (1952) 'Living under the shadow',. *Atlantic Monthly* **189**: 25–30.

Sigerist, Henry E. (1953a) 'Johannes Hartlieb's gynaecological collection and the Johns Hopkins Manuscript', in E. Ashworth Underwood (ed.) (1953) *Science, medicine and history. Essays on the evolution of scientific thought and medical practice, written in honour of Charles Singer* 2 vols (London), vol 1, 231–246.

Sigerist, Henry E. (1953b) 'Erinnerungen an Karl Sudhoff', *Archiv für Geschichte der Medizin*, **37**: 97–103.

Sigerist, Henry E. (1955) 'Review of Antonio Benivieni *De abditis nunnullis ac mirandis morborum et sanationum causis*' in *Centaurus* **4**: 175–176.

Sigerist, Henry E. (1956a) *Landmarks in the history of hygiene* (London).

Sigerist, Henry E. (1956b) 'Erinnerungen an meine Leipziger Tätigkeit', *Wissenschaftliche Zeitschrift der Karl-Marx-Universität Leipzig*, Mathematisch-Naturwissenschaftliche Reihe, **5**: 17–21.

Sigerist, Henry E. (1956c) 'Review of E.H.Ackerknecht *A short history of medicine*' in *Bulletin of the History of Medicine*, **30**: 278–279.

Sigerist, Henry E. (1958) 'The Latin medical literature in the Early Middle Ages', *Journal of the History of Medicine and Allied Sciences*, **13**: 127–146.

Sigerist, Henry E (1961) *A history of medicine* Vol. II (New York).

Singer, Charles (1915) 'Allegorical representation of the Synagogue in a twelfth century illuminated MS. of Hildegard von Bingen' *Jewish Quarterly Review*, **5**: 267–288.

Singer, Charles (1916–17) 'A review of the medical literature of the Dark Ages', *Proceedings of the Royal Society of Medicine*, Section History of Medicine, **10**: 107–160.

Singer, Charles (1918–19) 'The Lorica of Gildas the Briton (? 547). A magico-medical text containing an anatomical vocabulary. *Proceedings of the Royal Society of Medicine*, **12**: 124–144.

Singer, Charles (1921a) 'Review of *Opera hactenus inedita Rogeri Baconi, Fasc. V, Secretum Secretorum ....*, ed. by R. Steele', in *Nature*, **107**: 771–772.

Singer, Charles (1921b) 'Biology', in R. W. Livingstone (ed.) (1921) *The legacy of Greece* (Oxford), 163–200.

Singer, Charles (1921c) 'Medicine' in R. W. Livingstone (ed.) (1921) *The legacy of Greece* (Oxford), 201–248.

Singer, Charles (1921d) 'Greek biology and its relation to the rise of modern biology', in Charles Singer (ed.) (1921) *Studies in the history and method of science*, vol. 2 (Oxford: Clarendon Press), 1–101.

Singer, Charles (1923a) 'Ancient medicine', in F. S. Marvin (ed.) (1923) *Science and civilization* (London), 43–71.

Singer, Charles (1923b) 'The Dark Ages and the dawn', in F. S. Marvin (ed.) (1923) *Science and civilization* (London), 112–160.

Singer, Charles (1923c) [chapter on] 'Science', in C. Baily (ed.) (1923) The Legacy of Rome (Oxford), 265–324.

Singer Charles (1923d) 'Review of L. Thorndike, *A history of magic and experimental science*' in *Observer* 13 May, 5.

Singer, Charles (1923e) 'Herbals' *Edinburgh Review*, **237**: 95–112.

Singer, Charles (ed.) (1924a) *The Fasciculus Medicinae of Johannes de Ketham, Alemanus*, with an introduction by Karl Sudhoff, translated by C. Singer. (Milan).

Singer, Charles (1924b) 'Jenner and vaccination', article on Jenner's *Enquiry* (facsimile), *Times Literary Supplement*, 20 Nov.

Singer, Charles (1924c) 'The Father of Medicine. Review of *Hippocrates*, vols i and ii by W. H. S. Jones; and *Hippocrates and his successors* by R. O. Moon, *Times Literary Supplement*, 3 April, 197–198.

Singer, Charles (1924d) 'The master of those that know. Review of *Aristotle* by W. D. Ross', *British Medical Journal*, 757–758.

Singer, Charles (1924e) 'Science in the Middle Ages. Review of *Studies in the history of Mediaeval science* by C. H. Haskins', *Times Literary Supplement*, 4 Dec., 813.

Singer, Charles (ed.) (1925a) *The Fasciculo di Medicina Venice 1493* (With translation of Anathomia by Mondino da Luzzi) (Florence).

Singer, Charles (ed.) (1925b) *The earliest printed literature on syphilis being ten tractates from the Years 1495–1498*, Adapted from Karl Sudhoff (Florence).

Singer, Charles (1925c) *The evolution of anatomy* (London).

Singer, Charles (1925d) 'Historical relations of religion and science', in Joseph Needham (ed.) *Science religion and reality* (London), 85–148.

Singer, Charles (1927) 'The herbal in antiquity and its transmission to Later Ages', *Journal of Hellenic Studies*, **47**: 1–52.

Singer, Charles (1928a) *From magic to science. Essays on the scientific twilight.* (London).

Singer, Charles (1928b) *A short history of medicine* (Oxford).

Singer, Charles (1928c) *Religion and science considered in their historical relations* (London).

Singer, Charles (1931) *A short history of biology* (Oxford).

Singer, Charles (1937a) 'German universities', *The New Outlook*, **12**: 16–18.

Singer, Charles, (1937b) *The Christian approach to Jews*, with a foreword by the Rt. Rev. the Lord Bishop of Chichester; and a preface by the Rev. H. W. Fox (London).

Singer, Charles (1939) 'The legacy of Germany', *Spectator*, 1031–1032.

Singer, Charles (1941) *A short history of science to the nineteenth century* (Oxford).

Singer, Charles (1942a) 'A great country doctor. Francis Adams of Banchory 1796–1861', *Bulletin of the History of Medicine*, 12: 1–17.

Singer, Charles (Anceps) (1942b) 'Christianity, science, and the religion of humanity', *Political Quarterly*, **13**: 280–293 and 414–425.

Singer, Charles (1943) *The Christian failure* (London).

Singer, Charles (1945a) 'An early use of the word 'America'', *Times Literary Supplement*, 14 July, 336.

Singer, Charles (1945b) 'Some Vesalian problems', *Bulletin of the History of Medicine*, **17**: 425–438.

Singer, Charles (1945c) 'Beginnings of academic practical anatomy'. Historical essay in the reissue of L. Choulant, *History and bibliography of anatomic illustration"*, trans. and annotated by M. Frank (New York), 21A-21R.

Singer, Charles (1946a) 'Review of the *Circulation of the Blood and Andrea Cesalpino*, by J.P. Arcieri', *Bulletin of the History of Medicine*, **19**: 122.

Singer, Charles (1946b) 'Cesalpino and the circulation', *British Medical Journal*, i: 436.

Singer, Charles (1946c) 'Mme Hélène Metzger-Brühl', *Bulletin of the History of Medicine*, **19**: 461–462.

Singer, Charles (1946d) 'Mme. H. Metzger-Brühl', *Nature*, **157**: 472.

Singer, Charles (1948) *The earliest chemical industry. An essay in the historical relations of economics and technology illustrated from the alum trade* (London [?])

Singer, Charles (1949) Articles in *The Oxford Classical Dictionary* (Oxford).

Singer, Charles (1950) *A history of biology*, Revised edition (New York).

Singer, Charles (1951a) 'Review of *A history of medicine*, vol. I, by H. E. Sigerist', *British Medical Journal*, **ii**: 587–588.

Singer, Charles (1951b) 'Review of *A history of medicine*, vol. I, by H. E. Sigerist', *Bulletin of the History of Medicine*, **15**: 91–93.

Singer, Charles (1951c) 'An early parallel to the Hippocratic Oath', *Gesnerus*, **8**: 177–180.

Singer, Charles (1951d) *New worlds and old* (London).

Singer, Charles (1952a) *Vesalius on the human brain* (London).

Singer, Charles (1952b) 'A MS. translation of the Arabic version of Galen's "De anatomicis administrationibus", *Journal of the History of Medicine and Allied Sciences*, **7**: 85–86.

Singer, Charles (1952c) 'Leonardo da Vinci', *British Medical Journal*, **ii**: 804–805.

Singer, Charles (1952d) 'Ancient Egyptian Medicine. Review of *The old Egyptian medical papyri* by Chauncey D. Leake', *British Medical Journal*, **ii**: 1201.

Singer, Charles (1952e) 'Galen's elementary course on bones', *Proceedings of the Royal Society of Medicine*, Section on the History of Medicine, **45**: 25–34.

Singer, Charles (1952f) 'Personal hygiene in Ancient Rome. Review of *A translation of Galen's Hygiene* by Robert Montraville Green', *British Medical Journal*, i: 1404.

Singer, Charles (1954a) 'Some early goldwork', *Endeavour*, **13**: 86–93.

Singer, Charles (1954b) 'How medicine became anatomical', *British Medical Journal*, **ii**: 1499–1503.

Singer, Charles, (ed.) (1956a) *Galen on Anatomical Procedures: de Anatomicis administrationibus / translation of the surviving books* (London).

322

Singer, Charles (1956b) 'Obituary George Sarton', *Nature* **178**: 67.

Singer, Charles (1956c) 'Review of *A short history of medicine* by E.H.Ackerknecht', *Nature* **177**: 909.

Singer, Charles (1959) *A short history of scientific ideas* (Oxford).

Singer, Charles and Grattan, John H. G. (1952) *Anglo-Saxon magic and medicine* (London).

Singer, Charles, Holmyard, Eric and Hall, A. R. (eds) (1954–1958) *History of technology* (Oxford).

Singer, Charles and Long, Esmond R. (1954) *De abditis nonnullis ac mirandis morborum et sanationum Causis* (Springfield, IL).

Singer, Charles and Rabin, Chaim (1946) *A Prelude to Modern Science. Being a Discussion of the History, Sources and Circumstances of the 'Tabulae Anatomicae Sex' of Vesalius* (Cambridge).

Singer, Charles and Sigerist, Henry E. (eds) (1924) *Essays in the history of medicine presented to Karl Sudhoff on the occasion of his seventieth birthday November 25th 1923* (London/Zurich).

Singer, Charles and Singer, Dorothea (1919) 'On a miniature, ascribed to Mantegna, of an operation by Cosmas and Damian', in *Contributions to medical and biological research, dedicated to Sir William Osler*, vol. 1 (New York), 166–176.

Singer Charles and Singer, Dorothea (1924) 'The origin of the medical school of Salerno', in Charles Singer and Henry E. Sigerist (eds) (1924) *Essays in the history of medicine presented to Karl Sudhoff on the occasion of his seventieth birthday November 25th 1923* (London and Zurich), 121–138.

Singer, Dorothea W. (1924) *Selections from the works of Ambroise Paré* (London).

Sloane, Hans (1707–1725) *A voyage to the islands, Madera, Barbados, Nieves, S. Christophers and Jamaica* (London).

Smith, Frederick and Bullock, Fred (1919–1933) *Early history of veterinary literature* (London).

Spencer, Walter G. (1924) 'The 'Epitome' of Vesalius on vellum in the British Museum Library', in Charles Singer and Henry E. Sigerist (eds) (1924) *Essays in the history of medicine presented to Karl Sudhoff on the occasion of his seventieth birthday November 25th 1923* (London and Zurich), 237–244.

Steele, Robert (1921) 'Roger Bacon', in Charles Singer (ed.) (1921) *Studies in the history and method of science*, vol. 2 (Oxford), 121–150.

Stelluti, Francesco (1630) *Persio/tradotto in verso* (Roma).

Streeter, Edward C. and Singer, Charles (1924) 'Fifteenth century miniatures of extramural dissections', in Charles Singer and Henry E. Sigerist (eds) (1924) *Essays in the history of medicine presented to Karl Sudhoff on the occasion of his seventieth birthday November 25th 1923* (London and Zurich), 207–210.

Sudhoff, Karl (1912a) *Graphische und typographische Erstlinge der Syphilisliteratur aus den Jahren 1495 und 1496*, Alte Meister der Medizin und Naturkunde 4, (Munich).

Sudhoff, Karl (1912b) *Aus der Frühgeschichte der Syphilis*, Studien zur Geschichte der Medizin, Heft 9, (Leipzig).

Sudhoff, Karl (1922) *Kurzes Handbuch der Geschichte der Medizin* (Berlin).

Sudhoff, Karl (ed.) (1923) *Der Fasciculus medicinae des Johannes de Ketham, Alemannus* (Milan).

Sudhoff, Karl (1924) *Zehn Syphilis-Drucke aus den Jahren 1495–1498* (Milan).

Taylor, F. Sherwood (1938) *Galileo and the freedom of thought* (London).

Temkin, Owsei (1945) *Falling sickness, a history of epilepsy* (Baltimore).

Thierfelder, Johann G. (1943) *Additamenta ad Henrici Haeseri bibliothecam epidemiographicam* (Meissen).

Tietsch, F. L. (1939) 'Self-portrait of Fielding H. Garrison. Autobiographical excerpts compiled from his letters', *Bulletin of the History of Medicine*, **7**: 365–373.

Thorndike, Lynn (1923–1958) *History of magic and experimental science during the first thirteen centuries of our era* (New York).

Thorndike, Lynn (1924) 'Disputed dates, civilization and climate, and traces of magic in the scientific treatises ascribed to Theophrastus', in Charles Singer and Henry E. Sigerist (eds) (1924) *Essays in the history of medicine presented to Karl Sudhoff on the occasion of his seventieth birthday November 25th 1923* (London and Zurich), 73–86.

Townend, B. R. (1944) 'The Story of the Toothworm', *Bulletin of the History of Medicine*, **15**: 37–58.

Underwood, E. Ashworth (ed.) (1953) *Science, medicine and history. Essays on the evolution of scientific thought and medical practice, written in honour of Charles Singer*, 2 vols (London).

Underwood, E. Ashworth (1960) 'Charles Singer (1876–1960)', *Medical History*, **4**: 353–358.

Vesalius, Andreas (1552) *De humani corporis fabrica* (Leyden).

Wake, William Charles (1966) 'Who was Hippocrates?' *The Listener*, 19 Dec.

Walzer, Richard (1944) *Galen on medical experience* (New York).

Wedel, Theodore O. (1920) *The Medieval attitude towards astrology* (New Haven).

Wehrli, Gustav Adolf (1920) 'Die inneren Körperorgane in den Kinderzeichnungen mit einigen ethnographischen Parallelen', *Mitteilungen der Geographisch-Ethnographischen Gesellschaft Zürich*, 35–51.

Wissowa, Georg (ed.) (1893-) *Paulys Realencyclopädie der klassischen Altertumswissenschaft* (Stuttgart).

Withington, Edward T. (1924) 'Roger Bacon,On the Errors of Physicians', in Charles Singer and Henry E. Sigerist (eds) (1924) *Essays in the history of medicine presented to Karl Sudhoff on the occasion of his seventieth birthday November 25th 1923* (London and Zurich) 139–157.

Zimmermann, Ernst H. (1916) *Vorkarolingische Miniaturen* (Berlin).

Index

Rolleston, Sir Humphry 8, 9n2, 19, 50–51, 61, 87, 92, 165
  as a baronet 105
  in First World War 73–4
  as Physician-in-Ordinary to George V 73, 74n1
  'The reception of Harvey's doctrine ...' 50, 51n3, 53, 60–61, 61n3, 69, 73, 74
  death/obituary notices 226, 229, 232, 233
Rolleston, John D. (brother of Sir Humphry Rolleston) 87, 88n3, 92
Rome
  Biblioteca Lancisiana 43, 180, 205
  catacombs, rediscovered painted anatomical scenes 312–13, 313n5, 315
  Sigerist in 293
  Vatican Library 154, 156
  see also Italy
Rome University 195, 245
Rosen, George 177, 177n4, 208
  Sigerist, correspondence with vii
Ross, W.D. 199
  Aristotle 99n2
Rossiter, Arthur Percival: *The growth of science...* 206, 206n9
Royal Academy, Leonardo da Vinci quincentenary lectures, May 1952 279, 280
  Singer's lecture 279, 279n3
Royal Army Medical Corps, Singer in xii
Royal College of Physicians of London 71, 294, 300
  Sigerist as Fellow 293, 294
  Singer's Fitzpatrick Lectures 69, 70n5, 76, 117
Royal College of Surgeons 71, 300
Royal Society of London 169, 170, 176
Royal Society of Medicine 73–4, 294
  Rolleston as President 73–4
  Sigerist as member 8, 9n1, 10
Royal Society of Medicine Historical Section 14, 19, 207, 267
  Power as Vice-president 19
  Singer as President 5
Rudolf II, Duke of Austria *see* Hohenburg
Ryle, John Alfred 226, 227n3(a), 229, 231
Russia
  in Second World War 208, 209, 210n3, 216, 230
  Sigerist in xi, 156, 158, 163, 169, 170, 175, 176, 178, 178n1, 181, 182, 183, 184n4
  Sigerist's interest in 148; in socialized medicine 177, 177n6, 178, 179

St Bartholomew's Hospital, London 164, 164n2(b)
Salazar, Antonio de Oliveira 250, 250n2
Salerno School of Medicine
  Capparoni on 77, 77n2
  Kristeller on 234, 234n6, 237
  pre-Salernitan 6, 7n1
  the Singers on 7n1, 28–9, 29n2, 34, 41, 46, 60, 64, 65, 69, 76, 77, 102, 106–7, 106n1
Salzmann, Charles 268n3

Sanchez de Rivera y Moset, Daniel: *Siluetas de médicos y libros de antaño...* 100, 100n1
Sarton, George 29, 30n8, 35, 121, 129, 144, 152, 153, 167, 199, 223, 244, 256, 265, 303
  A guide to the history of science, Singer on 258n2(b)
  A history of science 281n1(b), 283 ; Sigerist on 281, 290 ; Singer on 282, 288, 288n2(b)
  Sigerist's open letter to, on history of medicine 172, 173, 173n1
  Singer: *Short history of science ...* dedicated to 209, 211, 213n3
  Singer on 282 ; his obituary notice of 311, 312n1
  Singer, Charles et. al : *History of technology Volume 1*, his review of 306, 306n3b
  death/obituary notices 311, 312n1
W.B. Saunders (publishers) 194
Saxl, Fritz 132, 133n1, 238
Schaxel, Julius 164, 164n1(b)
Schmidt, Dr (of Köln) 142
Henry Schuman (publisher/bookseller) 222, 223, 223n3, 229, 232, 245, 271, 296
science 155, 241–2
  Singer on religion and 30n1, 117, 118n9, 130, 136, 136n1, 219, 219n7
  see also International Congress on History of Science Museum, London 191, 200
Scott, Mrs Eleanor (née Dobson) 108n2
Scott, Walter 127n2
  Hermetica... 126, 127n2, 141, 141n1(a)
Scottish Beekeepers Association 205
Second World War (1939–45) 187n7, 193n2, 197, 197n1(b), 197n2, 203, 207n3, 212, 217n14, 224n4
  food supplies 205, 207, 209
  France in 201, 201n1(b), 203, 204n2, 234, 234n1, 238
  Italy in 203, 208, 208n2, 225
  Japan in 208n4, 210n4, 226n4
  London, German bombing of 203, 204
  Russia in 208, 209, 210n3, 216, 230
  Sigerist in xi, xvii, 198
  Sigerist on 208, 208n2, 224, 225, 230; on aftermath of 230, 234
  Singer in xiii, xviii, 199
  Singer on 185, 188, 193, 201, 202, 204–5, 207, 209, 214, 216–17, 223, 224, 226, 227; on hardships of 205, 209–10
  Dorothea Singer in 204
Seebohn, Almuth
  Apokalypse, ars moriendi... 219n5
  'Texts and images in a fifteenth-century German miscellany' 219n5
Seldwyla (publisher), Zurich 40, 40n6, 43, 44, 63, 69, 70, 71, 77, 79–80, 93, 94, 95, 96, 98, 102, 107, 112
Semitic language 243–4
  see also Singer, Charles and Chaim Rabin: *A prelude ...*

336